Introduction to
Matrices and Determinants

Introduction to Matrices and Determinants

F. Max Stein

COLORADO STATE UNIVERSITY

Wadsworth Publishing Company, Inc., Belmont, California

To Judith, Karen, and Kenneth

L.C. Cat. Card No.: 68-10353

Printed in the United States of America

Preface

This text is written to provide a firm basis for an introductory course in matrices and determinants. It is suitable for students who have had a minimum of two semesters of elementary calculus, although some additional mathematical training is helpful. The presentation is selective rather than exhaustive; the topics included have been chosen carefully to give the student a solid foundation for more advanced work.

Chapters 1 through 5 are directed primarily toward establishing methods for solving systems of linear equations. Chapter 6 introduces the characteristic value problem, and Chapter 7 discusses briefly the calculus of matrices and determinants. Throughout the book, the language of modern algebra is used, to make the material easily understandable. For the student who is not familiar with this terminology, an Appendix provides the necessary background.

This book includes ample material for a one-semester course in matrices. The instructor can adapt it for a one-quarter course by omitting (with little loss of continuity) some or all of the sections indicated by (†). Those more interested in the calculus of matrices may wish to omit some of the earlier material (such as Chapter 4) so that the material in Chapter 7 can be covered at greater length.

Some of the exercises require more mathematical sophistication than is generally assumed. These exercises are indicated by (*).

I wish to acknowledge my debt to the many people who have written texts and journal articles on matrices and determinants. I was particularly influenced by the text of Professor Franz E. Hohn on *Elementary Matrix Algebra*, especially in preparing the first portion of this book.

F. Max Stein

Contents

6

Linear Transformations and The Characteristic Equation 131

7

The Calculus of Matrices 184

Appendix †

Introduction to
Matrices and Determinants

1

The Algebra of Matrices

1.1 Introduction

Sets of numbers or functions frequently occur in mathematics. For example, one often encounters the sets of coefficients for the linear equations

$$\begin{aligned} 2x + y &= 5, \\ x - y &= 1, \end{aligned} \tag{1.1.1}$$

or the sets of all possible coefficients for the polynomial

$$ax^2 + bx + c. \tag{1.1.2}$$

If we concern ourselves solely with the coefficients of x and y in Eq. (1.1.1) and write them in a rectangular (in this case square) array,

$$\begin{bmatrix} 2 & 1 \\ 1 & -1 \end{bmatrix}, \tag{1.1.3}$$

we have an elementary example of a *matrix*. The set of coefficients in Eq. (1.1.2), $[a \;\; b \;\; c]$, would be another example of a matrix.

In this chapter we shall define what is meant by a matrix and discuss the various operations needed to construct an algebra of matrices. We shall then consider some other operations that are useful in the further study of matrices.

1.2. *The Definition of a Matrix; Addition of Matrices*

A matrix is defined as a *rectangular array* of *elements*. These elements are scalars from a number field $\mathscr{F}$, or functions that assume values from $\mathscr{F}$. (Throughout this book, the number field $\mathscr{F}$ is $\mathscr{F}_c$ unless specifically restricted to $\mathscr{F}_r$. The definition of a field in general and definitions of other terms from modern algebra introduced in this chapter are given in the Appendix.) A matrix is represented by

$$\text{(1.2.1)} \qquad \mathbf{A} = \begin{bmatrix} a_{11} & a_{12} & \cdots & a_{1n} \\ a_{21} & a_{22} & \cdots & a_{2n} \\ \cdots & & & \\ a_{m1} & a_{m2} & \cdots & a_{mn} \end{bmatrix} = [a_{ij}];$$

the first subscript on each element is called the *row subscript*, and the second subscript is called the *column subscript*. Thus a_{34} is the element in the third row and fourth column of the matrix.

Examples of matrices are:

$$\text{(1.2.2)} \qquad \begin{bmatrix} -2 \\ 1 \end{bmatrix}, \quad [3 \quad 2 \quad 5], \quad \begin{bmatrix} 1 & 3 \\ 2 & -1 \end{bmatrix}, \quad \begin{bmatrix} \cos\theta & \sin\theta \\ -\sin\theta & \cos\theta \end{bmatrix},$$
$$\begin{bmatrix} 1 & x \\ x^2 & x^3 \end{bmatrix}, \quad \begin{bmatrix} 2 & 1 & 5 & 3 \\ 1 & 0 & 0 & 4 \end{bmatrix}.$$

The first is called a *column matrix*, the second is called a *row matrix*, the next three are all *square matrices* (since they have as many rows as columns), and the final one is a 2×4 (or 2 by 4) matrix.

Note that a matrix is simply an array; so far, no value or number has been assigned to, or associated with, a given matrix.

Equation (1.2.1) shows two alternative methods for referring to a matrix: either by a boldface capital letter **A**, or by a general element enclosed in square brackets $[a_{ij}]$. In this book, whenever the full array is shown, it is also enclosed in square brackets. Other texts sometimes use parentheses or two vertical lines on each side of the array to indicate a matrix; the notation of one vertical line on each side of the array is reserved for a determinant (defined in Chapter 2).

We shall refer to the *order* of a matrix when we wish to talk about its size. Thus a matrix with m rows and n columns, such as **A** in Eq. (1.2.1), is said to be a *matrix of order* $m \times n$ (read "*m by n*"); it is designated by $\mathbf{A}_{m,n}$ when it is necessary to emphasize the number of rows and columns.

If $m = n$, the matrix is a *square matrix*; it is called a *matrix of order n* and is written as

$$\mathbf{A}_n = \begin{bmatrix} a_{11} & a_{12} & \cdots & a_{1n} \\ a_{21} & a_{22} & \cdots & a_{2n} \\ \cdots & & & \\ a_{n1} & a_{n2} & \cdots & a_{nn} \end{bmatrix}.$$

When $\mathbf{A}$ is square, the elements $a_{11}, a_{22}, \cdots, a_{nn}$ make up, or lie on, the *principal diagonal* of $\mathbf{A}$. We write $\mathbf{A}_n$ for a square matrix in case we need to call attention to its order.

Two matrices $\mathbf{A}$ and $\mathbf{B}$ are *equal* if and only if each element of $\mathbf{A}$ is equal to the corresponding element of $\mathbf{B}$:

$$\mathbf{A} = \begin{bmatrix} a_{11} & a_{12} & \cdots & a_{1n} \\ a_{21} & a_{22} & \cdots & a_{2n} \\ \cdots \\ a_{m1} & a_{m2} & \cdots & a_{mn} \end{bmatrix} = \begin{bmatrix} b_{11} & b_{12} & \cdots & b_{1n} \\ b_{21} & b_{22} & \cdots & b_{2n} \\ \cdots \\ b_{m1} & b_{m2} & \cdots & b_{mn} \end{bmatrix} = \mathbf{B},$$

where $a_{ij} = b_{ij}$ for each pair of subscripts i and j. The definition of equality implies that the two matrices must be of the same order.

If $\mathbf{A}$ and $\mathbf{B}$ are each of the order $m \times n$, we define the *sum* by

$$\mathbf{A} + \mathbf{B} = \mathbf{C}, \tag{1.2.3}$$

where $c_{ij} = a_{ij} + b_{ij}$. The addition of matrices is defined only for matrices of the same order.

The *zero matrix* (or *null matrix*) is defined as the matrix of any order which consists entirely of zeros; its use determines its order in any particular case. The zero matrix is denoted by $\mathbf{0}$; it is the *identity matrix* under addition.

The *inverse* operation of matrix addition is called *subtraction*. The inverse of $\mathbf{A}$ under addition is a matrix $\mathbf{B}$ such that

$$\mathbf{A} + \mathbf{B} = \mathbf{0}. \tag{1.2.4}$$

That is, $\mathbf{B}$ is that matrix which, when added to $\mathbf{A}$, gives the zero matrix. It readily follows that $\mathbf{B}$ is a matrix of the same order as $\mathbf{A}$, and that the elements of $\mathbf{B}$ are the negatives of the elements of $\mathbf{A}$. We find it convenient to denote $\mathbf{B}$ by $-\mathbf{A}$, so that

$$\mathbf{A} + (-\mathbf{A}) = \mathbf{A} - \mathbf{A} = \mathbf{0}. \tag{1.2.5}$$

If we examine the set of matrices of order $m \times n$ under the operation of addition, we notice that:

(1) The *closure property* holds, since the sum of matrices of the same order gives a matrix of the same order.
(2) The *associative property* holds. (The proof of this result is left as an exercise for the reader.)
(3) The *identity matrix* under addition is the zero matrix.
(4) The *inverse* under addition of any matrix $\mathbf{A}$ is $-\mathbf{A}$, where $-\mathbf{A}$ is a matrix whose elements are the negatives of the corresponding elements of $\mathbf{A}$.
(5) The *commutative* property holds. (The proof of this result is also left as an exercise for the reader.)

These observations enable us to state the following theorem:

Theorem 1.2.1. *The set of matrices of order $m \times n$ forms an Abelian group under the operation of addition.*

By using the associative property of matrix addition, we can extend the definition of a sum to any finite number of matrices of the same order.

Example 1.2.1. Find the sum of the $m \times n$ matrices, **A**, **B**, **C**, **D**, **E**.

By the associative property we may write the sum as

$$\mathbf{A} + \mathbf{B} + \mathbf{C} + \mathbf{D} + \mathbf{E} = \mathbf{A} + (\mathbf{B} + (\mathbf{C} + (\mathbf{D} + \mathbf{E}))).$$

Each sum in parentheses is a matrix; the entire sum is a matrix whose general element is

$$a_{ij} + b_{ij} + c_{ij} + d_{ij} + e_{ij}.$$

The associative property enables us to perform the addition in any manner we choose; thus the parentheses may be omitted entirely.

Example 1.2.2. Find $\mathbf{A} + \mathbf{B} + \mathbf{C}$ and $\mathbf{A} - \mathbf{B} + \mathbf{C}$, where

$$\mathbf{A} = \begin{bmatrix} 2 & 3 & 1 \\ 4 & 2 & -1 \end{bmatrix}, \quad \mathbf{B} = \begin{bmatrix} 3 & 3 & -1 \\ 7 & 3 & 3 \end{bmatrix}, \quad \mathbf{C} = \begin{bmatrix} 1 & 0 & -2 \\ 3 & 1 & 4 \end{bmatrix}.$$

$$\mathbf{A} + \mathbf{B} + \mathbf{C} = \begin{bmatrix} 2 & 3 & 1 \\ 4 & 2 & -1 \end{bmatrix} + \begin{bmatrix} 3 & 3 & -1 \\ 7 & 3 & 3 \end{bmatrix} + \begin{bmatrix} 1 & 0 & -2 \\ 3 & 1 & 4 \end{bmatrix}$$
$$= \begin{bmatrix} 6 & 6 & -2 \\ 14 & 6 & 6 \end{bmatrix}.$$

$$\mathbf{A} - \mathbf{B} + \mathbf{C} = \begin{bmatrix} 2 & 3 & 1 \\ 4 & 2 & -1 \end{bmatrix} - \begin{bmatrix} 3 & 3 & -1 \\ 7 & 3 & 3 \end{bmatrix} + \begin{bmatrix} 1 & 0 & -2 \\ 3 & 1 & 4 \end{bmatrix}$$
$$= \begin{bmatrix} 2 & 3 & 1 \\ 4 & 2 & -1 \end{bmatrix} + \begin{bmatrix} -3 & -3 & 1 \\ -7 & -3 & -3 \end{bmatrix} + \begin{bmatrix} 1 & 0 & -2 \\ 3 & 1 & 4 \end{bmatrix}$$
$$= \begin{bmatrix} 0 & 0 & 0 \\ 0 & 0 & 0 \end{bmatrix}$$
$$= \mathbf{0}.$$

Exercises 1.2

Use the following matrices in exercises 1 through 4:

$$\mathbf{A} = \begin{bmatrix} 4 & 1 & 0 \\ 2 & 1 & 3 \end{bmatrix}, \quad \mathbf{B} = \begin{bmatrix} 2 & -7 & 2 \\ -1 & 3 & 4 \end{bmatrix}, \quad \mathbf{C} = \begin{bmatrix} -2 & -8 & 2 \\ -3 & 2 & 1 \end{bmatrix},$$

$$\mathbf{D} = \begin{bmatrix} 0 & 2 & -1 \\ 1 & 0 & 3 \end{bmatrix}.$$

1. Find $\mathbf{A} + \mathbf{B}$; $\mathbf{A} - \mathbf{D}$.

2. Find $\mathbf{B} + \mathbf{C} + \mathbf{C}$.

3. Verify that $\mathbf{A} - \mathbf{B} + \mathbf{C} = \mathbf{0}$.

4. Solve for $\mathbf{X}$ if $\mathbf{X} + \mathbf{D} = \mathbf{A}$, and

$$\mathbf{X} = \begin{bmatrix} x_{11} & x_{12} & x_{13} \\ x_{21} & x_{22} & x_{23} \end{bmatrix}.$$

5. Show that the associative property for matrix addition holds. (Hint: Consider the nature of the general element in each term.)

6. Prove that the commutative property under addition holds for the set of matrices of order $m \times n$.

7. Determine a matrix $\mathbf{Q}$ such that $\mathbf{P} + \mathbf{Q} = \mathbf{X}$, where $a_{ij} = i + j$,

$$\mathbf{P} = \begin{bmatrix} 2 & -1 & 4 \\ 3 & 2 & 0 \\ -1 & 4 & 4 \end{bmatrix}, \quad \text{and} \quad \mathbf{X} = \begin{bmatrix} a_{11} & a_{12} & a_{13} \\ 0 & a_{22} & a_{23} \\ 0 & 0 & a_{33} \end{bmatrix}.$$

8. Using the matrix $\mathbf{P}$ in exercise 7, determine a matrix $\mathbf{Q}$ such that $\mathbf{P} + \mathbf{Q} = \mathbf{X}$, where $a_{ii} = 2i$ and

$$\mathbf{X} = \begin{bmatrix} a_{11} & 0 & 0 \\ 0 & a_{22} & 0 \\ 0 & 0 & a_{33} \end{bmatrix}.$$

9. Using the matrix $\mathbf{P}$ in exercise 7, determine a matrix $\mathbf{Q}$ such that $\mathbf{P} + \mathbf{Q} = \mathbf{X}$, where $\mathbf{X}$ consists entirely of zeros except on the main diagonal, and entirely of fives on the main diagonal:

$$\mathbf{X} = \begin{bmatrix} 5 & 0 & 0 \\ 0 & 5 & 0 \\ 0 & 0 & 5 \end{bmatrix}.$$

10. Using the matrix $\mathbf{P}$ of exercise 7 and the matrix $\mathbf{Q}$ of exercise 9, determine $\mathbf{Y}$ such that $\mathbf{Q} - \mathbf{P} = \mathbf{Y}$.

11. Prove that the inverse of a general matrix $\mathbf{G}$ under addition is a matrix consisting of the negatives of the elements of $\mathbf{G}$.

1.3. Combining Scalars and Matrices

The reader is already familiar with the algebra of scalars. We now define an operation combining scalars and matrices. The symbol for multiplication of a matrix $\mathbf{A}$ by a scalar k is

(1.3.1) $$k\mathbf{A} = \mathbf{A}k;$$

it means that every element of the matrix **A** is multiplied by the scalar k. That is,

$$
(1.3.2) \qquad k\mathbf{A} = k\begin{bmatrix} a_{11} & a_{12} & \cdots & a_{1n} \\ a_{21} & a_{22} & \cdots & a_{2n} \\ \cdots & & & \\ a_{m1} & a_{m2} & \cdots & a_{mn} \end{bmatrix}
= \begin{bmatrix} ka_{11} & ka_{12} & \cdots & ka_{1n} \\ ka_{21} & ka_{22} & \cdots & ka_{2n} \\ \cdots & & & \\ ka_{m1} & ka_{m2} & \cdots & ka_{mn} \end{bmatrix}
= [ka_{ij}].
$$

In accordance with the definition of a linear space given in Section A.3 (Appendix), we are able to state the following theorem:

Theorem 1.3.1. *The set of $m \times n$ matrices forms a linear space over the scalar field $\mathcal{F}$.*

Proof: We have already seen (in Section 1.2) that the set of $m \times n$ matrices forms an Abelian group under the operation of addition. Therefore, to prove the theorem, we need only to verify that the properties required by Eq. (A.3.1) hold. This verification is left as an exercise for the reader.

Exercises 1.3

1. Complete the proof of Theorem 1.3.1.
2. Which field postulates (if any) for the scalar field are not actually needed in the proof of Theorem 1.3.1?
3. Using the matrices **A**, **B**, and **C** of Exercises 1.2, determine $2\mathbf{A} - 2\mathbf{B}$; $\mathbf{A} + 2\mathbf{C} - 3\mathbf{B}$; $3(\mathbf{B} - \mathbf{C})$.
4. Determine **Q** so that $\mathbf{Q} = \mathbf{P}/2$; $\mathbf{Q} = 3\mathbf{P}$, where

$$
\mathbf{P} = \begin{bmatrix} 6 & 4 & 5 \\ 8 & 1 & 6 \end{bmatrix}.
$$

5. Write a square matrix of order 4 with threes on the main diagonal and zeros off the main diagonal. Write this matrix as equal to a scalar multiple of a matrix with only ones on the main diagonal.
6. Write any non-zero 3×4 matrix **A**. Now find a matrix **B** such that $\mathbf{A} = 5\mathbf{B}$.
7. Work exercise 6 if **A** is a 1×4 matrix; if **A** is a 3×1 matrix.

1.4. *The Product of Matrices*

The *product* of two matrices **A** and **B**, which we shall denote by **AB**, is defined if and only if matrix **A** is of order $m \times n$ and matrix **B** is of order $n \times p$; that is, the number of columns of the matrix on the left must be the same as the number of rows of the matrix on the right. This product is a matrix **C** of order $m \times p$; that is,

(1.4.1) $$\mathbf{AB} = \mathbf{C}.$$

Matrix **B** is *premultiplied* by **A**, and matrix **A** is *postmultiplied* by **B**.

The elements of **C** are:

(1.4.2) $$c_{ij} = \sum_{k=1}^{n} a_{ik} b_{kj} = a_{i1} b_{1j} + a_{i2} b_{2j} + \cdots + a_{in} b_{nj}.$$

Thus to multiply matrix **A** by matrix **B**, we multiply the elements of the ith row of **A** by the corresponding elements of the jth column of **B**, then add the results to obtain the element in the ith row and jth column of **C**, the product matrix.

Example 1.4.1. Determine the product of **A** and **B**, where

$$\mathbf{A} = \begin{bmatrix} 2 & -1 & 3 \\ 4 & 2 & 0 \end{bmatrix}, \qquad \mathbf{B} = \begin{bmatrix} 3 & 0 \\ 1 & 4 \\ 2 & 2 \end{bmatrix}.$$

We note that the multiplication of **A** and **B** is defined. Then,

$$\begin{aligned} \mathbf{AB} &= \begin{bmatrix} 2 & -1 & 3 \\ 4 & 2 & 0 \end{bmatrix} \begin{bmatrix} 3 & 0 \\ 1 & 4 \\ 2 & 2 \end{bmatrix} \\ &= \begin{bmatrix} 2\cdot 3 - 1\cdot 1 + 3\cdot 2 & 2\cdot 0 - 1\cdot 4 + 3\cdot 2 \\ 4\cdot 3 + 2\cdot 1 + 0\cdot 2 & 4\cdot 0 + 2\cdot 4 + 0\cdot 2 \end{bmatrix} \\ &= \begin{bmatrix} 11 & 2 \\ 14 & 8 \end{bmatrix}. \end{aligned}$$

Example 1.4.2. If

$$\mathbf{A} = \begin{bmatrix} 2 & 1 & 2 \\ 1 & 0 & 3 \\ 2 & 1 & 5 \end{bmatrix}, \qquad \mathbf{x} = \begin{bmatrix} x \\ y \\ z \end{bmatrix}, \qquad \mathbf{d} = \begin{bmatrix} 1 \\ 3 \\ 5 \end{bmatrix},$$

set $\mathbf{Ax} = \mathbf{d}$ and use the definition of the equality of matrices to write the result as a system of linear equations.

The equation $\mathbf{Ax} = \mathbf{d}$ may be written as

$$\begin{bmatrix} 2 & 1 & 2 \\ 1 & 0 & 3 \\ 2 & 1 & 5 \end{bmatrix} \begin{bmatrix} x \\ y \\ z \end{bmatrix} = \begin{bmatrix} 2x + y + 2z \\ x \quad\;\; + 3z \\ 2x + y + 5z \end{bmatrix} = \begin{bmatrix} 1 \\ 3 \\ 5 \end{bmatrix}.$$

From the equality of matrices we have:

$$\begin{aligned} 2x + y + 2z &= 1, \\ x \qquad + 3z &= 3, \\ 2x + y + 5z &= 5. \end{aligned}$$

There are three major points to note about matrix multiplication. *First,* the matrices must have the correct sizes for multiplication to be defined. *Second,* the resulting matrix has the same number of rows as the matrix on the left and the same number of columns as the matrix on the right. *Third,* if matrices **A** and **B** are of orders such that **AB** and **BA** are both defined, in general **AB** ≠ **BA**. In Example 1.4.1, **AB** is a matrix of order 2 × 2 while **BA** would be a matrix of order 3 × 3; obviously, these two matrices could not be equal. In Example 1.4.2 **Ax** is defined while **xA** is not. Except for special cases (to be considered later), matrix multiplication is *not commutative.*

From the preceding definition of multiplication of matrices, a kind of *closure property* is satisfied. The product of two matrices is a matrix; however, unless the matrices are square, the product is not a matrix of the same order.

For scalars, $ab = 0$ implies that $a = 0$ or $b = 0$. For matrices, however, $\mathbf{AB} = \mathbf{0}$ can hold without $\mathbf{A} = \mathbf{0}$ or $\mathbf{B} = \mathbf{0}$.

Example 1.4.3. Multiply **A** by **B** and then **B** by **A** if

$$\mathbf{A} = \begin{bmatrix} 2 & 1 \\ -2 & -1 \end{bmatrix}, \qquad \mathbf{B} = \begin{bmatrix} 1 & -1 \\ -2 & 2 \end{bmatrix}.$$

$$\mathbf{AB} = \begin{bmatrix} 2 & 1 \\ -2 & -1 \end{bmatrix}\begin{bmatrix} 1 & -1 \\ -2 & 2 \end{bmatrix} = \begin{bmatrix} 0 & 0 \\ 0 & 0 \end{bmatrix} = \mathbf{0}.$$

$$\mathbf{BA} = \begin{bmatrix} 1 & -1 \\ -2 & 2 \end{bmatrix}\begin{bmatrix} 2 & 1 \\ -2 & -1 \end{bmatrix} = \begin{bmatrix} 4 & 2 \\ -8 & -4 \end{bmatrix}.$$

For matrices (unlike scalars), $\mathbf{AB} = \mathbf{AC}$ can hold without $\mathbf{B} = \mathbf{C}$ or $\mathbf{A} = \mathbf{0}$.

Example 1.4.4. Determine **AB** and **AC** and note that $\mathbf{AB} = \mathbf{AC}$ but $\mathbf{B} \neq \mathbf{C}$ if

$$\mathbf{A} = \begin{bmatrix} 2 & 0 \\ 0 & 0 \end{bmatrix}, \qquad \mathbf{B} = \begin{bmatrix} 0 & 3 \\ 0 & 4 \end{bmatrix}, \qquad \mathbf{C} = \begin{bmatrix} 0 & 3 \\ 0 & 2 \end{bmatrix}.$$

$$\mathbf{AB} = \begin{bmatrix} 2 & 0 \\ 0 & 0 \end{bmatrix}\begin{bmatrix} 0 & 3 \\ 0 & 4 \end{bmatrix} = \begin{bmatrix} 0 & 6 \\ 0 & 0 \end{bmatrix} = \begin{bmatrix} 2 & 0 \\ 0 & 0 \end{bmatrix}\begin{bmatrix} 0 & 3 \\ 0 & 2 \end{bmatrix} = \mathbf{AC}.$$

The *associative property* for multiplication is

$$(1.4.3) \qquad (\mathbf{AB})\mathbf{C} = \mathbf{A}(\mathbf{BC}).$$

To prove this property we note first that the orders of the matrices must be such that multiplication is defined in all cases. For example, the matrices could have the orders of $m \times n$, $n \times r$, and $r \times s$ respectively (written $\mathbf{A}_{m,n}$, $\mathbf{B}_{n,r}$, $\mathbf{C}_{r,s}$). From the definition of multiplication, the element in the ith row and kth column of **AB** (a matrix of order $m \times r$) would be

$$\sum_{j=1}^{n} a_{ij} b_{jk}. \tag{1.4.4}$$

We now multiply this result on the right by **C** to get, as the element in the ith row and pth column of the product (**AB**)**C**,

$$\sum_{k=1}^{r} \left(\sum_{j=1}^{n} a_{ij} b_{jk} \right) c_{kp} = \sum_{k=1}^{r} \sum_{j=1}^{n} a_{ij} b_{jk} c_{kp}. \tag{1.4.5}$$

Since we can consider the terms in any order in a finite sum,

$$\sum_{j=1}^{n} \sum_{k=1}^{r} a_{ij} b_{jk} c_{kp} = \sum_{j=1}^{n} a_{ij} \left(\sum_{k=1}^{r} b_{jk} c_{kp} \right). \tag{1.4.6}$$

But the final result is merely the element in the ith row and pth column of **A**(**BC**). Thus, we have proved the following theorem:

Theorem 1.4.1. *The associative property holds for the multiplication of matrices.*

Up to this point, we have avoided associating a particular scalar with a given matrix. One scalar which can be associated with a *square* matrix is its *trace*, defined by

$$tr\, \mathbf{A} = \sum_{i=1}^{n} a_{ii}. \tag{1.4.7}$$

That is, the trace of a square matrix is the sum of the elements on the principal diagonal.

Exercises 1.4

1. Extend the definition of the product of matrices to find the product **ABCDE**, in that order, if none of the matrices is square but the multiplications are all defined. What is the order of the product?

2. Perform the indicated matrix multiplications:

(a) $\begin{bmatrix} 2 & 2 & 1 \\ 1 & 2 & -1 \\ 0 & 2 & 2 \end{bmatrix} \begin{bmatrix} 2 & 1 \\ -1 & 1 \\ 1 & 0 \end{bmatrix}$ (b) $\begin{bmatrix} 2 & 1 & 4 & 3 \end{bmatrix} \begin{bmatrix} 3 \\ 2 \\ 1 \\ 1 \end{bmatrix}$

(c) $\begin{bmatrix} 3 \\ 2 \\ 1 \\ 1 \end{bmatrix} [2 \quad 1 \quad 4 \quad 3]$ (d) $\begin{bmatrix} 1 & 2 & 3 \\ 3 & 2 & 1 \end{bmatrix} \begin{bmatrix} 1 & 3 \\ 2 & 2 \\ 3 & 1 \end{bmatrix}$

3. (a) Perform the indicated matrix multiplication:

$$\begin{bmatrix} \cos\theta & -\sin\theta \\ \sin\theta & \cos\theta \end{bmatrix} \begin{bmatrix} \cos\theta & \sin\theta \\ -\sin\theta & \cos\theta \end{bmatrix}$$

(b) Reverse the order of the matrices in (a) and multiply.

4. The matrices

$$\mathbf{X} = \begin{bmatrix} 0 & 1 \\ 1 & 0 \end{bmatrix}, \quad Y = \begin{bmatrix} 0 & -i \\ i & 0 \end{bmatrix}, \text{ and } \quad \mathbf{Z} = \begin{bmatrix} 1 & 0 \\ 0 & -1 \end{bmatrix},$$

in which $i = \sqrt{-1}$, are the *Pauli spin matrices*. Determine other matrices so that the entire set forms a group under matrix multiplication.

5. Write a system of four linear equations in four unknowns as a matrix equation. Can a system of three linear equations in two unknowns be written as a matrix equation? Illustrate your answer by an example.

6. (a) If k is a scalar, prove that $\operatorname{tr}(k\mathbf{A}) = k \operatorname{tr} \mathbf{A}$.
(b) Prove that $\operatorname{tr}(\mathbf{A} + \mathbf{B}) = \operatorname{tr} \mathbf{A} + \operatorname{tr} \mathbf{B}$.
(c) Prove that $\operatorname{tr}(\mathbf{AB}) = \operatorname{tr}(\mathbf{BA})$.

7. In exercise 2, reverse the orders of the matrices, and find the products in those cases where multiplication is still defined.

1.5. The Distributive Law for Matrices

Since an associative multiplication is now defined for matrices, it is natural to ask whether the linear space of all $m \times n$ matrices (Theorem 1.3.1) forms a linear algebra or a field under this multiplication. (See Sections A.2 and A.4.) Of course, we can only multiply $m \times n$ matrices if $m = n$. Thus we restrict ourselves to square matrices of an arbitrary but fixed order n.

For square matrices, the closure property, Eq. (A.4.1)(1), obviously holds from the definition of the product of matrices. Also the associative property, Eq. (A.4.1)(2), holds since it is a special case of Theorem 1.4.1. Hence, we need only check the distributive properties, Eq. (A.4.1)(3) and (4), to verify that our set of square matrices forms a linear algebra. (Actually, these properties hold even if the matrices are not square. All that is required is that the matrices be of proper size so that the various operations involved are defined.) We state this result as a theorem:

Theorem 1.5.1. *For elements α, β of a scalar field and for $n \times p$ matrices* **B** *and* **C** *and $m \times n$ matrix* **A**, *then*

(1.5.1) $$\mathbf{A}(\alpha\mathbf{B} + \beta\mathbf{C}) = \alpha\mathbf{AB} + \beta\mathbf{AC}.$$

If **A** *is a* $p \times m$ *matrix, then*

(1.5.2) $$(\alpha\mathbf{B} + \beta\mathbf{C})\mathbf{A} = \alpha\mathbf{BA} + \beta\mathbf{CA}.$$

If $\alpha = \beta = 1$ and **A**, **B**, and **C** are all square matrices, then we have the following corollary:

Corollary 1.5.1. *For square matrices, matrix multiplication is distributive with respect to addition; that is,*

(1.5.3) $$\mathbf{A}(\mathbf{B} + \mathbf{C}) = \mathbf{AB} + \mathbf{AC}, \qquad \textit{and also}$$

(1.5.4) $$(\mathbf{B} + \mathbf{C})\mathbf{A} = \mathbf{BA} + \mathbf{CA}.$$

Proof: To prove the theorem we first note that, since α is a scalar, $\mathbf{A}\alpha = \alpha\mathbf{A}$, and $\mathbf{A}(\alpha\mathbf{B}) = (\mathbf{A}\alpha)\mathbf{B} = \alpha\mathbf{AB}$. Then we observe that **B** and **C** must be of proper size for addition, and that the various products must be defined. (The matrices need not be square.) We shall expand only Eq. (1.5.1); Eq. (1.5.2) may be treated similarly.

$$\begin{aligned}
\mathbf{A}(\alpha\mathbf{B} + \beta\mathbf{C}) &= [a_{ij}][(\alpha b_{jk} + \beta c_{jk})] \\
&= \left[\sum_{j=1}^{n} a_{ij}(\alpha b_{jk} + \beta c_{jk})\right] \\
&= \left[\sum_{j=1}^{n} a_{ij}\alpha b_{jk} + \sum_{j=1}^{n} a_{ij}\beta c_{jk}\right] \\
&= \alpha\left[\sum_{j=1}^{n} a_{ij} b_{jk}\right] + \beta\left[\sum_{j=1}^{n} a_{ij} c_{jk}\right] \\
&= \alpha\mathbf{AB} + \beta\mathbf{AC}.
\end{aligned}$$

The companion result, Eq. (1.5.2), does *not* follow from Eq. (1.5.1), since matrix multiplication is not in general commutative. However, Eq. (1.5.2) is true provided the various matrices are such that the additions and multiplications are defined. The proof of Eq. (1.5.2) is left as an exercise.

Exercises 1.5

1. Prove Eq. (1.5.2).
2. (a) If $\mathbf{A}^2 = \mathbf{AA}$, what conditions must be imposed on **A** and **B** for $(\mathbf{A} + \mathbf{B})^2$ to have meaning?
   (b) Does $(\mathbf{A} + \mathbf{B})^2 = (\mathbf{A} + \mathbf{B})(\mathbf{A} + \mathbf{B})$?
   (c) Does $(\mathbf{A} + \mathbf{B})^2 = \mathbf{A}^2 + 2\mathbf{AB} + \mathbf{B}^2$?

3. (a) Does $(\mathbf{A}+\mathbf{B})(\mathbf{A}-\mathbf{B})=\mathbf{A}^2-\mathbf{B}^2$?
   (b) Does $(\mathbf{A}-\mathbf{B})(\mathbf{A}+\mathbf{B})=\mathbf{A}^2-\mathbf{B}^2$?
   (c) Does $(\mathbf{A}-\mathbf{B})(\mathbf{A}+\mathbf{B})=(\mathbf{A}+\mathbf{B})(\mathbf{A}-\mathbf{B})$?
4. Define what is meant by $\mathbf{A}^3$; by $\mathbf{A}^4$.
5. If none of the matrices is square, indicate their orders so that $\mathbf{A}((\mathbf{B}+\mathbf{C})\mathbf{D})$ has meaning. Is the result the same as $(\mathbf{A}(\mathbf{B}+\mathbf{C}))\mathbf{D}$? Why?
6. Expand $\mathbf{A}(\mathbf{B}+\mathbf{C})$ and also $(\mathbf{B}+\mathbf{C})\mathbf{A}$ if

$$\mathbf{A}=\begin{bmatrix}2 & 1\\ 3 & 2\end{bmatrix},\qquad \mathbf{B}=\begin{bmatrix}0 & 2\\ 2 & 4\end{bmatrix},\qquad \mathbf{C}=\begin{bmatrix}3 & 1\\ 1 & -1\end{bmatrix}.$$

1.6. The Multiplicative Identity and Multiplicative Inverse

Theorem 1.3.1 states that $m \times n$ matrices, and hence square matrices of order n, form a linear space over the scalar field $\mathscr{F}$. Section 1.5 shows that the set of square matrices of order n forms a linear algebra over the scalar field $\mathscr{F}$. Section 1.4 shows that matrix multiplication is not generally commutative even if the matrices are square. Since fields require commutativity, sets of square matrices do not usually form fields under the operation of addition and multiplication.

Despite this conclusion, we will consider the remaining two field postulates. These postulates deal with the existence of a multiplicative identity and multiplicative inverses.

An identity matrix **I** under the operation of multiplication, can only exist if

$$\mathbf{AI}=\mathbf{IA}=\mathbf{A} \tag{1.6.1}$$

for all matrices **A**. This implies that both **A** and **I** must be square. If we let $\mathbf{I}=[b_{ij}]$, then for each a_{ij} we must have

$$\sum_{j=1}^{n} a_{ij}b_{jk}=a_{ik}=\sum_{j=1}^{n} b_{ij}a_{jk}. \tag{1.6.2}$$

Equation (1.6.2) implies that $b_{jk}=0$ except when $j=k$, and also that $b_{kk}=1$ for all k, since this result must hold for an arbitrary square matrix. (The reader might write out a few terms of Eq. (1.6.2).) Thus the *identity matrix*, under the operation of multiplication, must be

$$\mathbf{I}=\begin{bmatrix}1 & 0 & \cdots & 0\\ 0 & 1 & \cdots & 0\\ \cdots & & & \\ 0 & 0 & \cdots & 1\end{bmatrix}; \tag{1.6.3}$$

it is also called the *unit matrix*. It is left as an exercise for the reader to prove that Eq. (1.6.3) is sufficient (as well as necessary) to satisfy Eq. (1.6.1).

If $\mathbf{A}$ has an *inverse* $\mathbf{A}^{-1}$, that is, if there exists a matrix $\mathbf{A}^{-1}$ such that

$$\mathbf{A}^{-1}\mathbf{A} = \mathbf{A}\mathbf{A}^{-1} = \mathbf{I}, \tag{1.6.4}$$

then $\mathbf{A}$ must be square. However, this condition is not sufficient, since some square matrices do not have multiplicative inverses, such as

$$\begin{bmatrix} 1 & 0 \\ 0 & 0 \end{bmatrix} \quad \text{or} \quad \begin{bmatrix} 3 & 1 & 2 \\ 4 & 0 & 1 \\ 2 & 2 & 3 \end{bmatrix}.$$

Although the procedures for determining the inverse (if any) of a matrix are not given until Chapter 3, we can now prove the following theorem:

Theorem 1.6.1. *If a matrix has an inverse, the inverse is unique.*

Proof: If we assume that $\mathbf{B}$ and $\mathbf{C}$ are both inverses of $\mathbf{A}$, then

$$\mathbf{AB} = \mathbf{BA} = \mathbf{I} \quad \text{and} \tag{1.6.5}$$

$$\mathbf{AC} = \mathbf{CA} = \mathbf{I}. \tag{1.6.6}$$

From Eqs. (1.6.5) and (1.6.6) we can write that

$$\mathbf{AB} - \mathbf{AC} = \mathbf{A}(\mathbf{B} - \mathbf{C}) = \mathbf{0}.$$

Then from

$$\mathbf{0} = \mathbf{B0} = \mathbf{B}(\mathbf{A}(\mathbf{B} - \mathbf{C})) = (\mathbf{BA})(\mathbf{B} - \mathbf{C}) = \mathbf{I}(\mathbf{B} - \mathbf{C}) = \mathbf{B} - \mathbf{C}$$

we conclude that

$$\mathbf{B} = \mathbf{C}.$$

That is, if $\mathbf{A}$ has an inverse, the inverse is unique.

Although addition, subtraction, and multiplication of matrices have been defined, *division* of matrices has not been (and will not be) defined. That is, it is *not* correct to attempt to solve for $\mathbf{B}$ in $\mathbf{AB} = \mathbf{I}$ by writing $\mathbf{B} = \mathbf{I}/\mathbf{A}$ since the operation on the right has been given no meaning. However, by premultiplying on both sides by $\mathbf{A}^{-1}$, we are able to solve for $\mathbf{B}$:

$$\mathbf{A}^{-1}(\mathbf{AB}) = \mathbf{A}^{-1}\mathbf{I},$$

$$\mathbf{IB} = \mathbf{A}^{-1}\mathbf{I},$$

$$\mathbf{B} = \mathbf{A}^{-1}.$$

In general, if $\mathbf{A}$ has an inverse, we can solve for $\mathbf{B}$ in $\mathbf{AB} = \mathbf{C}$ in a similar manner to get $\mathbf{B} = \mathbf{A}^{-1}\mathbf{C}$. If $\mathbf{A}$ does not have an inverse, $\mathbf{B}$ cannot be uniquely determined. (See Example 1.4.4.)

Theorem 1.6.2. *If* $\mathbf{A}$ *and* $\mathbf{B}$ *have inverses and if* $\mathbf{C} = \mathbf{AB}$, *then* $\mathbf{C}^{-1} = \mathbf{B}^{-1}\mathbf{A}^{-1}$.

Proof: It is easy to *verify* that $\mathbf{C}^{-1} = \mathbf{B}^{-1}\mathbf{A}^{-1}$ and thus complete the proof of the theorem, since the inverse of the product $\mathbf{AB}$ is unique by Theorem 1.6.1. Instead, we shall *derive* this result. That is, we seek a matrix $\mathbf{C}^{-1}$ such that $\mathbf{CC}^{-1} = \mathbf{I}$. Since $\mathbf{C} = \mathbf{AB}$, then

$$\mathbf{CC}^{-1} = \mathbf{I},$$

$$(\mathbf{AB})\mathbf{C}^{-1} = \mathbf{I},$$

$$\mathbf{A}(\mathbf{BC}^{-1}) = \mathbf{I}.$$

Multiplying on the left by $\mathbf{A}^{-1}$,

$$(\mathbf{A}^{-1}\mathbf{A})(\mathbf{BC}^{-1}) = \mathbf{A}^{-1}\mathbf{I},$$

$$\mathbf{BC}^{-1} = \mathbf{A}^{-1}.$$

Multiplying on the left again, this time by $\mathbf{B}^{-1}$, yields the desired result:

$$(\mathbf{B}^{-1}\mathbf{B})\mathbf{C}^{-1} = \mathbf{B}^{-1}\mathbf{A}^{-1},$$

$$\mathbf{C}^{-1} = \mathbf{B}^{-1}\mathbf{A}^{-1}.$$

Exercises 1.6

1. Verify Theorem 1.6.2, using the following matrices:

$$\mathbf{A} = \begin{bmatrix} 1 & 2 & 1 \\ 0 & 1 & 0 \\ 0 & 0 & 1 \end{bmatrix}, \qquad \mathbf{A}^{-1} = \begin{bmatrix} 1 & -2 & -1 \\ 0 & 1 & 0 \\ 0 & 0 & 1 \end{bmatrix}, \qquad \mathbf{B} = \mathbf{B}^{-1} = \begin{bmatrix} 0 & 1 & 0 \\ 1 & 0 & 0 \\ 0 & 0 & 1 \end{bmatrix}.$$

2. If A is a 3×3 matrix, and

$$\mathbf{x} = \begin{bmatrix} x_1 \\ x_2 \\ x_3 \end{bmatrix}, \qquad \mathbf{c} = \begin{bmatrix} c_1 \\ c_2 \\ c_3 \end{bmatrix}, \qquad \text{and} \qquad \mathbf{A}^{-1} = [b_{ij}]:$$

   (a) Write $\mathbf{Ax} = \mathbf{c}$ out completely as a system of scalar equations.
   (b) Solve symbolically for $\mathbf{x}$.

3. Determine $\mathbf{D}^{-1}$, where $\mathbf{D}$ is a matrix with non-zero elements on the principal diagonal and zero elements otherwise,

4. Find $\mathbf{S}^{-1}$ if

$$\mathbf{S} = \begin{bmatrix} 1 & 0 & \cdots & 0 \\ 0 & 2 & \cdots & 0 \\ \cdots & & & \\ 0 & 0 & \cdots & n \end{bmatrix}; \qquad \mathbf{S} = \begin{bmatrix} 0 & 0 & \cdots & n \\ \cdots & & & \\ 0 & 2 & \cdots & 0 \\ 1 & 0 & \cdots & 0 \end{bmatrix}.$$

5. By inspection, find the inverses of

$$\begin{bmatrix} 1 & 0 & 0 & 0 \\ 0 & 1 & 0 & 0 \\ 0 & 0 & 1 & 0 \\ 0 & 0 & 0 & 1 \end{bmatrix}, \quad \begin{bmatrix} 1 & 0 & 0 & 1 \\ 0 & 0 & 0 & 1 \\ 0 & 0 & 1 & 1 \\ 0 & 1 & 0 & 1 \end{bmatrix}, \quad \text{and} \quad \begin{bmatrix} 1 & 0 & 0 & 1 \\ 0 & 2 & 0 & 0 \\ 0 & 0 & 3 & 0 \\ 0 & 0 & 0 & 4 \end{bmatrix}.$$

6. If **A** is such that $\mathbf{A}^2 = \mathbf{I}$, then **A** is its own inverse. Find matrices of order 3 meeting this condition.

7. Where

$$\mathbf{A} = \begin{bmatrix} a & b \\ c & d \end{bmatrix} \quad \text{and} \quad \mathbf{B} = \begin{bmatrix} e & 0 \\ 0 & f \end{bmatrix},$$

prove that if the elements of **A** are all non-zero, then no inverse of the type **B** exists. Also prove that if **A** has non-zero elements only on the principal diagonal, then the elements of **B** are completely determined.

8. Prove the theorem: $(\mathbf{A}^{-1})^{-1} = \mathbf{A}$.

9. Prove that Eq. (1.6.1) implies that both **A** and **I** must be square.

10. Prove that Eq. (1.6.2) implies that $b_{ik} = \delta_{ik}$, where $i, k = 1, 2, \cdots, n$ and δ_{ik} is the *Kronecker delta*. The Kronecker delta is defined to be 1 if $i = k$ and 0 if $i \neq k$.

11. Prove that if the identity matrix under multiplication is given in Eq. (1.6.3), then Eq. (1.6.1) is satisfied.

12. Write any 4×4 matrix **A**; first premultiply **A** by **I**, and then postmultiply **A** by **I**. Change one of the zeros in **I** to a non-zero scalar and determine if the same result is obtained when **A** is premultiplied and then postmultiplied by the new matrix.

13. (a) Show that the Pauli spin matrices **X**, **Y**, and **Z** are such that each is its own inverse. (Hint: See number 4 of Exercises 1.4.)
    (b) Are any other of the matrices found in the group in number 4 of Exercises 1.4 their own inverse?

14. For the matrices

$$\mathbf{A} = \begin{bmatrix} -1 & 1 & 2 \\ -1 & 0 & 1 \\ 1 & 1 & 1 \end{bmatrix} \quad \text{and} \quad \mathbf{B} = \begin{bmatrix} -1 & 1 & 1 \\ 2 & -3 & -1 \\ -1 & 2 & 1 \end{bmatrix},$$

    (a) Find **AB** and **BA**.
    (b) Find **ABA** and **BAB**.

15. (a) Write the system of equations

$$\begin{aligned} -x + y + 2z &= 2, \\ -x \phantom{{}+y} + z &= 0, \\ x + y + z &= 3 \end{aligned}$$

    in the form $\mathbf{Au} = \mathbf{c}$.
    (b) Use the results of exercise 14 to solve for **u**.

1.7. *Diagonal Matrices and Scalar Matrices*

A square matrix which consists of zeros off the principal diagonal is defined to be a *diagonal matrix*. The elements on the principal diagonal may or may not be non-zero. Thus the matrix

$$\mathbf{D} = \begin{bmatrix} d_1 & 0 & \cdots & 0 \\ 0 & d_2 & \cdots & 0 \\ \cdots & & & \\ 0 & 0 & \cdots & d_n \end{bmatrix} \tag{1.7.1}$$

is a diagonal matrix. That is, $\mathbf{D}$ is a diagonal matrix if and only if $d_{ij} = d_i\,\delta_{ij}$, where $d_i(i = 1, 2, \cdots, n)$ is a scalar, and δ_{ij} is the Kronecker delta. (See number 10 of Exercises 1.6.)

We have already considered some examples of diagonal matrices, such as the matrix $\mathbf{D}$ in number 3 of Exercises 1.6. From that exercise, we learned that if the principal diagonal elements of a diagonal matrix are all non-zero, the matrix possesses an inverse that is also a diagonal matrix. The principal diagonal elements of the inverse are the reciprocals of the corresponding elements of the original matrix.

Example 1.7.1. What is the inverse of the diagonal matrix

$$\mathbf{D} = \begin{bmatrix} 2 & 0 & 0 \\ 0 & 1 & 0 \\ 0 & 0 & 1/5 \end{bmatrix}?$$

The inverse of $\mathbf{D}$ is

$$\mathbf{D}^{-1} = \begin{bmatrix} 1/2 & 0 & 0 \\ 0 & 1 & 0 \\ 0 & 0 & 5 \end{bmatrix}$$

since $\mathbf{DD}^{-1} = \mathbf{D}^{-1}\mathbf{D} = \mathbf{I}$.

A diagonal matrix whose elements on the principal diagonal are all the same scalar λ is said to be a *scalar matrix*. Every scalar matrix may be written as a scalar times the identity matrix:

$$\mathbf{S} = \begin{bmatrix} \lambda & 0 & \cdots & 0 \\ 0 & \lambda & \cdots & 0 \\ \cdots & & & \\ 0 & 0 & \cdots & \lambda \end{bmatrix} = \lambda \begin{bmatrix} 1 & 0 & \cdots & 0 \\ 0 & 1 & \cdots & 0 \\ \cdots & & & \\ 0 & 0 & \cdots & 1 \end{bmatrix} = \lambda\mathbf{I} = \mathbf{I}\lambda. \tag{1.7.2}$$

The set of scalar matrices of order n, Eq. (1.7.2), forms a field under the definitions of addition and multiplication given earlier. First, since scalar matrices are square, addition is defined; they form an Abelian group under the operation of addition with the square zero matrix as the additive identity. (See Theorem 1.2.1.)

Second, scalar matrices with $\lambda \neq 0$ are diagonal matrices with non-zero elements on the principal diagonal. The closure property holds for such matrices from the definition of matrix multiplication; the associative property holds by Theorem 1.4.1; and the scalar matrix $\mathbf{I}$ is the identity matrix. Thus, non-zero scalar matrices form a group under the operation of multiplication. Since $\mathbf{A} = a\mathbf{I}$ and $\mathbf{B} = b\mathbf{I}$, then by Eq. (1.3.1)

$$\mathbf{AB} = a\mathbf{I}b\mathbf{I} = ab\mathbf{I} = ba\mathbf{I} = b\mathbf{I}a\mathbf{I} = \mathbf{BA};$$

the commutative property under multiplication is thus satisfied, and hence non-zero scalar matrices form an Abelian group under multiplication.

Third, the distributive property is satisfied. (See Corollary 1.5.1.) Therefore all of the field properties are satisfied for scalar matrices, and:

Theorem 1.7.1. *Scalar matrices form a field under the operations of addition and multiplication.*

Since for a field in general the additive identity is not required to have a multiplicative inverse, the zero matrix of the set of scalar matrices is not required to have an inverse. (In fact, it does not.) Note that operating with scalar matrices is equivalent to operating with scalars under the defined operations.

Exercises 1.7

1. Is a scalar matrix commutative with every other matrix of the same order? That is, does $\mathbf{AS} = \mathbf{SA}$ where $\mathbf{S}$ is a scalar matrix?

2. Does $\mathbf{AB} = \mathbf{BA}$, where

$$\mathbf{A} = \begin{bmatrix} a & 0 & 0 \\ 0 & b & 0 \\ 0 & 0 & c \end{bmatrix} \quad \text{and} \quad \mathbf{B} = \begin{bmatrix} d & 0 & 0 \\ 0 & e & 0 \\ 0 & 0 & f \end{bmatrix}?$$

   Do diagonal matrices of order n commute if $n > 3$?

3. If $\mathbf{D}$ is a diagonal matrix, evaluate $\mathbf{D}^k$ (where k is a positive integer).

4. Find the inverse of the matrix

$$\mathbf{D} = \begin{bmatrix} 2 & 0 & 0 \\ 0 & 3 & 0 \\ 0 & 0 & 4 \end{bmatrix}.$$

5. Do diagonal matrices of order n form a field? Why?

6. Prove the theorem: *If A is a diagonal matrix having no two diagonal elements equal, then the only matrices that commute with* **A** *are diagonal matrices.*

7. Prove the theorem: *The only matrices that commute with every square matrix of order n are scalar matrices of order n.*

8. If **A** is a given square matrix and **D** is a diagonal matrix, describe in words what has happened to **A** under **DA**; under **AD**.

1.8. Vectors

A matrix that consists of only one row is said to be a *row matrix* or a $1 \times n$ *matrix*. A matrix that consists of only one column is said to be a *column matrix* or an $m \times 1$ *matrix*.

(1.8.1) $$\mathbf{x} = [x_1 \quad x_2 \quad \cdots \quad x_n],$$

(1.8.2) $$\mathbf{y} = \begin{bmatrix} y_1 \\ y_2 \\ \vdots \\ y_m \end{bmatrix}.$$

Thus Eq. (1.8.1) is a row matrix, and Eq. (1.8.2) is a column matrix.

Row and column matrices will be referred to as *vectors*; lowercase (rather than uppercase) boldfaced letters will be used to distinguish vectors from general $m \times n$ matrices. The vectors studied in a course in Vector Analysis customarily have only three components or elements, while the vectors we study in courses in matrices may have n elements, where $n \gtreqless 3$. Whenever $n = 2$ or $n = 3$, the operations considered here are the same as the corresponding operations considered in Vector Analysis. Therefore vectors in those two instances may be referred to as *geometric vectors.*

1.9. Transpose of a Matrix

If the rows and columns of a matrix are interchanged the resulting matrix is said to be the *transpose* of the original matrix; the transpose of **A** is written as **A′**. That is, if a_{ij} is the element in the ith row and jth column of **A**, it is also the element in the jth row and ith column of **A′**. A matrix need not be square to have a transpose; if **A** is of order $m \times n$, then **A′** is of order $n \times m$. For example, if

$$\mathbf{A} = \begin{bmatrix} 2 & 3 \\ 1 & 4 \\ 0 & 5 \end{bmatrix}, \qquad \text{then} \qquad \mathbf{A}' = \begin{bmatrix} 2 & 1 & 0 \\ 3 & 4 & 5 \end{bmatrix}.$$

Using this notation, we can write the column vector in Eq. (1.8.2) as

$$\mathbf{y} = [y_1 \quad y_2 \quad \cdots \quad y_m]', \qquad \text{or as} \qquad \mathbf{y}' = [y_1 \quad y_2 \quad \cdots \quad y_m].$$

In this book, one of these representations is generally used instead of the column representation. However, in each instance, $\mathbf{y}$ remains a column vector.

If $\mathbf{A}$ and $\mathbf{B}$ are matrices for which addition is defined and if λ is a scalar, then

(1.9.1) $$\mathbf{A}' = \mathbf{B}' \quad \text{if and only if} \quad \mathbf{A} = \mathbf{B},$$

(1.9.2) $$(\mathbf{A}')' = \mathbf{A},$$

(1.9.3) $$(\mathbf{A} + \mathbf{B})' = \mathbf{A}' + \mathbf{B}', \quad \text{and}$$

(1.9.4) $$(\lambda\mathbf{A})' = \lambda\mathbf{A}'.$$

The proofs of these equations are left as exercises for the reader.

The following theorem gives an important result for the transpose of the product of matrices; it is slightly more complicated to prove.

Theorem 1.9.1. *If* $\mathbf{A}$ *and* $\mathbf{B}$ *are such that the multiplication is defined, then*

(1.9.5) $$(\mathbf{AB})' = \mathbf{B}'\mathbf{A}'.$$

Proof: Note first that if $\mathbf{AB}$ is defined, $(\mathbf{AB})'$ is defined, and that $\mathbf{B}'\mathbf{A}'$ is defined while $\mathbf{A}'\mathbf{B}'$ may not be. (When is $\mathbf{A}'\mathbf{B}'$ defined?) If $\mathbf{A}$ is an $m \times n$ matrix and $\mathbf{B}$ is an $n \times r$ matrix, then

(1.9.6) $$\mathbf{AB} = \mathbf{C}, \qquad \text{where} \qquad c_{ik} = \sum_{j=1}^{n} a_{ij}\, b_{jk}$$

is the element in the ith row and kth column of $\mathbf{C}$, an $m \times r$ matrix. It is sufficient to show that the element in the ith row and kth column of $\mathbf{C}$ is the same as the element in the kth row and ith column of $\mathbf{B}'\mathbf{A}'$.

For the transposed matrices we have $\mathbf{B}'_{r,n}$ and $\mathbf{A}'_{n,m}$, so $\mathbf{B}'\mathbf{A}' = [d_{ki}]$ is defined. The element d_{ki} is obtained by multiplying the elements of the kth row of $\mathbf{B}'$ by the corresponding elements of the ith column of $\mathbf{A}'$ and adding. That is,

(1.9.7) $$d_{ki} = [b_{1k} \quad b_{2k} \quad \cdots \quad b_{nk}] \begin{bmatrix} a_{i1} \\ a_{i2} \\ \cdots \\ a_{in} \end{bmatrix} = \sum_{j=1}^{n} b_{jk}\, a_{ij},$$

recalling that the vector $[b_{1k}\ b_{2k}\ \cdots\ b_{nk}]$ is the transpose of the vector that is the kth column of $\mathbf{B}$, and similarly $[a_{i1}\ a_{i2}\ \cdots\ a_{in}]'$ is the transpose of the vector that is the ith row of $\mathbf{A}$. Thus, since the summation in Eq. (1.9.7) can be written as

$$\sum_{j=1}^{n} a_{ij} b_{jk},$$

we see that $d_{ki} = c_{ik}$. That is,

(1.9.8) $$\mathbf{B}'\mathbf{A}' = \left[\sum_{j=1}^{n} a_{ij} b_{jk}\right] = (\mathbf{AB})';$$

the sum in the brackets is the element in the kth row and ith column of the product $\mathbf{B}'\mathbf{A}'$. The following example should help to clarify the result.

Example 1.9.1. Find $(\mathbf{AB})'$ and $\mathbf{B}'\mathbf{A}'$ if

$$\mathbf{A} = \begin{bmatrix} 2 & 1 & 3 \\ 1 & 0 & 2 \end{bmatrix} \quad \text{and} \quad \mathbf{B} = \begin{bmatrix} 1 & 4 \\ 0 & 2 \\ 3 & 1 \end{bmatrix}.$$

Now $$\mathbf{AB} = \begin{bmatrix} 2 & 1 & 3 \\ 1 & 0 & 2 \end{bmatrix} \begin{bmatrix} 1 & 4 \\ 0 & 2 \\ 3 & 1 \end{bmatrix} = \begin{bmatrix} 11 & 13 \\ 7 & 6 \end{bmatrix}, \quad \text{so}$$

$$(\mathbf{AB})' = \begin{bmatrix} 11 & 7 \\ 13 & 6 \end{bmatrix}.$$

Also $$\mathbf{A}' = \begin{bmatrix} 2 & 1 \\ 1 & 0 \\ 3 & 2 \end{bmatrix} \quad \text{and} \quad \mathbf{B}' = \begin{bmatrix} 1 & 0 & 3 \\ 4 & 2 & 1 \end{bmatrix}, \quad \text{so}$$

$$\mathbf{B}'\mathbf{A}' = \begin{bmatrix} 1 & 0 & 3 \\ 4 & 2 & 1 \end{bmatrix} \begin{bmatrix} 2 & 1 \\ 1 & 0 \\ 3 & 2 \end{bmatrix} = \begin{bmatrix} 11 & 7 \\ 13 & 6 \end{bmatrix}.$$

Note that $(\mathbf{AB})' = \mathbf{B}'\mathbf{A}'$.

Theorem 1.9.2. *If* $\mathbf{A}^{-1}$ *exists, then*

(1.9.9) $$(\mathbf{A}')^{-1} = (\mathbf{A}^{-1})'.$$

Proof: We have that $\mathbf{AA}^{-1} = \mathbf{I}$; taking the transpose in accordance with Theorem 1.9.1,

$$(\mathbf{A}^{-1})'\mathbf{A}' = \mathbf{I}' = \mathbf{I}.$$

Thus, to prove Theorem 1.9.2, we need only write

$$(\mathbf{A}^{-1})' = (\mathbf{A}^{-1})'\mathbf{A}'(\mathbf{A}')^{-1} = (\mathbf{A}')^{-1}.$$

By using the transpose, we are able to multiply row (or column) vectors together within the definition of matrix multiplication. The following three definitions, which are quite useful in our further study of vectors and matrices and which are discussed more fully later, are stated in terms of row vectors; similar definitions can be made for column vectors.

The product of a row vector **x** and a column vector **y** is a *scalar product*; it is customarily written as the scalar itself. (See Sections 2.2 and 2.3.) For instance,

$$[2 \quad 1 \quad 4]\begin{bmatrix} -1 \\ 0 \\ 2 \end{bmatrix} = 6.$$

If the scalar product of two vectors is zero, the vectors are *orthogonal.* The vectors $[2 \quad -1 \quad 4]$ and $[-1 \quad 2 \quad 1]'$ are orthogonal because

$$[2 \quad -1 \quad 4]\begin{bmatrix} -1 \\ 2 \\ 1 \end{bmatrix} = 0.$$

If we multiply a row vector and its transpose, and obtain a scalar product of 1, the vector is a *unit vector.* The row vector $[3/5 \quad 4/5]$ is a unit vector, because

$$[3/5 \quad 4/5]\begin{bmatrix} 3/5 \\ 4/5 \end{bmatrix} = 1.$$

Exercises 1.9

1. If **x** is the row vector $[x_1 \quad x_2 \quad \cdots \quad x_n]$ and **y** is the column vector $[y_1 \quad y_2 \quad \cdots \quad y_n]'$ find $\mathbf{xx}'$, $\mathbf{y'y}$ and $\mathbf{xy}$.
2. For any vector **a**, show that $\mathbf{a'a} = (\mathbf{a'a})'$.
3. Find $(\mathbf{ABC})'$ in terms of $\mathbf{A}'$, $\mathbf{B}'$, and $\mathbf{C}'$. Extend the result to the transpose of the product of n matrices.
4. Prove Eq. (1.9.1).
5. Prove Eq. (1.9.2).
6. Prove Eq. (1.9.3).
7. Prove Eq. (1.9.4).
8. Using the matrices of Example 1.9.1, verify that $(\mathbf{BA})' = \mathbf{A'B'}$.
9. Verify Eqs. (1.9.1) through (1.9.5) if

$$\mathbf{A} = \begin{bmatrix} 1 & 1 \\ 0 & 1 \end{bmatrix} \quad \text{and} \quad \mathbf{B} = \begin{bmatrix} 1 & 2 \\ 3 & 4 \end{bmatrix}.$$

10. If $\mathbf{x} = [2 \quad -1 \quad 0 \quad 5]$ and $\mathbf{y} = [1 \quad 7 \quad 4 \quad 1]$, show that $\mathbf{xy}' = 0$ (so that **x** and **y** are orthogonal).
11. Find the scalar product of $[3 \quad -1 \quad 2]$ and $[x^2 \quad x \quad 1]'$. (See exercise 1.)

12. Find two vectors, each containing 3 non-zero elements, such that their scalar product is zero.

13. Find a row vector $\mathbf{x}$ with three elements such that $\mathbf{xx}' = 1$ (so that $\mathbf{x}$ is a unit vector).

1.10. Special Matrices

A square matrix having only zero elements on one side of the principal diagonal is a *triangular matrix*. If the zeros are below the principal diagonal, the matrix is an *upper triangular matrix*; if the zeros are above the principal diagonal, the matrix is a *lower triangular matrix*. If each of the principal diagonal elements of a triangular matrix is zero, the matrix is a *strictly triangular matrix*. All diagonal matrices and scalar matrices, as well as the identity matrix and the zero matrix, are triangular matrices.

Among the following matrices, **A** and **D** are upper triangular matrices, **B** is a lower triangular matrix, and **C** is strictly triangular.

$$\mathbf{A} = \begin{bmatrix} 1 & 2 & 1 \\ 0 & 3 & 0 \\ 0 & 0 & 2 \end{bmatrix}, \quad \mathbf{B} = \begin{bmatrix} 2 & 0 & 0 \\ 2 & -1 & 0 \\ 0 & 4 & 0 \end{bmatrix}, \quad \mathbf{C} = \begin{bmatrix} 0 & 0 & 0 \\ 2 & 0 & 0 \\ 3 & 2 & 0 \end{bmatrix},$$

$$\mathbf{D} = \begin{bmatrix} 1 & 2 & 0 \\ 0 & 0 & 3 \\ 0 & 0 & 0 \end{bmatrix}.$$

The matrix **J** is a matrix consisting entirely of ones, and the vector **j** is a vector of ones:

$$(1.10.1) \qquad \mathbf{J} = \begin{bmatrix} 1 & 1 & \cdots & 1 \\ 1 & 1 & \cdots & 1 \\ \cdots & & & \\ 1 & 1 & \cdots & 1 \end{bmatrix}, \quad \text{and} \quad \mathbf{j} = \begin{bmatrix} 1 \\ 1 \\ \cdots \\ 1 \end{bmatrix}.$$

Unfortunately the symbols **J** and **j** are often used to represent other mathematical objects. (See Section 7.8 for another use of **J**, or any text on Vector Analysis for another use of **j**.) In general, however, the context will indicate which use is intended in each instance.

If $\mathbf{A} = \mathbf{A}'$, then **A** is a *symmetric matrix*. If $\mathbf{A} = -\mathbf{A}'$, then **A** is a *skew symmetric* matrix. Only square matrices can be symmetric or skew symmetric. Consequences of these definitions (that are often taken as definitions) are that $a_{ij} = a_{ji}$ for symmetric matrices and $a_{ij} = -a_{ji}$ for skew symmetric matrices.

The matrix **A** in Eq. (1.10.2) is symmetric while **B** is skew symmetric:

$$(1.10.2) \qquad \mathbf{A} = \begin{bmatrix} 0 & 2 & -3 \\ 2 & 1 & 4 \\ -3 & 4 & -2 \end{bmatrix}, \quad \mathbf{B} = \begin{bmatrix} 0 & -4 & 0 & 3 \\ 4 & 0 & 1 & -2 \\ 0 & -1 & 0 & 5 \\ -3 & 2 & -5 & 0 \end{bmatrix}.$$

In our work we shall be primarily concerned with matrices all of whose elements are real. Such matrices are called *real matrices*. However, matrices with complex elements occur frequently in the applications, see number 4 of Exercises 1.4 for example.

If each element of a matrix **A** is replaced by its complex conjugate, the resulting matrix is said to be the *conjugate* of **A** and is denoted by $\bar{\mathbf{A}}$.

Theorem 1.10.1. *The matrix* **A** *is real if and only if* $\mathbf{A} = \bar{\mathbf{A}}$.

Proof: If the general element of **A** is $a_{jk} = \alpha_{jk} + i\beta_{jk}$, for which $i = \sqrt{-1}$ and α_{jk} and β_{jk} are real, then $\bar{a}_{jk} = \alpha_{jk} - i\,\beta_{jk}$ is the corresponding element of $\bar{\mathbf{A}}$.

Thus if $\mathbf{A} = \bar{\mathbf{A}}$, $a_{jk} = \bar{a}_{jk}$ which implies that $\beta_{jk} = 0$ and thus each a_{jk} is real. Conversely if **A** is real, $\beta_{jk} = 0$, $a_{jk} = \bar{a}_{jk}$, and thus $\mathbf{A} = \bar{\mathbf{A}}$.

If we take the *transpose* of the *conjugate* of **A** we obtain a matrix denoted by $\bar{\mathbf{A}}' = \mathbf{A}^*$.

For example, if

$$\mathbf{A} = \begin{bmatrix} i & 3-i \\ 2+i & 1+i2 \end{bmatrix}, \quad \text{then} \quad \bar{A} = \begin{bmatrix} -i & 3+i \\ 2-i & 1-i2 \end{bmatrix}, \quad \text{and}$$

$$\mathbf{A}^* = \begin{bmatrix} -i & 2-i \\ 3+i & 1-i2 \end{bmatrix}.$$

If $\mathbf{A} = \mathbf{A}^*$, then **A** is said to be a *Hermitian*† matrix. If the elements of A are all real, then $\mathbf{A}' = \mathbf{A}^*$; thus *a real Hermitian matrix is a symmetric matrix.*

Example 1.10.1. If **A** is any square matrix, prove that $\mathbf{A} + \mathbf{A}'$ is symmetric and $\mathbf{A} - \mathbf{A}'$ is skew symmetric.

If **A** is square, **A** and $\mathbf{A}'$ can be added. If $\mathbf{A} + \mathbf{A}' = \mathbf{B}$,

$$\mathbf{B}' = (\mathbf{A} + \mathbf{A}')' = \mathbf{A}' + (\mathbf{A}')' = \mathbf{A}' + \mathbf{A} = \mathbf{A} + \mathbf{A}' = \mathbf{B},$$

so that $\mathbf{A} + \mathbf{A}'$ is symmetric.

Similarly, if $\mathbf{A} - \mathbf{A}' = \mathbf{C}$,

$$\mathbf{C}' = (\mathbf{A} - \mathbf{A}')' = \mathbf{A}' - (\mathbf{A}')' = \mathbf{A}' - \mathbf{A} = -\mathbf{C},$$

so that $\mathbf{A} - \mathbf{A}'$ is skew symmetric.

Special types of matrices are encountered in various places in the applications. This section concludes with a listing and brief discussion of a few such matrices.

If the matrix **A** is squared and the result is **A**, then **A** is said to be *idempotent*.

†Named after the French mathematician, Charles Hermite (1822–1901).

That is, **A** is idempotent if and only if

$$\mathbf{A}^2 = \mathbf{A}. \tag{1.10.3}$$

The zero matrix and the identity matrix are both idempotent; so are many others, such as

$$\begin{bmatrix} 1 & 0 \\ 2 & 0 \end{bmatrix}.$$

A matrix **A** is said to be *nilpotent* if

$$\mathbf{A}^k = \mathbf{0} \tag{1.10.4}$$

for some positive integer k. The matrix **A** is said to be nilpotent of *index* k if $\mathbf{A}^k = \mathbf{0}$ but $\mathbf{A}^{k-1} \neq \mathbf{0}$. Considering the matrices

$$\mathbf{A} = \begin{bmatrix} 2 & 1 \\ -4 & -2 \end{bmatrix} \quad \text{and} \quad \mathbf{B} = \begin{bmatrix} 3 & 1 \\ 0 & 2 \end{bmatrix};$$

A is nilpotent of index 2, but **B** is not nilpotent, since $\mathbf{B}^k \neq \mathbf{0}$ for any integer k.

A matrix **A** such that

$$\mathbf{A}^2 = \mathbf{I} \tag{1.10.5}$$

is said to be *involutory*. That is, if **A** is involutory it is its own inverse. A necessary and sufficient condition that **A** be involutory is that

$$(\mathbf{A} + \mathbf{I})(\mathbf{A} - \mathbf{I}) = \mathbf{0}. \tag{1.10.6}$$

Equation (1.10.6) does not imply, however, that only **I** and $-\mathbf{I}$ are involutory. For example, another involutory matrix is

$$\begin{bmatrix} 0 & 1 \\ 1 & 0 \end{bmatrix}.$$

Finally, the symbol δ_{ij}, the *Kronecker delta*, is a function such that

$$\delta_{ij} = \begin{Bmatrix} 1, \text{ if } i \neq j \\ 0, \text{ if } i \neq j \end{Bmatrix}, \tag{1.10.7}$$

where i and j are positive integers. (See number 10 in Exercises 1.6.) The square matrix $\mathbf{A} = [\delta_{ij}]$ is the identity matrix: when $i = j$, the elements are on the principal diagonal (and are all ones), and when $i \neq j$, the elements are off the principal diagonal (and are all zeros). What is $[d_i \delta_{ij}]$ if the d_i are scalars?

Exercises 1.10

1. Prove that the elements on the principal diagonal of a skew symmetric matrix must all be equal. What stronger result have you proved?
2. Prove that the principal diagonal elements of a Hermitian matrix are all real.

3. Prove the theorem: *If* **A** *is any matrix, then* **AA′** *is symmetric.*

4. Prove that any square matrix may be written as the sum of a symmetric matrix and a skew symmetric matrix.

5. If **A** is square and **A** = −**A*** (that is, if $a_{ij} = -\bar{a}_{ji}$ for all i and j), **A** is said to be *skew Hermitian*. Show that i**A** is skew Hermitian if **A** is Hermitian; also show that i**A** is Hermitian if **A** is skew Hermitian.

6. If **A** is Hermitian, write **A** = **B** + i**C** where **B** and **C** are real matrices. Describe **B** and **C** further.

7. If **A** is symmetric or skew symmetric, show that **AA′** = **A′A**.

8. Prove the theorem: *If* **A** *is real and* **A′A** = **0**, *then* **A** = **0**.

9. If **A** and **B** are symmetric, is **AB** symmetric? Give an example involving 2 × 2 matrices **A** and **B** supporting your answer.

10. Show that (**A***)* = **A**, (**AB**)* = **B*A***, (**AB** ⋯ **H**)* = **H*** ⋯ **B*A***.

11. If **A** is symmetric or skew symmetric, show that both **AA′** and $\mathbf{A}^2$ are symmetric.

12. Prove that if **A** is a symmetric matrix, then $\mathbf{A}^{-1}$ is also symmetric.

13. (a) Determine an idempotent matrix of order 2 that has 1 in the lower left-hand corner.
    (b) Determine an idempotent diagonal matrix of order 3. Generalize.

14. Prove that any matrix of order 3 that is strictly triangular is nilpotent. What is the index of the most general such matrix?

15. Determine the form of every nilpotent matrix of order 2 and index 2.

16. (a) By referring to Eq. (1.10.6) explain why matrices other than **I** and −**I** can be involutory.
    (b) Give at least two numerical examples of 3 × 3 matrices other than **I** and −**I** that are involutory.

1.11. *Submatrices and Block Matrices*

Since a matrix **A** is defined to be an array of scalars, any matrix of order greater than one can be broken up into other arrays, called *submatrices of* **A**, by deleting from **A** some rows, some columns, both, or neither.

The matrices $\mathbf{A}_1$ and $\mathbf{A}_2$ of Eq. (1.11.1) are both submatrices of **A** of Eq. (1.11.2):

(1.11.1)
$$\mathbf{A}_1 = \begin{bmatrix} a & c \\ d & f \end{bmatrix} \qquad \mathbf{A}_2 = [h \quad i]$$

(1.11.2)
$$\mathbf{A} = \begin{bmatrix} a & b & c \\ d & e & f \\ g & h & i \end{bmatrix}.$$

The matrix $\mathbf{A}_1$ was obtained by deleting the third row and second column of $\mathbf{A}$, and $\mathbf{A}_2$ was obtained by deleting the first and second rows and the first column of $\mathbf{A}$. The matrix $\mathbf{A}$ itself, as well as each of its elements, may also be considered a submatrix of $\mathbf{A}$.

The rows of an $m \times n$ matrix $\mathbf{A}$ are $1 \times n$ submatrices or *row vectors*; the columns of $\mathbf{A}$ are $m \times 1$ submatrices or *column vectors*.

A matrix $\mathbf{A}$ is *partitioned* if it is broken into submatrices by horizontal lines between rows and vertical lines between columns. The matrix in Eq. (1.11.3) has been partitioned into nine submatrices. In a partitioned matrix, each element is contained in one and only one submatrix.

(1.11.3)

$$\mathbf{A} = \left[\begin{array}{cc:ccc:ccc} a_{11} & a_{12} & a_{13} & \cdots & a_{1j} & a_{1,j+1} & \cdots & a_{1n} \\ \hdashline a_{21} & a_{22} & a_{23} & \cdots & a_{2j} & a_{2,j+1} & \cdots & a_{2n} \\ \cdots & & & & & & & \\ a_{k1} & a_{k2} & a_{k3} & \cdots & a_{kj} & a_{k,j+1} & \cdots & a_{kn} \\ \hdashline a_{k+1,1} & a_{k+1,2} & a_{k+1,3} & \cdots & a_{k+1,j} & a_{k+1,j+1} & \cdots & a_{k+1,n} \\ \cdots & & & & & & & \\ a_{m1} & a_{m2} & a_{m3} & \cdots & a_{mj} & a_{m,j+1} & \cdots & a_{mn} \end{array}\right]$$

While the matrix of Eq. (1.11.3) has been partitioned, the matrix

(1.11.4)
$$\mathbf{B} = \begin{bmatrix} \begin{bmatrix} 2 \\ 0 \end{bmatrix} & \begin{bmatrix} 1 & 3 \end{bmatrix} \\ \begin{bmatrix} 2 \end{bmatrix} & \begin{bmatrix} 1 & 4 \\ 1 & 7 \end{bmatrix} \end{bmatrix}$$

has been broken into submatrices but is not partitioned.

We now broaden the definition of a matrix to permit the elements of a matrix to be matrices themselves (instead of restricting the elements only to scalars). For instance, Eq. (1.11.3) may be written as

(1.11.5)
$$\mathbf{A} = \begin{bmatrix} \mathbf{A}_{11} & \mathbf{A}_{12} & \mathbf{A}_{13} \\ \mathbf{A}_{21} & \mathbf{A}_{22} & \mathbf{A}_{23} \\ \mathbf{A}_{31} & \mathbf{A}_{32} & \mathbf{A}_{33} \end{bmatrix},$$

in which each element $\mathbf{A}_{ij}$ is defined in an obvious manner from $\mathbf{A}$. (Note that the subscripts *do not* refer to the orders of the submatrices.)

The matrix in Eq. (1.11.5) is a *block matrix*. The submatrices $\mathbf{A}_{ij}$ for which $i = j$ are *diagonal blocks* of the matrix. If the number of rows of submatrices equals the number of columns of submatrices, the matrix is a *square block matrix*. If each diagonal block of a square block matrix is a square matrix, the matrix is said to be *regularly partitioned*. (Only square matrices can be regularly partitioned.)

If a square block matrix is such that the submatrices $\mathbf{A}_{ij} = \mathbf{0}$ for $i \neq j$, the matrix is said to be a *diagonal block matrix*. If a square block matrix is such that the elements above (or below) the diagonal blocks are all zero, the matrix is said to be a *triangular block matrix*. Note that in either case the matrix itself need not be square, provided it is a square block matrix.

In forming a submatrix **B** from a matrix **A**, the elements from certain rows and columns are used. If we now construct a submatrix **C** from the remaining rows and columns, taken in the same order, we obtain a submatrix which has no rows or columns in common with **B**. For example, if

$$\mathbf{A} = \begin{bmatrix} 2 & 1 & 7 & 3 \\ -1 & 0 & 9 & 4 \\ 3 & 8 & 7 & 2 \\ 1 & 0 & 5 & 6 \end{bmatrix} \quad \text{and} \quad \mathbf{B} = \begin{bmatrix} -1 & 9 \\ 3 & 7 \end{bmatrix}, \tag{1.11.6}$$

$$\text{then} \quad \mathbf{C} = \begin{bmatrix} 1 & 3 \\ 0 & 6 \end{bmatrix}.$$

One use of partitioned matrices is the following: Given **A** and **B** we may write

$$\mathbf{AB} = \begin{bmatrix} \mathbf{A}_1 \\ \mathbf{A}_2 \\ \vdots \\ \mathbf{A}_m \end{bmatrix} [\mathbf{B}_1 \quad \mathbf{B}_2 \quad \cdots \quad \mathbf{B}_p] = [\mathbf{A}_i\mathbf{B}_j], \tag{1.11.7}$$

where $i = 1, 2, \cdots, m$, and $j = 1, 2, \cdots, p$. Here $\mathbf{A}_i$ is a $1 \times n$ row vector and $\mathbf{B}_j$ is an $n \times 1$ column vector; the subscripts i and j do not refer to the order of the matrix. Written out more completely, the result in Eq. (1.11.7) is

$$\mathbf{AB} = \begin{bmatrix} \mathbf{A}_1\mathbf{B}_1 & \mathbf{A}_1\mathbf{B}_2 & \cdots & \mathbf{A}_1\mathbf{B}_p \\ \mathbf{A}_2\mathbf{B}_1 & \mathbf{A}_2\mathbf{B}_2 & \cdots & \mathbf{A}_2\mathbf{B}_p \\ \cdots & & & \\ \mathbf{A}_m\mathbf{B}_1 & \mathbf{A}_m\mathbf{B}_2 & \cdots & \mathbf{A}_m\mathbf{B}_p \end{bmatrix} \tag{1.11.8}$$

where the element $\mathbf{A}_i\mathbf{B}_j$ is the scalar product, a 1×1 matrix that we may write as the scalar itself. (See Section 1.9.).

Similarly, after partitioning **A** and **B** as

$$\mathbf{A} = \begin{bmatrix} \mathbf{A}_{11} & \mathbf{A}_{12} \\ \mathbf{A}_{21} & \mathbf{A}_{22} \end{bmatrix} \quad \text{and} \quad \mathbf{B} = \begin{bmatrix} \mathbf{B}_{11} & \mathbf{B}_{12} \\ \mathbf{B}_{21} & \mathbf{B}_{22} \end{bmatrix} \tag{1.11.9}$$

such that the various submatrices can be multiplied, the product **AB** may be written as

$$\mathbf{AB} = \begin{bmatrix} \mathbf{A}_{11}\mathbf{B}_{11} + \mathbf{A}_{12}\mathbf{B}_{21} & \mathbf{A}_{11}\mathbf{B}_{12} + \mathbf{A}_{12}\mathbf{B}_{22} \\ \mathbf{A}_{21}\mathbf{B}_{11} + \mathbf{A}_{22}\mathbf{B}_{21} & \mathbf{A}_{21}\mathbf{B}_{12} + \mathbf{A}_{22}\mathbf{B}_{22} \end{bmatrix}. \tag{1.11.10}$$

Note that after **A** has been partitioned by columns, **B** must be partitioned correspondingly by rows so that the submatrices can be multiplied. The rows of **A** and the columns of **B** may each be partitioned entirely arbitrarily, since the multiplication remains defined in any case.

Example 1.11.1. Perform the following matrix multiplication by using the indicated submatrices:

$$\left[\begin{array}{ccc|cc} 2 & 1 & 3 & 5 & 4 \\ 0 & 1 & 6 & 2 & 1 \\ \hline 3 & 1 & 4 & 7 & 1 \end{array}\right]\left[\begin{array}{ccc|c} 2 & 1 & 4 & 3 \\ 1 & 1 & 2 & 1 \\ 0 & 1 & 0 & 0 \\ \hline 2 & 1 & 3 & 0 \\ 4 & 1 & 3 & 1 \end{array}\right].$$

By referring to Eq. (1.11.10), we first write the product as

$$\begin{bmatrix} \begin{bmatrix} 5 & 6 & 10 \\ 1 & 7 & 2 \end{bmatrix} + \begin{bmatrix} 26 & 9 & 27 \\ 8 & 3 & 9 \end{bmatrix} & \begin{bmatrix} 7 \\ 1 \end{bmatrix} + \begin{bmatrix} 4 \\ 1 \end{bmatrix} \\ [7 \quad 8 \quad 14] + [18 \quad 8 \quad 24] & [10] + [1] \end{bmatrix}$$

$$= \begin{bmatrix} \begin{bmatrix} 31 & 15 & 37 \\ 9 & 10 & 11 \end{bmatrix} & \begin{bmatrix} 11 \\ 2 \end{bmatrix} \\ [25 \quad 16 \quad 38] & [11] \end{bmatrix} = \begin{bmatrix} 31 & 15 & 37 & 11 \\ 9 & 10 & 11 & 2 \\ 25 & 16 & 38 & 11 \end{bmatrix}.$$

Note that if the matrices contain blocks that are zero matrices after partitioning, the multiplication is considerably simplified.

Example 1.11.2. Find the product **AB** of the partitioned matrices

$$\mathbf{A} = \left[\begin{array}{cc|c} 2 & 1 & 0 \\ 0 & 3 & 0 \\ \hline 0 & 0 & 0 \\ \hline 0 & 1 & 4 \end{array}\right] \quad \text{and} \quad \mathbf{B} = \left[\begin{array}{c|cc|cc} 1 & 0 & 0 & 1 & 0 \\ 2 & 0 & 0 & 0 & 0 \\ \hline 0 & 0 & 0 & 0 & 0 \end{array}\right].$$

$$\mathbf{AB} = \begin{bmatrix} \begin{bmatrix} 4 \\ 6 \end{bmatrix} + \begin{bmatrix} 0 \\ 0 \end{bmatrix} & \begin{bmatrix} 0 & 0 \\ 0 & 0 \end{bmatrix} + \begin{bmatrix} 0 & 0 \\ 0 & 0 \end{bmatrix} & \begin{bmatrix} 2 & 0 \\ 0 & 0 \end{bmatrix} + \begin{bmatrix} 0 & 0 \\ 0 & 0 \end{bmatrix} \\ [0] + [0] & [0 \quad 0] + [0 \quad 0] & [0 \quad 0] + [0 \quad 0] \\ [2] + [0] & [0 \quad 0] + [0 \quad 0] & [0 \quad 0] + [0 \quad 0] \end{bmatrix}$$

$$= \begin{bmatrix} \begin{bmatrix} 4 \\ 6 \end{bmatrix} & \begin{bmatrix} 0 & 0 \\ 0 & 0 \end{bmatrix} & \begin{bmatrix} 2 & 0 \\ 0 & 0 \end{bmatrix} \\ [0] & [0 \quad 0] & [0 \quad 0] \\ [2] & [0 \quad 0] & [0 \quad 0] \end{bmatrix} = \begin{bmatrix} 4 & 0 & 0 & 2 & 0 \\ 6 & 0 & 0 & 0 & 0 \\ 0 & 0 & 0 & 0 & 0 \\ 2 & 0 & 0 & 0 & 0 \end{bmatrix}.$$

Exercises 1.11

1. Partition **A** properly and find the product **AB** by the methods of this section.

$$\mathbf{AB} = \begin{bmatrix} 6 & 3 & 5 & 1 \\ 2 & 7 & -4 & 3 \end{bmatrix} \begin{bmatrix} 2 & 0 & 1 \\ 1 & -1 & 1 \\ 0 & 1 & 0 \\ 0 & 0 & 1 \end{bmatrix}.$$

2. Using the partitioned form, find the product **AB** if

$$\mathbf{A} = \begin{bmatrix} \mathbf{I}_2 & \mathbf{0} \\ \mathbf{0} & \mathbf{A}_1 \end{bmatrix}, \qquad \mathbf{B} = \begin{bmatrix} \mathbf{B}_1 & \mathbf{0} & \mathbf{B}_2 \\ \mathbf{0} & \mathbf{I}_1 & \mathbf{B}_3 \end{bmatrix},$$

where

$$\mathbf{I}_2 = \begin{bmatrix} 1 & 0 \\ 0 & 1 \end{bmatrix}, \qquad \mathbf{A}_1 = [3],$$

$$\mathbf{B}_1 = \begin{bmatrix} 1 & 2 \\ 3 & 4 \end{bmatrix}, \qquad \mathbf{B}_2 = \begin{bmatrix} 6 \\ 5 \end{bmatrix}, \qquad \mathbf{B}_3 = [7], \qquad \mathbf{I}_1 = [1],$$

and the **0** matrices are of appropriate order.

3. In number 2, determine at least two more partitionings of **B** such that the partitioned form of the product **AB** is defined. Verify that these new partitionings give the same value for **AB**.

4. Partition the following matrices to take advantage of the zero elements, and perform the indicated multiplication:

$$\begin{bmatrix} 5 & 2 & 0 & 0 \\ 2 & 1 & 0 & 0 \\ 0 & 0 & 8 & 3 \\ 0 & 0 & 5 & 2 \end{bmatrix} \begin{bmatrix} 1 & -2 & 0 & 0 \\ -2 & 5 & 0 & 0 \\ 0 & 0 & 2 & -3 \\ 0 & 0 & -5 & 8 \end{bmatrix}.$$

5. Write the submatrix obtained by deleting the first row and second column of **A**, where

$$\mathbf{A} = \begin{bmatrix} a_{11} & a_{12} & a_{13} \\ a_{21} & a_{22} & a_{23} \\ a_{31} & a_{32} & a_{33} \end{bmatrix}.$$

6. In Example 1.11.2, with **A** partitioned as shown, partition **B** in two other ways, and show that the final product is the same in all three cases.

7. Partition the matrix in exercise 5 so that it may be written as a column matrix of row vectors; as a row matrix of column vectors.

8. Using the vector form of the matrices in Eq. (1.11.7), assume that $m = p$, then find **BA** and write the result in the expanded form corresponding to Eq. (1.11.8).

9. For the matrix

$$\mathbf{P} = \begin{bmatrix} 1 & 2 & -1 \\ 3 & 0 & -2 \end{bmatrix},$$

how many submatrices can be obtained from **P**? Write out completely all possible submatrices.

10. Give a numerical example of a 4×5 triangular block matrix with 9 submatrices.

11. Give a numerical example of the product of matrices $\mathbf{A}_{4,5}$ and $\mathbf{B}_{5,6}$, each a diagonal block matrix with 9 submatrices, which illustrates the advantage of block matrix multiplication.

2

Determinants

2.1. Introduction

This chapter considers some aspects of determinant theory needed in the further study of matrices. Although the reader is no doubt familiar with some of the elementary uses and manipulations of determinants, the chapter includes a systematic treatment of the subject in general. The special cases of determinants of orders 2 and 3 are used to illustrate the general definitions and theorems.

In Section 1.2 we defined a matrix as an *array* of scalars with no value or number associated with it. We now wish to associate a scalar with a matrix in some reasonable manner. Although this may be done in a variety of ways, not all definitions are equally valuable; in addition, a definition useful for one purpose might not be useful for another. For example (as will be shown later), the determinant of a square matrix of real numbers may be either positive, negative, or zero. Thus this definition would not be satisfactory if the associated scalar must always be non-negative.

Before defining a determinant, we shall consider a few other definitions useful for certain special matrices.

2.2. Matrices of One Element

For a matrix of one element, it appears reasonable to associate the scalar element itself with the matrix. One reason is that such matrices are scalar matrices; operating with the scalar is equivalent to operating with the matrix.

Another reason is that, since a matrix of one element is a square matrix, its determinant is the element itself. (See Section 2.5.)

Finally, matrices of one element generally arise as a product of vectors. For the product of column vectors $\mathbf{x}$ and $\mathbf{y}$ we write $\mathbf{x}'\mathbf{y} = [c]$, a 1×1 matrix, considering the result as a *product of matrices*. However, if this product is considered as a *scalar product* (defined in Sections 1.9 and 2.3), this operation is a mapping of a set of vectors onto a set of scalars, and we write $\mathbf{x}'\mathbf{y} = c$, a scalar.

Thus, except for a few isolated cases, we shall associate the scalar itself with the matrix of one element. Note, however, that $[c] \neq c$, since the matrix and the scalar are not members of the same set.

2.3. *Scalars Associated with Vectors*

Next, what scalar should be associated with a vector, another special matrix? Using the results of the preceding section, then for the special *scalar products* $\mathbf{x}\mathbf{x}'$ and $\mathbf{y}'\mathbf{y}$, where $\mathbf{x}$ is a row vector and $\mathbf{y}$ is a column vector, we can associate the scalar of $\mathbf{x}\mathbf{x}'$ with $\mathbf{x}$ and of $\mathbf{y}'\mathbf{y}$ with $\mathbf{y}$. For example, the vector $\mathbf{x} = [2\ \ 1\ \ 3]$ can have the scalar 14 associated with it, since $\mathbf{x}\mathbf{x}' = 14$.

A *scalar product* is defined as the scalar obtained by taking the product of a row vector and a column vector. Thus if $\mathbf{x}$ and $\mathbf{y}$ are row vectors and $\mathbf{u}$ and $\mathbf{v}$ are column vectors, each with the same number of elements, then $\mathbf{x}\mathbf{y}'$, $\mathbf{u}'\mathbf{v}$, $\mathbf{x}\mathbf{u}$, and $\mathbf{v}'\mathbf{y}'$ are all examples of scalar products. As stated in the previous section, we associate the scalar element of the scalar product of two vectors with that scalar product.

After determining the scalar element of the scalar product of a vector $\mathbf{x}$ and its transpose $\mathbf{x}'$ (or the transposed conjugate $\mathbf{x}^*$ if the elements are from $\mathscr{F}_c$), we can take the positive square root of this element. The result is called the *length* or the *magnitude of the vector*. This quantity may also be called a *norm* of the vector, denoted in general by $\|\mathbf{x}\|$, since it satisfies the three properties:

(2.3.1)
(a) $\|\mathbf{x}\| \geqq 0;\ \|\mathbf{x}\| = 0 \quad$ if and only if $\mathbf{x} = \mathbf{0}$,
(b) $\|\alpha\| = |\alpha|\ \|\mathbf{x}\|$, and
(c) $\|\mathbf{x} + \mathbf{y}\| \leqq \|\mathbf{x}\| + \|\mathbf{y}\|$, the triangular inequality.

It is left as an exercise for the reader to prove that the length of a vector actually satisfies the properties required for a norm. Note that both the scalar product and the length of a vector are always non-negative if the elements of the vector belong to $\mathscr{F}_r$, the real number field. Note also that $\sqrt{\mathbf{x}^*\mathbf{x}} \geqq 0$ if the elements of $\mathbf{x}$ are from $\mathscr{F}_c$.

Example 2.3.1. Determine the magnitude of the vector $\mathbf{x} = [4\ 2\ 4]$.

The scalar product is

$$\mathbf{xx}' = [4 \quad 2 \quad 4]\,[4 \quad 2 \quad 4]' = 16 + 4 + 16 = 36,$$

so the magnitude is $\sqrt{36} = 6$. Observe that this is merely the distance from the origin to the point (4, 2, 4) in a rectangular coordinate system.

Exercises 2.3

1. Find the scalar associated with $\mathbf{d}$ if $\mathbf{d}' = [2\ 4\ 1\ 3]$; with $\mathbf{h} = [1\ 0\ 5\ 1]$.
2. Divide each element of the vector $\mathbf{c} = [2\ 1\ -2]$ by the proper scalar so that the length of $\mathbf{c}$ is 1. The resulting vector is a unit vector.
3. Find the scalar product of $\mathbf{p}$ and $\mathbf{q}$ if $\mathbf{p} = [2\ 1\ 7\ 3]$ and $\mathbf{q}' = [4\ -1\ 0\ 2]$.
4. Which pairs of the following vectors are orthogonal?

$$\mathbf{p} = [\ \ 1 \quad 2 \quad \ \ 1 \quad 2]$$
$$\mathbf{q} = [-2 \quad 1 \quad -2 \quad 1]$$
$$\mathbf{r} = [-2 \quad 1 \quad \ \ 0 \quad 0]$$
$$\mathbf{s} = [\ \ 0 \quad 0 \quad \ \ 1 \quad 2]$$

5. Find the length of each vector in exercise 4.

6.* Prove that the length of a vector satisfies the properties required for a norm.

2.4. *Signs Associated with Permutations*

Before we can define a determinant, we need to associate a +1 or a −1 with a *permutation* of the first n natural numbers $1, 2, \cdots, n$. If the integers 1 through n are in their *natural order*, or if these integers are permuted by an *even number of interchanges* from their natural order, we associate a +1 with the permutation. If the integers are permuted by an *odd number of interchanges* from their natural order, we associate a −1 with the permutation.

For example, consider the permutations 1 4 3 2 and 2 3 4 1. The interchange of 2 and 4 (1 interchange from the natural order) gives the first permutation; the interchange of 1 and 2, then 1 and 3, then 1 and 4 (3 interchanges from the natural order), gives the second permutation. In each instance, the number of interchanges is odd; thus, each permutation has a −1 associated with it. Although the number of interchanges may not be unique, the sign associated with a permutation is always unique.

2.5. *Definition of a Determinant*

Finally we define the *determinant* of the square matrix **A** to be the particular scalar associated with **A** as follows:

$$\det \mathbf{A} = |\mathbf{A}| = A = \begin{bmatrix} a_{11} & a_{12} & \cdots & a_{1n} \\ a_{21} & a_{22} & \cdots & a_{2n} \\ \cdots & & & \\ a_{n1} & a_{n2} & \cdots & a_{nn} \end{bmatrix} \tag{2.5.1}$$

$$= \sum_{(j)} (-1)^j a_{1j_1} a_{2j_2} \cdots a_{nj_n}.$$

The symbol $\sum_{(j)}$ denotes the summation of $n!$ terms. Each term consists of a product of n elements of **A** in which the first subscripts are in their natural order, and the second subscripts take on all of their $n!$ possible permutations. The symbol $(-1)^j$ is $+1$ or -1, the sign to be associated with the permutation of the second subscripts for each term.

In other words, the scalar det **A**, associated with the square matrix **A**, is the sum of all possible products of elements, where one element is chosen from each row and each column in the matrix. Each term in the sum is multiplied by either $+1$ or -1, depending on whether the second subscripts in the product are permuted by an even or odd number of interchanges when the first subscripts are arranged in their natural order.

At this point, scalars are associated only with scalar matrices, vectors, and square matrices (including one-element matrices). (See Sections 1.7, 1.9, 2.2, and 2.3.) Later (in Chapter 7), the norm of matrix will be used to associate a scalar with a matrix of any size. The process of finding the scalar associated with a square matrix **A** will be called *evaluating* the determinant of **A**. In this book, whenever we refer to det **A**, we imply that **A** is a square matrix.

One vertical line on each side of the array of elements is universally used to indicate a determinant. Note that in Eq. (2.5.1) the capital letter A is used to indicate the determinant, while the boldface letter **A** denotes the matrix; both have the same elements. The symbol $|\mathbf{A}|$ also denotes the determinant of **A**. On the other hand, $\|\mathbf{A}\|$ denotes some type of norm associated with **A**; several such norms are to be found in the literature. (See Section 2.3.)

Example 2.5.1. Find the determinant of the matrix

$$\mathbf{A} = \begin{bmatrix} a_{11} & a_{12} \\ a_{21} & a_{22} \end{bmatrix}.$$

$$\det \mathbf{A} = a_{11}a_{22} - a_{12}a_{21}; \tag{2.5.2}$$

note the signs associated with the permutations of the second subscripts.

Example 2.5.2. Find the determinant of

$$\mathbf{A} = \begin{bmatrix} 2 & 1 \\ 3 & -4 \end{bmatrix}; \quad \text{of} \quad \mathbf{B} = \begin{bmatrix} x & 2 \\ 1 & 2 \end{bmatrix}.$$

Using the results of Example 2.5.1, we can write

$$A = \begin{vmatrix} 2 & 1 \\ 3 & -4 \end{vmatrix} = -8 - 3 = -11, \quad \text{and} \quad B = \begin{vmatrix} x & 2 \\ 1 & 2 \end{vmatrix} = 2x - 2.$$

Example 2.5.3. Find the determinant of the matrix

$$\mathbf{A} = \begin{bmatrix} a_{11} & a_{12} & a_{13} \\ a_{21} & a_{22} & a_{23} \\ a_{31} & a_{32} & a_{33} \end{bmatrix}.$$

(2.5.3)
$$A = \begin{vmatrix} a_{11} & a_{12} & a_{13} \\ a_{21} & a_{22} & a_{23} \\ a_{31} & a_{32} & a_{33} \end{vmatrix}$$

$$\det \mathbf{A} = a_{11}a_{22}a_{33} - a_{11}a_{23}a_{32} - a_{12}a_{21}a_{33} + a_{12}a_{23}a_{31} + a_{13}a_{21}a_{32} - a_{13}a_{22}a_{31};$$

again note the signs.

Example 2.5.4. Find det **C** and det **D** if

$$\mathbf{C} = \begin{bmatrix} 1/3 & -2/3 & -2/3 \\ 2/3 & -1/3 & 2/3 \\ -2/3 & -2/3 & 1/3 \end{bmatrix}; \qquad \mathbf{D} = \begin{bmatrix} (2-\lambda) & 1 & 0 \\ 0 & (3-\lambda) & 1 \\ 0 & 0 & (4-\lambda) \end{bmatrix}.$$

Using the results of Example 2.5.3, we can write

$$|\mathbf{C}| = -1/27 - (-4/27) - (-4/27) + 8/27 + 8/27 - (-4/27) = 1.$$

$$|\mathbf{D}| = (2-\lambda)(3-\lambda)(4-\lambda).$$

Exercises 2.5

1. Find the signs associated with the permutations

25134; 654321; 135246.

2. Find the determinants of the following matrices:

(a) $\begin{bmatrix} 2x & 2y \\ x & y \end{bmatrix}$ (b) $\begin{bmatrix} x & 0 & 0 \\ 2 & y & 0 \\ 3 & 4 & z \end{bmatrix}$ (c) $\begin{bmatrix} 1 & 2 & 3 \\ 4 & 1 & 2 \\ 3 & 4 & 3 \end{bmatrix}$

(d) $\begin{bmatrix} (1-\lambda) & -2 \\ -7 & (2-\lambda) \end{bmatrix}$ (e) $\begin{bmatrix} 0 & 1 & 0 \\ 1 & 0 & 0 \\ 0 & 0 & 1 \end{bmatrix}$ (f) $\begin{bmatrix} 0 & 1 & 1 \\ 1 & 0 & 1 \\ 1 & 1 & 0 \end{bmatrix}$

3. Solve for x if

(a) $$\begin{vmatrix} x & x^2 & x^3 \\ -1 & 1 & -1 \\ 2 & 4 & 8 \end{vmatrix} = 0,$$

(b) $$\begin{vmatrix} \sin x & \cos x \\ \cos x & \sin x \end{vmatrix} = 0,$$

(c) $$\begin{vmatrix} 2-x & 1 \\ 3 & 1-x \end{vmatrix} = 0,$$

4. Show that a 3×3 skew-symmetric matrix has determinant of zero.

5. (a) Evaluate

$$\begin{vmatrix} 1 & 2 & 3 & -1 \\ 3 & 4 & -1 & 2 \\ 0 & 0 & 1 & 0 \\ 0 & 0 & 2 & 1 \end{vmatrix}.$$

(b) Evaluate

$$\begin{vmatrix} 1 & 2 \\ 3 & 4 \end{vmatrix} \cdot \begin{vmatrix} 1 & 0 \\ 2 & 1 \end{vmatrix}$$

and note that the result is the same as in (a).

6. (a) Examine

$$\begin{vmatrix} x & y & 1 \\ 2 & 2 & 1 \\ 3 & -1 & 1 \end{vmatrix} = 0$$

and name the geometric figure represented by the result without expanding the determinant.

(b) Expand the determinant in (a) and check your conclusion regarding the geometric figure represented.

7. (a) If

$$\mathbf{A} = \begin{bmatrix} -1 & 2 & 2 \\ 2 & -1 & 2 \\ 2 & 2 & -1 \end{bmatrix},$$

divide each element of **A** by the proper number k so that

$$\left| \frac{\mathbf{A}}{k} \right| = 1.$$

(b) Show that the rows of **A** are mutually orthogonal.
(c) Show that the columns of **A** are mutually orthogonal.
(d) After completing (a), show that the rows and columns of the result are each unit vectors.

2.6 *Properties of Determinants*

From the definition of a determinant and its expansion given in Section 2.5, we can associate a scalar with any square matrix. However, the form of the expansion makes the evaluation of a determinant difficult, especially if the order of the associated matrix is large.

The following seven basic properties or rules follow directly from the definition of a determinant and are given as theorems. These theorems are listed together so that they are available for ready reference; they are then proved individually.

Theorem 2.6.1. *All rows of a matrix may be interchanged with the corresponding columns of the matrix without changing the determinant of the matrix.*

Theorem 2.6.2. *Any theorem about det* **A** *that is true for rows (columns) of a matrix* **A** *is also true for columns (rows).*

Theorem 2.6.3. *If two rows of a matrix are interchanged, the determinant of the matrix changes sign.*

Theorem 2.6.4. *If each element of the ith row of a matrix* **D** *contains a given factor k, then we may write* $|\mathbf{D}| = k|\mathbf{\Delta}|$, *where the rows of* $\mathbf{\Delta}$ *are the same as the rows of* **D** *except that the factor k has been removed from each element of the ith row of* **D** *to produce* $\mathbf{\Delta}$.

Theorem 2.6.5. *If each element of a row of the matrix* **D** *is zero, then* $|\mathbf{D}| = 0$.

Theorem 2.6.6. *If two rows of a matrix* **D** *are identical, then* $|\mathbf{D}| = 0$.

Theorem 2.6.7. *The determinant of a matrix is not changed if the elements of the ith row are multiplied by the scalar k and the results are added to the corresponding elements of the hth row,* $h \neq i$.

We now prove the preceding theorems, after which we shall discuss some of the implications of these theorems; we also consider some examples in which the theorems are applied.

Proof of Theorem 2.6.1: From the definition of the expansion of the determinant of a matrix **A**,

$$|\mathbf{A}| = \sum_{(j)} (-1)^j a_{1j_1} a_{2j_2} \cdots a_{nj_n}, \tag{2.6.1}$$

the first subscripts on the factors in each term in Eq. (2.6.1) are in their natural order, while the second subscripts present a permutation. If instead, we place the second subscripts in their natural order, the first subscripts present a permutation. It is left as an exercise to prove that the signs associated with the two permutations are the same. Thus the sign associated with each term in the expansion of the determinant of a matrix is the same in both instances, and the factors remain the same. One factor is still taken from each row and each column for each term; the factors are not changed but merely rearranged. Thus the determinant of the matrix **A** is not altered (except for a rearrangement of terms), and the definition,

$$|\mathbf{A}| = \sum_{(i)} (-1)^i a_{i_1 1} a_{i_2 2} \cdots a_{i_n n}, \tag{2.6.2}$$

is equivalent to that given in Eq. (2.6.1). The sign for each term, however, is determined by the permutation of the first subscripts.

The result of Theorem 2.6.1 may be stated as

$$\det \mathbf{A} = \det \mathbf{A}'. \tag{2.6.3}$$

Example 2.6.1. Find det $\mathbf{C}'$ for the matrix **C** given in Example 2.5.4.

$$\text{For } \mathbf{C} = \begin{bmatrix} 1/3 & -2/3 & -2/3 \\ 2/3 & -1/3 & 2/3 \\ -2/3 & -2/3 & 1/3 \end{bmatrix}, \qquad \mathbf{C}' = \begin{vmatrix} 1/3 & 2/3 & -2/3 \\ -2/3 & -1/3 & -2/3 \\ -2/3 & 2/3 & 1/3 \end{vmatrix}$$

$$|\mathbf{C}'| = -1/27 - (-4/27) - (-4/27) + 8/27 + 8/27 - (-4/27) = 1,$$

using Eq. (2.5.3). Note that this is the same result that was obtained in Example 2.5.4.

Proof of Theorem 2.6.2: This theorem is an immediate consequence of Theorem 2.6.1 since the interchange of all rows and columns of a matrix does not alter the determinant of the matrix.

Proof of Theorem 2.6.3: The interchange of two rows of a matrix causes an odd number of adjacent interchanges of the first subscripts in the determinant of the transformed matrix. This causes a change in the permutation of the first subscripts, which in turn causes the sign to be changed for each term.

Example 2.6.2. Find det **B** if the 3×3 matrix **B** is obtained from **A** in Eq. (2.5.3) by interchanging the first and third columns.

The expansion of det **B** is given in terms of columns instead of rows so that the result may be compared term by term with that in Eq. (2.5.3). Theorem 2.6.2 assures us that the result is the same as if rows had been used. Note the sign associated with each term.

(2.6.4)
$$\mathbf{B} = \begin{vmatrix} a_{13} & a_{12} & a_{11} \\ a_{23} & a_{22} & a_{21} \\ a_{33} & a_{32} & a_{31} \end{vmatrix}$$
$$= a_{13}a_{22}a_{31} - a_{13}a_{21}a_{32} - a_{12}a_{23}a_{31} + a_{12}a_{21}a_{33} + a_{11}a_{23}a_{32} - a_{11}a_{22}a_{33}.$$

Note that the terms in the final sum are merely the negatives of the terms in Eq. (2.5.3).

Proof of Theorem 2.6.4: If

(2.6.5)
$$\mathbf{D} = \begin{bmatrix} a_{11} & a_{12} & \cdots & a_{1n} \\ a_{21} & a_{22} & \cdots & a_{2n} \\ \cdots & & & \\ kb_{i1} & kb_{i2} & \cdots & kb_{in} \\ \cdots & & & \\ a_{n1} & a_{n2} & \cdots & a_{nn} \end{bmatrix} \quad \text{and} \quad \mathbf{\Delta} = \begin{vmatrix} a_{11} & a_{12} & \cdots & a_{1n} \\ a_{21} & a_{22} & \cdots & a_{2n} \\ \cdots & & & \\ b_{i1} & b_{i2} & \cdots & b_{in} \\ \cdots & & & \\ a_{n1} & a_{n2} & \cdots & a_{nn} \end{vmatrix},$$

then

(2.6.6)
$$\begin{aligned} |\mathbf{D}| &= \sum_{(j)} (-1)^j a_{1j_1} a_{2j_2} \cdots kb_{ij_i} \cdots a_{nj_n} \\ &= k \sum_{(j)} (-1)^j a_{1j_1} a_{2j_2} \cdots b_{ij_i} \cdots a_{nj_n} \\ &= k|\mathbf{\Delta}|; \end{aligned}$$

in other words, k is a common factor in each term of the expansion of det **D**.

Example 2.6.3. Simplify by removing common factors from rows or columns of

$$|\mathbf{D}| = \begin{vmatrix} 2 & 6 & 4 \\ 1 & 9 & 0 \\ 5 & 3 & 2 \end{vmatrix}.$$

We can factor 2 from the first row, 3 from the second column, and also 2 from the third column. Thus,

$$|\mathbf{D}| = 2\begin{vmatrix} 1 & 3 & 2 \\ 1 & 9 & 0 \\ 5 & 3 & 2 \end{vmatrix} = 2\cdot 3\begin{vmatrix} 1 & 1 & 2 \\ 1 & 3 & 0 \\ 5 & 1 & 2 \end{vmatrix} = 2\cdot 3\cdot 2\begin{vmatrix} 1 & 1 & 1 \\ 1 & 3 & 0 \\ 5 & 1 & 1 \end{vmatrix}.$$

Proof of Theorem 2.6.5: This theorem follows directly from the observation that if each element of the ith row of a matrix is zero, each term in the expansion Eq. (2.5.1) must be zero, since each term contains an element of the ith row.

Proof of Theorem 2.6.6: If the matrix $\mathbf{D}_1$ is obtained from **D** by interchanging two rows, then

(2.6.7)
$$|\mathbf{D}| = -|\mathbf{D}_1|,$$

by Theorem 2.6.3. Now if the rows interchanged are identical, then

$$|\mathbf{D}| = |\mathbf{D}_1|, \tag{2.6.8}$$

since the elements of **D** are the same as those of $\mathbf{D}_1$. Thus, from Eqs. (2.6.7) and (2.6.8), we see that $|\mathbf{D}| = 0$.

Proof of Theorem 2.6.7: If $\mathbf{A} = [a_{ij}]$ and

$$\mathbf{A}_1 = \begin{bmatrix} a_{11} & a_{12} & \cdots & a_{1n} \\ a_{21} & a_{22} & \cdots & a_{2n} \\ \cdots \\ a_{i1} & a_{i2} & \cdots & a_{in} \\ \cdots \\ a_{h1} + ka_{i1} & a_{h2} + ka_{i2} & \cdots & a_{hn} + ka_{in} \\ \cdots \\ a_{n1} & a_{n2} & \cdots & a_{nn} \end{bmatrix},$$

$$\begin{aligned} |\mathbf{A}_1| &= \sum_{(j)} (-1)^j a_{1j_1} a_{2j_2} \cdots a_{ij_i} \cdots (a_{hj_h} + ka_{ij_h}) \cdots a_{nj_n} \\ &= \sum_{(j)} (-1)^j a_{1j_1} a_{2j_2} \cdots a_{nj_n} \\ &\quad + k \sum_{(j)} (-1)^j a_{1j_1} a_{2j_2} \cdots a_{ij_i} \cdots a_{ij_h} \cdots a_{nj_n} \\ &= |\mathbf{A}| + k0, \end{aligned} \tag{2.6.9}$$

since, in accordance with Theorem 2.6.6, the determinant of a matrix with two rows identical is zero.

Example 2.6.4. Multiply the first row of the 3 × 3 matrix of Eq. (2.5.3) by k, and add each element to the corresponding element of the second row. Show that the determinant of the result is the same as det **A**.

If we perform the indicated operations and use the expansion of Eq. (2.5.3) we get

$$\begin{vmatrix} a_{11} & a_{12} & a_{13} \\ a_{21} + ka_{11} & a_{22} + ka_{12} & a_{23} + ka_{13} \\ a_{31} & a_{32} & a_{33} \end{vmatrix} \tag{2.6.10}$$

$$\begin{aligned} &= a_{11}(a_{22} + ka_{12})a_{33} - a_{11}(a_{23} + ka_{13})a_{32} - a_{12}(a_{21} + ka_{11})a_{33} \\ &\quad + a_{12}(a_{23} + ka_{13})a_{31} + a_{13}(a_{21} + ka_{11})a_{32} - a_{13}(a_{22} + ka_{12})a_{31} \\ &= a_{11}a_{22}a_{33} - a_{11}a_{23}a_{32} - a_{12}a_{21}a_{33} + a_{12}a_{23}a_{31} + a_{13}a_{21}a_{32} \\ &\quad - a_{13}a_{22}a_{31} + k(a_{11}a_{12}a_{33} - a_{11}a_{13}a_{32} - a_{12}a_{11}a_{33} \\ &\quad + a_{12}a_{13}a_{31} + a_{13}a_{11}a_{32} - a_{13}a_{12}a_{31}) \\ &= |\mathbf{A}| + k0. \end{aligned}$$

The final term in the last expression is zero, since the terms in the coefficient of k of the preceding expression cancel one another.

We could also write

(2.6.11)
$$\begin{vmatrix} a_{11} & a_{12} & a_{13} \\ a_{21}+ka_{11} & a_{22}+ka_{12} & a_{23}+ka_{13} \\ a_{31} & a_{32} & a_{33} \end{vmatrix} = \begin{vmatrix} a_{11} & a_{12} & a_{13} \\ a_{21} & a_{22} & a_{23} \\ a_{31} & a_{32} & a_{33} \end{vmatrix} + k \begin{vmatrix} a_{11} & a_{12} & a_{13} \\ a_{11} & a_{12} & a_{13} \\ a_{31} & a_{32} & a_{33} \end{vmatrix};$$

the last determinant is zero by Theorem 2.6.6 since two rows are identical.

Example 2.6.5. Use Theorem 2.6.7 to simplify

(2.6.12)
$$|\mathbf{C}| = \begin{vmatrix} 2 & 5 & -1 & 0 \\ 0 & 4 & -3 & 2 \\ 0 & -3 & 3 & 1 \\ 0 & 0 & 0 & -2 \end{vmatrix}.$$

By Theorems 2.6.2 and 2.6.7, we may add the third column of $|\mathbf{C}|$ to the second to get

(2.6.13)
$$|\mathbf{C}| = \begin{vmatrix} 2 & 4 & -1 & 0 \\ 0 & 1 & -3 & 2 \\ 0 & 0 & 3 & 1 \\ 0 & 0 & 0 & -2 \end{vmatrix}.$$

The expansion of this determinant is -12, the product of elements on the principal diagonal, since all other terms involve one or more zero factors.

By applying one or more of the preceding theorems, the expansion of the determinant of a matrix can often be considerably simplified. In particular, if $\mathbf{A}$ can be transformed into a matrix $\mathbf{B}$ such that every element in one row (column) of $\mathbf{B}$ consists entirely of zeros, then

$$\det \mathbf{A} = \det \mathbf{B} = 0.$$

Also, by extending the idea in Eq. (2.6.13) to matrices of order n, the determinant of a triangular matrix or of a diagonal matrix can be expanded readily.

Example 2.6.6. If

$$\mathbf{A} = \begin{bmatrix} 1 & 3 & 1 & 0 \\ 2 & 1 & 4 & 1 \\ 0 & 1 & -2 & 1 \\ 8 & 12 & 16 & 0 \end{bmatrix},$$

simplify det **A** and expand. (It is left as an exercise for the reader to determine the theorems used in each step of the following simplification.)

$$\begin{vmatrix} 1 & 3 & 1 & 0 \\ 2 & 1 & 4 & 1 \\ 0 & 1 & -2 & 0 \\ 8 & 12 & 16 & 0 \end{vmatrix} = 2\begin{vmatrix} 1 & 3 & 1 & 0 \\ 2 & 1 & 4 & 1 \\ 0 & 1 & -2 & 1 \\ 4 & 6 & 8 & 0 \end{vmatrix} = 2\begin{vmatrix} 1 & 3 & 1 & 0 \\ 2 & 1 & 4 & 1 \\ 0 & 1 & -2 & 1 \\ 0 & -1 & 2 & -1 \end{vmatrix}$$

$$= 2\begin{vmatrix} 1 & 3 & 1 & 0 \\ 2 & 1 & 4 & 1 \\ 0 & 1 & -2 & 1 \\ 0 & 0 & 0 & 0 \end{vmatrix} = 0.$$

Example 2.6.7. Simplify det **B** and expand if

$$\mathbf{B} = \begin{bmatrix} 1 & 2 & 1 & 0 \\ 2 & 3 & 4 & 1 \\ 0 & 1 & -2 & 1 \\ 3 & 0 & 2 & 2 \end{bmatrix}.$$

$$|\mathbf{B}| = \begin{vmatrix} 1 & 2 & 1 & 0 \\ 2 & 3 & 4 & 1 \\ 0 & 1 & -2 & 1 \\ 3 & 0 & 2 & 2 \end{vmatrix} = \begin{vmatrix} 1 & 2 & 1 & 0 \\ 2 & 3 & 4 & 1 \\ 0 & 1 & -2 & 1 \\ 0 & -6 & -1 & 0 \end{vmatrix} = \begin{vmatrix} 1 & 2 & 1 & 0 \\ 0 & -1 & 2 & 1 \\ 0 & 1 & -2 & 1 \\ 0 & -6 & -1 & 0 \end{vmatrix}$$

$$= \begin{vmatrix} 1 & 2 & 1 & 0 \\ 0 & 1 & -2 & -1 \\ 0 & 1 & -2 & 1 \\ 0 & 6 & 1 & 0 \end{vmatrix} = \begin{vmatrix} 1 & 2 & 1 & 0 \\ 0 & 1 & -2 & -1 \\ 0 & 0 & 0 & 2 \\ 0 & 0 & 13 & 6 \end{vmatrix}$$

$$= -\begin{vmatrix} 1 & 2 & 1 & 0 \\ 0 & 1 & -2 & -1 \\ 0 & 0 & 13 & 6 \\ 0 & 0 & 0 & 2 \end{vmatrix} = -26.$$

Exercises 2.6

1. Name, in order, the theorems of this section that are applied in Example 2.6.6.
2. Without expanding, prove that det $\mathbf{A} = 0$ is the equation of a straight line through the points (2, 1) and (3, 4) if

$$\mathbf{A} = \begin{bmatrix} x & y & 1 \\ 2 & 1 & 1 \\ 3 & 4 & 1 \end{bmatrix}.$$

3. Without expanding, name the configuration in space determined by det $\mathbf{B} = 0$ if

$$|\mathbf{B}| = \begin{vmatrix} x & y & z & 1 \\ 1 & 0 & 2 & 1 \\ 1 & 3 & 1 & 1 \\ 2 & 1 & 0 & 1 \end{vmatrix}.$$

4. Simplify and expand:

(a) $\begin{vmatrix} 1 & 1 & 5 & 6 & 3 \\ 2 & -2 & 2 & 2 & 0 \\ 6 & -8 & 2 & 1 & -3 \\ 0 & 2 & 4 & 5 & 3 \\ 3 & -3 & -1 & 1 & -2 \end{vmatrix}$ (b) $\begin{vmatrix} 1 & 2 & 1 & 1 \\ -3 & 4 & 2 & 4 \\ 1 & 1 & -1 & 2 \\ -2 & 3 & -2 & -1 \end{vmatrix}.$

5. Without expanding, prove:

$$\begin{vmatrix} x+y & y+z & z+x \\ w+u & u+v & v+w \\ f+g & g+h & h+f \end{vmatrix} = 2\begin{vmatrix} x & y & z \\ w & u & v \\ f & g & h \end{vmatrix}.$$

6. Evaluate:

$$\begin{vmatrix} 1 & \omega & \omega^2 \\ \omega & \omega^2 & 1 \\ \omega^2 & 1 & \omega \end{vmatrix} \quad \text{where } \omega^3 = 1,\ \omega \neq 1.$$

7. Evaluate:

$$\begin{vmatrix} -i & 1 & 2 & i+2 \\ 2 & 3 & i-1 & 3 \\ 1 & 0 & 4 & -1 \\ 0 & -i & 0 & 1 \end{vmatrix}.$$

8. Evaluate:

$$\begin{vmatrix} 1 & i & -i \\ 0 & -1 & 2i \\ 1+i & 0 & 1 \end{vmatrix}.$$

9. Prove $|k\mathbf{A}| = k^n|\mathbf{A}|$ where k is a scalar and $\mathbf{A}$ is an $n \times n$ matrix.

10. Show that

$$A = \begin{vmatrix} 1 & 1 & 1 & -3 \\ 1 & 1 & -3 & 1 \\ 1 & -3 & 1 & 1 \\ -3 & 1 & 1 & 1 \end{vmatrix} = 0$$

without expanding.

11. The following determinant is known as the *Vandermonde determinant*.

$$V = \begin{vmatrix} 1 & x_1 & \cdots & x_1^{n-2} & x_1^{n-1} \\ 1 & x_2 & \cdots & x_2^{n-2} & x_2^{n-1} \\ \cdots & & & & \\ 1 & x_n & \cdots & x_n^{n-2} & x_n^{n-1} \end{vmatrix}$$

(a) Write the Vandermonde determinant for $n = 3$ and $n = 4$ and expand in each case.
(b) By induction, show that $V = \Pi_{1 \leqq i < j \leqq n}(x_j - x_i)$.
(c) From (b) show that $V = 0$ if and only if two of the x_i's are equal.

12. Prove the theorem: *If* **S** *is a skew symmetric matrix of order n, then*
(a) *det* $\mathbf{S} = 0$ *if n is odd.*
(b) *det* **S** *may or may not be zero if n is even.*

13.* By considering V in exercise 11 as a polynomial of degree $n - 1$ in x_1, say, we can say that $(x_1 - x_2)$, $(x_1 - x_3)$, $\cdots$, $(x_1 - x_n)$ are all factors of V. Proceed with this type of argument to complete the proof of exercise 11(b).

14.* Prove that the sign associated with a term in the expansion of a determinant is the same whether (a) the first subscripts are in their natural order, and the second subscripts present a permutation of the integers 1 through n, or (b) the roles of the subscripts are interchanged from (a).

2.7. *Minors and Cofactors*

So far, we have expanded the determinant of a matrix only by using the definition, Eq. (2.5.1). Examples 2.6.5 and 2.6.7 hint that matrices in triangular form can be expanded more simply. We now seek some systematic methods for expanding determinants routinely, and for taking advantage of the form of the matrix in that expansion. This section covers various preliminary aspects of the problem; the following two sections cover some specific methods.

Methods for expanding det **A** if **A** is of order 2 or 3 have been established. (See Examples 2.5.1 and 2.5.3.) The reader may have used a "diagonal process" to memorize

$$\text{(2.7.1)} \qquad \begin{vmatrix} a_{11} & a_{12} \\ a_{21} & a_{22} \end{vmatrix} = a_{11}a_{22} - a_{12}a_{21}, \quad \text{and}$$

$$\text{(2.7.2)} \qquad \begin{vmatrix} a_{11} & a_{12} & a_{13} \\ a_{21} & a_{22} & a_{23} \\ a_{31} & a_{32} & a_{33} \end{vmatrix} = \begin{aligned} &a_{11}a_{22}a_{33} + a_{12}a_{23}a_{31} + a_{13}a_{21}a_{32} \\ &- a_{31}a_{22}a_{13} - a_{21}a_{12}a_{33} - a_{11}a_{32}a_{23}. \end{aligned}$$

However, such a "diagonal process" is *not* valid when the order of the associated matrix is greater than 3 (except for very special matrices). To verify this statement, compare the number of terms obtained by the "diagonal process" from det **A** if **A** is of order 4 with the number of terms obtained by the definition, Eq. (2.5.1).

In Section 1.11, *submatrices* of **A** were defined as matrices obtained by deleting some rows and some columns of **A**. We now delete $n - r$ rows and

$n-r$ columns of **A**, a square matrix of order n. The remaining elements, taken in their natural order by rows and by columns, then constitute a square submatrix of order r. The determinant of this submatrix is called a *minor determinant* of order r, or simply an rth order *minor* of **A**. Thus

(2.7.3)
$$\begin{vmatrix} a_{12} & a_{13} \\ a_{32} & a_{33} \end{vmatrix}$$

is the minor of order two of the matrix

(2.7.4)
$$A = \begin{bmatrix} a_{11} & a_{12} & a_{13} \\ a_{21} & a_{22} & a_{23} \\ a_{31} & a_{32} & a_{33} \end{bmatrix}.$$

This minor is the determinant of the submatrix of **A** resulting from the deletion of the second row and first column of **A**.

If the same r rows and columns of a square matrix **A** are deleted, the matrix of the remaining elements is called a *principal submatrix* of **A** of order $n-r$; the determinant of this submatrix is called a *principal minor* of **A** of order $n-r$. If the last r rows and columns of **A** are deleted, the remaining submatrix is called the *leading principal submatrix* of **A** of order $n-r$; the determinant of this submatrix is called the *leading principal minor* of **A** of order $n-r$.

If we delete the ith row and jth column of **A**, the determinant of the remaining submatrix is denoted by M_{ij}, and is called the minor of a_{ij}. Thus the determinant in Eq. (2.7.3) is the minor of a_{21}.

We define

(2.7.5)
$$A_{ij} = (-1)^{i+j} M_{ij}$$

as the *cofactor* of a_{ij}. That is, the cofactor of any element a_{ij} of a matrix is obtained by forming the determinant M_{ij} of the submatrix remaining after the ith row and jth column have been deleted, and then multiplying M_{ij} by $(-1)^{i+j}$, where $i+j$ is the sum of the row and column subscripts of a_{ij}. Thus, a cofactor is simply a signed minor; in a sense, this associates a sign with each of the n^2 positions in **A**.

Exercises 2.7

1. Expand each of the following by using the "diagonal process."

(a) $\begin{vmatrix} 2 & 1 & 1 \\ 4 & 3 & 0 \\ 2 & 4 & 1 \end{vmatrix}$, (b) $\begin{vmatrix} 0 & 1 & 1 \\ 3 & -2 & 0 \\ 3 & 0 & 2 \end{vmatrix}$, (c) $\begin{vmatrix} 3 & 2 & 0 \\ 6 & 4 & 0 \\ 0 & 5 & 1 \end{vmatrix}$.

2. (a) Write the cofactor of each element in the second column of

$$\mathbf{A} = \begin{bmatrix} 1 & 2 & 0 \\ 2 & 3 & 1 \\ 1 & 1 & 2 \end{bmatrix}.$$

(b) Find the sum of the products of the elements of the second column of **A** with the corresponding cofactors found in (a).
(c) Find the sum of the products of the elements of the first column of **A** with the corresponding cofactors found in (a).
(d) Expand det **A** directly.

3. (a) From the matrix

$$\mathbf{C} = \begin{bmatrix} 2 & 1 & 2 \\ 1 & 1 & 2 \\ 1 & 0 & 1 \end{bmatrix},$$

construct a matrix **B** whose element b_{ij} is C_{ji}.
(b) Find the product **CB**.
(c) Describe **B** in relation to **C**.

4. Work exercise 3 using **A** from exercise 2.

5. How many terms arise in the expansion of det **A** if **A** is of order 4? of order 6? of order 15?

6. If $\mathbf{A} = [a_{ij}]$ is a 5×5 matrix, write the minor and cofactor for a_{22}; for a_{45}; for a_{31}; for a_{53}; for a_{42}.

2.8. *The Expansion of Determinants by Minors*

This section provides the proofs of two theorems useful for evaluating determinants. The first theorem permits us to simplify our work so that we need only expand determinants of matrices of order 2 or 3: (See Eqs. (2.7.1) and (2.7.2).)

Theorem 2.8.1. *If A_{ij} is the cofactor of a_{ij}, then*

$$\text{(2.8.1)} \qquad \det \mathbf{A} = \sum_{j=1}^{n} a_{ij} A_{ij} = a_{i1}A_{i1} + a_{i2}A_{i2} + \cdots + a_{in}A_{in}$$

for any i, or

$$\text{(2.8.2)} \qquad \det \mathbf{A} = \sum_{i=1}^{n} a_{ij} A_{ij} = a_{1j}A_{1j} + a_{2j}A_{2j} + \cdots + a_{nj}A_{nj}$$

for any j.

Proof: The second part of the theorem, Eq. (2.8.2), follows directly from Theorem 2.6.2, so we concern ourselves only with the proof of the first part.

Now, from Eq. (2.7.5) and the definitions of a determinant and of the cofactor of a_{ij},

(2.8.3)
$$A_{ij} = (-1)^{i+j} M_{ij}$$

$$= (-1)^{i+j} \begin{vmatrix} a_{11} & a_{12} & \cdots & a_{1,j-1} & a_{1,j+1} & \cdots & a_{1n} \\ a_{21} & a_{22} & \cdots & a_{2,j-1} & a_{2,j+1} & \cdots & a_{2n} \\ \cdots \\ a_{i-1,1} & a_{i-1,2} & \cdots & a_{i-1,j-1} & a_{i-1,j+1} & \cdots & a_{i-1,n} \\ a_{i+1,1} & a_{i+1,2} & \cdots & a_{i+1,j-1} & a_{i+1,j+1} & \cdots & a_{i+1,n} \\ \cdots \\ a_{n1} & a_{n2} & \cdots & a_{n,j-1} & a_{n,j+1} & \cdots & a_{nn} \end{vmatrix},$$

the determinant of a matrix with $n - 1$ rows and columns; the ith row and jth column of det **A** are missing. The expansion of M_{ij} contains $(n - 1)!$ terms. Then, if we use $\sum_{(j')}$ to indicate the summation over all possible permutations of the $n - 1$ subscripts, $j_1, \cdots, j_{i-1}, j_{i+1}, \cdots, j_n$, we may write

(2.8.4)
$$A_{ij} = (-1)^{i+j} \sum_{(j')} (-1)^{j'} a_{1j_1} \cdots a_{i-1\,j_{i-1}} a_{i+1\,j_{i+1}} \cdots a_{nj_n}.$$

For the remainder of the proof we let $i = 1$ in order to simplify the notation; it is obvious that the same steps could be used for the general row i. Thus if $i = 1$, Eq. (2.8.4) becomes

(2.8.5)
$$A_{1j} = (-1)^{1+j} \sum_{(j')} (-1)^{j'} a_{2j_2} a_{3j_3} \cdots a_{nj_n}.$$

From the definition of a determinant, after introducing the factor $(-1)^{1+1} = 1$ to get our equation in the form to use Eq. (2.8.5), we have

(2.8.6)
$$\begin{aligned} \det \mathbf{A} &= (-1)^{1+1} \sum_{(j)} (-1)^{j} a_{1j_1} a_{2j_2} \cdots a_{nj_n} \\ &= (-1)^{1+1} \sum_{(j')} (-1)^{j'} a_{11} a_{2j_2} \cdots a_{nj_n} \\ &\quad + (-1)^{1+1} \sum_{(j')} (-1)^{j'} a_{12} a_{2j_2} \cdots a_{nj_n} \\ &\quad + \cdots + (-1)^{1+1} \sum_{(j')} (-1)^{j'} a_{1n} a_{2j_2} \cdots a_{nj_n} \\ &= (-1)^{1+1} a_{11} \sum_{(j')} (-1)^{j'} a_{2j_2} \cdots a_{nj_n} \\ &\quad + (-1)^{1+2} a_{12} \sum_{(j')} (-1)^{j'} a_{2j_2} \cdots a_{nj_n} \\ &\quad + \cdots + (-1)^{1+n} a_{1n} \sum_{(j')} (-1)^{j'} a_{2j_2} \cdots a_{nj_n}. \end{aligned}$$

The $\sum_{(j')}$ in the final expressions indicate that the summation is over all possible permutations of the second subscripts, $j_2, j_3, \cdots, j_n$. The factors

$a_{11}, a_{12}, \cdots, a_{1n}$ have been removed from the summations in the final expression since they do not enter into the summations in those terms in which they occur. Finally, the factor $(-1)^{k-1}$ is removed as a common factor from the kth summation; since there are only $n-1$ integers as second subscripts, the sign associated with each permutation must be altered accordingly.

From the final result in Eq. (2.8.6), we can write

(2.8.7) $$\det \mathbf{A} = a_{11}A_{11} + a_{12}A_{12} + \cdots + a_{1n}A_{1n}.$$

This is simply Eq. (2.8.1) for the case $i = 1$; it is called the *expansion by minors* of elements of the first row of det **A**.

Example 2.8.1. Expand det **A** by minors of the first row if

(2.8.8) $$\det \mathbf{A} = \begin{vmatrix} a_{11} & a_{12} & a_{13} \\ a_{21} & a_{22} & a_{23} \\ a_{31} & a_{32} & a_{33} \end{vmatrix}.$$

One method is to follow the steps used in the proof of Theorem 2.8.1:

(2.8.9)
$$\begin{aligned}
\det \mathbf{A} &= (-1)^{1+1} \sum_{(j)} (-1)^{j} a_{1j_1} a_{2j_2} a_{3j_3} \\
&= (-1)^{1+1} \sum_{(j')} (-1)^{j'} a_{11} a_{2j_2} a_{3j_3} \\
&\quad + (-1)^{1+1} \sum_{(j')} (-1)^{j'} a_{12} a_{2j_2} a_{3j_3} \\
&\quad + (-1)^{1+1} \sum_{(j')} (-1)^{j'} a_{13} a_{2j_2} a_{3j_3} \\
&= (-1)^{1+1} a_{11} \sum_{(j')} (-1)^{j'} a_{2j_2} a_{3j_3} \\
&\quad + (-1)^{1+2} a_{12} \sum_{(j')} (-1)^{j'} a_{2j_2} a_{3j_3} \\
&\quad + (-1)^{1+3} a_{13} \sum_{(j')} (-1)^{j'} a_{2j_2} a_{3j_3} \\
&= a_{11}[a_{22}a_{33} - a_{23}a_{32}] - a_{12}[a_{21}a_{33} - a_{23}a_{31}] \\
&\quad + a_{13}[a_{21}a_{32} - a_{22}a_{31}] \\
&= a_{11}a_{22}a_{33} - a_{11}a_{23}a_{32} - a_{12}a_{21}a_{33} + a_{12}a_{23}a_{31} \\
&\quad + a_{13}a_{21}a_{32} - a_{13}a_{22}a_{31}.
\end{aligned}$$

An alternate method is to use Eq. (2.8.7) and write, from Eq. (2.8.8),

(2.8.10)
$$\det \mathbf{A} = a_{11}\begin{vmatrix} a_{22} & a_{23} \\ a_{32} & a_{33} \end{vmatrix} - a_{12}\begin{vmatrix} a_{21} & a_{23} \\ a_{31} & a_{33} \end{vmatrix} + a_{13}\begin{vmatrix} a_{21} & a_{22} \\ a_{31} & a_{32} \end{vmatrix}.$$

Since we know how to expand determinants of order 2, we arrive at the same result as in Eq. (2.8.9). Note that both results are the same as that in Example (2.5.3).

Example 2.8.2. Expand det $\mathbf{D}$ by minors of elements of the fourth column if

$$\mathbf{D} = \begin{bmatrix} 6 & 2 & 1 & 4 \\ 2 & 5 & 0 & 0 \\ 1 & 7 & 0 & 3 \\ 2 & 6 & 0 & 0 \end{bmatrix}.$$

We can write immediately

$$\det \mathbf{D} = (-1)^{1+4}\, 4 \begin{vmatrix} 2 & 5 & 0 \\ 1 & 7 & 0 \\ 2 & 6 & 0 \end{vmatrix} + (-1)^{3+4}\, 3 \begin{vmatrix} 6 & 2 & 1 \\ 2 & 5 & 0 \\ 2 & 6 & 0 \end{vmatrix}$$

$$= 0 - (-1)^{1+3}\, 3 \cdot 1 \begin{vmatrix} 2 & 5 \\ 2 & 6 \end{vmatrix} = -3(12 - 10) = -6.$$

Here we have used the elements of the third column of

$$\begin{vmatrix} 6 & 2 & 1 \\ 2 & 5 & 0 \\ 2 & 6 & 0 \end{vmatrix}$$

to simplify our result. All other terms arising have the factor zero.

The second theorem of this section is valuable in its own right. It will have particular application later when we establish Cramer's Rule. (See Section 2.11.)

Theorem 2.8.2. *The sum*

$$\sum_{j=1}^{n} a_{ij} A_{kj} = a_{i1} A_{k1} + a_{i2} A_{k2} + \cdots + a_{in} A_{kn} = 0 \qquad (2.8.11)$$

for $i \neq k$.

This theorem says that if each element of one row of a matrix $\mathbf{A}$ is multiplied by the cofactor of the corresponding element of a different row of $\mathbf{A}$, the sum is zero.

Proof: For simplicity of notation we let $i = 1$ and $k = 2$, although the same method is applicable for arbitrary i and k, $i \neq k$. For

$$\mathbf{A} = \begin{bmatrix} a_{11} & a_{12} & \cdots & a_{1n} \\ a_{21} & a_{22} & \cdots & a_{2n} \\ \cdots & & & \\ a_{n1} & a_{n2} & \cdots & a_{nn} \end{bmatrix}$$

we have

$$A_{21} = -\begin{vmatrix} a_{12} & a_{13} & \cdots & a_{1n} \\ a_{32} & a_{33} & \cdots & a_{3n} \\ \cdots & & & \\ a_{n2} & a_{n3} & \cdots & a_{nn} \end{vmatrix}, \quad A_{22} = \begin{vmatrix} a_{11} & a_{13} & \cdots & a_{1n} \\ a_{31} & a_{33} & \cdots & a_{3n} \\ \cdots & & & \\ a_{n1} & a_{n3} & \cdots & a_{nn} \end{vmatrix}, \ldots.$$

Thus we can write

$$\sum_{j=1}^{n} a_{1j}A_{2j} = -\begin{vmatrix} a_{11} & a_{12} & a_{13} & \cdots & a_{1n} \\ a_{11} & a_{12} & a_{13} & \cdots & a_{1n} \\ a_{31} & a_{32} & a_{33} & \cdots & a_{3n} \\ \cdots & & & & \\ a_{n1} & a_{n2} & a_{n3} & \cdots & a_{nn} \end{vmatrix},$$

which is obviously zero by Theorem 2.6.6, since the first two rows are the same.

Exercises 2.8

1. Let $|\mathbf{A}| = \begin{vmatrix} 1 & 2 & -3 & 1 \\ 0 & 1 & 2 & -1 \\ 0 & 0 & -1 & 2 \\ 1 & -1 & 0 & 1 \end{vmatrix}$.

   Expand $|\mathbf{A}|$ by minors of the third (a) column, (b) row.

2. Using $|\mathbf{A}|$ in exercise 1, compute $\sum_{j=1}^{4} a_{2j}A_{3j}$.

3. Expand the following determinants by minors of appropriate rows or columns, then expand the minors by minors. Continue until the 3×3 level is reached, then complete the evaluation.

(a) $\begin{vmatrix} 1 & -1 & 3 & 0 & 0 & 0 \\ 0 & 2 & -3 & 0 & 4 & 0 \\ 0 & 0 & -1 & 1 & 0 & 0 \\ 0 & 1 & 0 & 3 & -1 & 0 \\ 0 & 0 & 0 & 0 & 1 & 4 \\ 2 & 0 & 0 & 0 & 0 & 2 \end{vmatrix}$ (b) $\begin{vmatrix} 1 & 2 & 0 & 0 \\ 2 & 0 & -1 & 0 \\ 0 & 0 & 1 & 2 \\ 0 & -2 & 0 & -1 \end{vmatrix}$

(c) $\begin{vmatrix} 1 & 1 & 1 & 0 & 0 \\ 1 & 0 & 1 & 1 & 0 \\ 1 & 0 & 0 & 1 & 1 \\ 0 & 1 & 1 & 0 & 1 \\ 0 & 1 & 0 & 1 & 1 \end{vmatrix}$ (d) $\begin{vmatrix} -2 & -1 & 0 & 1 & 2 \\ 2 & -2 & -1 & 0 & 0 \\ 1 & 2 & -2 & -1 & 0 \\ 0 & 1 & 2 & 0 & 0 \\ 1 & 2 & 0 & 0 & 0 \end{vmatrix}$

2.9. Laplace's Expansion

In this section we state, but do not prove, a theorem for which the results of the last section is a special case. The theorem gives *Laplace's expansion** of det **A**, or Laplace's method for the expansion of det **A**. By using this theorem,

*Named after the French mathematician Pierre Simon de Laplace (1749–1827).

we can take advantage of the form of a matrix (especially if zeros are present) in expanding its determinant.

Theorem 2.9.1. *For matrix* **A**,

$$\det \mathbf{A} = \sum_{(j)} A_{i_1 \cdots i_r, j_1 \cdots j_r} M_{i_{r+1} \cdots i_n, j_{r+1} \cdots j_n}. \tag{2.9.1}$$

In Eq. (2.9.1) the symbol $M_{i_{r+1} \cdots i_n, j_{r+1} \cdots j_n}$ is the minor determinant of **A** obtained by deleting the $n - r$ rows $i_{r+1}, \cdots, i_n$ and the $n - r$ columns $j_{r+1}, \cdots, j_n$, while

$$A_{i_1 \cdots i_r, j_1 \cdots j_r} = (-1)^{i_1 + \cdots + i_r + j_1 + \cdots + j_r} M_{i_1 \cdots i_r, j_1 \cdots j_r}.$$

That is, r rows and columns of **A** are deleted to give the minor determinant appearing second in Eq. (2.9.1). The deleted elements (appearing in both the r deleted rows and the r deleted columns) are used to form the minor determinant appearing first. The proper sign is then associated with the minor appearing first (although it equally well could have been associated with the minor appearing second).

The symbol $\sum_{(j)}$ in Eq. (2.9.1) indicates that the summation is taken over all possible permutations of the n second subscripts of **A** taken r at a time in their natural order according to the first subscripts. The first r subscripts $i_1, \cdots, i_r$ (and hence the first $n - r$ first subscripts $i_{r+1}, \cdots, i_n$) are chosen arbitrarily but remain fixed for each term in the expansion. Notice that if $r = n - 1$, Eq. (2.9.1) reduces to Eq. (2.8.1), the expansion of the determinant by minors. The proof of Theorem 2.9.1 is similar to the proof of Theorem 2.8.1; it is not difficult but is tedious.

Example 2.9.1. Use Theorem 2.9.1 to expand det **A** by elements of the second and fourth rows of **A** if

$$\mathbf{A} = \begin{bmatrix} 2 & 1 & 3 & 1 \\ 1 & 0 & 2 & 5 \\ 2 & 1 & 1 & 3 \\ 1 & 3 & 0 & 2 \end{bmatrix}.$$

The expansion of det **A** written out is

$$\begin{aligned}
\det \mathbf{A} \\
&= (-1)^{2+4+1+2} \begin{vmatrix} 1 & 0 \\ 1 & 3 \end{vmatrix} \begin{vmatrix} 3 & 1 \\ 1 & 3 \end{vmatrix} + (-1)^{2+4+1+3} \begin{vmatrix} 1 & 2 \\ 1 & 0 \end{vmatrix} \begin{vmatrix} 1 & 1 \\ 1 & 3 \end{vmatrix} \\
&\quad + (-1)^{2+4+1+4} \begin{vmatrix} 1 & 5 \\ 1 & 2 \end{vmatrix} \begin{vmatrix} 1 & 3 \\ 1 & 1 \end{vmatrix} + (-1)^{2+4+2+3} \begin{vmatrix} 0 & 2 \\ 3 & 0 \end{vmatrix} \begin{vmatrix} 2 & 1 \\ 2 & 3 \end{vmatrix} \\
&\quad + (-1)^{2+4+2+4} \begin{vmatrix} 0 & 5 \\ 3 & 2 \end{vmatrix} \begin{vmatrix} 2 & 3 \\ 2 & 1 \end{vmatrix} + (-1)^{2+4+3+4} \begin{vmatrix} 2 & 5 \\ 0 & 2 \end{vmatrix} \begin{vmatrix} 2 & 1 \\ 2 & 1 \end{vmatrix} \\
&= -(3)(8) + (-2)(2) - (-3)(-2) - (-6)(4) + (-15)(-4) - (4)(0) \\
&= 50.
\end{aligned}$$

Example 2.9.2. Use Laplace's expansion to determine det **A** if

$$\mathbf{A} = \begin{bmatrix} 0 & 2 & 0 & 7 & 1 \\ 1 & 0 & 3 & 0 & 0 \\ 0 & 0 & 0 & 5 & 1 \\ 1 & 0 & 4 & 0 & 0 \\ 0 & 0 & 0 & 1 & 0 \end{bmatrix}.$$

An examination of **A** shows that the zeros can be used to advantage by expanding elements of the first and third columns. (Other choices could serve equally well.) Theorem 2.6.2 is used so that the expansion may be carried out in terms of columns rather than rows.

det **A**

$$= (-1)^{1+2+1+3}\begin{vmatrix} 0 & 0 \\ 1 & 3 \end{vmatrix}\begin{vmatrix} 0 & 5 & 1 \\ 0 & 0 & 0 \\ 0 & 1 & 0 \end{vmatrix} + (-1)^{1+3+1+3}\begin{vmatrix} 0 & 0 \\ 0 & 0 \end{vmatrix}\begin{vmatrix} 0 & 0 & 0 \\ 0 & 0 & 0 \\ 0 & 1 & 0 \end{vmatrix}$$

$$+ (-1)^{1+4+1+3}\begin{vmatrix} 0 & 0 \\ 1 & 4 \end{vmatrix}\begin{vmatrix} 0 & 0 & 0 \\ 0 & 5 & 1 \\ 0 & 0 & 0 \end{vmatrix} + (-1)^{1+5+1+3}\begin{vmatrix} 0 & 0 \\ 0 & 0 \end{vmatrix}\begin{vmatrix} 0 & 0 & 0 \\ 0 & 5 & 1 \\ 0 & 0 & 0 \end{vmatrix}$$

$$+ (-1)^{2+3+1+3}\begin{vmatrix} 1 & 3 \\ 0 & 0 \end{vmatrix}\begin{vmatrix} 2 & 7 & 1 \\ 0 & 0 & 0 \\ 0 & 1 & 0 \end{vmatrix} + (-1)^{2+4+1+3}\begin{vmatrix} 1 & 3 \\ 1 & 4 \end{vmatrix}\begin{vmatrix} 2 & 7 & 1 \\ 0 & 5 & 1 \\ 0 & 1 & 0 \end{vmatrix}$$

$$+ (-1)^{2+5+1+3}\begin{vmatrix} 1 & 3 \\ 0 & 0 \end{vmatrix}\begin{vmatrix} 2 & 7 & 1 \\ 0 & 5 & 1 \\ 0 & 0 & 0 \end{vmatrix} + (-1)^{3+4+1+3}\begin{vmatrix} 0 & 0 \\ 1 & 4 \end{vmatrix}\begin{vmatrix} 2 & 7 & 1 \\ 0 & 0 & 0 \\ 0 & 1 & 0 \end{vmatrix}$$

$$+ (-1)^{3+5+1+3}\begin{vmatrix} 0 & 0 \\ 0 & 0 \end{vmatrix}\begin{vmatrix} 2 & 7 & 1 \\ 0 & 0 & 0 \\ 0 & 0 & 0 \end{vmatrix} + (-1)^{4+5+1+3}\begin{vmatrix} 1 & 4 \\ 0 & 0 \end{vmatrix}\begin{vmatrix} 2 & 7 & 1 \\ 0 & 0 & 0 \\ 0 & 5 & 1 \end{vmatrix}$$

$$= (-1)^{10}\begin{vmatrix} 1 & 3 \\ 1 & 4 \end{vmatrix}\begin{vmatrix} 2 & 7 & 1 \\ 0 & 5 & 1 \\ 0 & 1 & 0 \end{vmatrix} = -2. \text{ (All other terms are zero.)}$$

Thus, this method takes advantage of the insight the individual may have in expanding the determinant of a matrix. However, for routine evaluation, Theorem 2.8.1 and the theorems of Section 2.6 (used to reduce the determinant to one of a matrix of triangular form) are generally as useful as Laplace's expansion.

Exercises 2.9

1. Use Laplace's expansion with appropriate 2×2 minors to evaluate

(a) $\begin{vmatrix} 0 & 1 & 0 & 1 \\ 0 & 0 & 1 & 1 \\ 1 & 0 & 1 & 1 \\ 1 & 1 & 1 & 1 \end{vmatrix}$ (b) $\begin{vmatrix} 0 & 0 & 1 & 2 \\ 0 & 0 & -1 & 0 \\ 1 & 1 & 0 & 0 \\ 2 & 1 & 0 & 0 \end{vmatrix}$ (c) $\begin{vmatrix} 2 & 6 & 5 & -4 & 1 \\ 0 & 1 & 0 & -1 & 0 \\ 1 & 0 & 0 & 1 & 0 \\ 0 & 3 & 1 & 0 & 5 \\ -1 & 0 & 2 & 0 & 0 \end{vmatrix}$

2. Show that

$$\begin{vmatrix} 1 & 2 & 0 & 0 \\ 3 & 4 & 0 & 0 \\ 0 & 0 & 1 & -1 \\ 0 & 0 & 0 & 1 \end{vmatrix} = \begin{vmatrix} 1 & 2 \\ 3 & 4 \end{vmatrix} \cdot \begin{vmatrix} 1 & -1 \\ 0 & 1 \end{vmatrix},$$

but that

$$\begin{vmatrix} 1 & 1 & 1 & 1 \\ 2 & 1 & 0 & 1 \\ 1 & 2 & 1 & 0 \\ -1 & 1 & 0 & 1 \end{vmatrix} \neq \begin{vmatrix} 1 & 1 \\ 2 & 1 \end{vmatrix} \cdot \begin{vmatrix} 1 & 0 \\ 0 & 1 \end{vmatrix} - \begin{vmatrix} 1 & 1 \\ 0 & 1 \end{vmatrix} \cdot \begin{vmatrix} 1 & 2 \\ -1 & 1 \end{vmatrix}.$$

3. In how many different ways can the determinant of a 4×4 matrix be expanded by Laplace's expansion using 2×2 minors?

2.10. The Determinant of the Product of Square Matrices

If we are given two square matrices **A** and **B**, each of order n, then det **A** and det **B**, as well as **AB** and det **AB**, are defined. The following theorem shows us that the product of the determinants is equal to the determinant of the product. The matrices must be square and of the same order, since otherwise some of the operations would not be defined.

Theorem 2.10.1. *If matrices* **A** *and* **B** *are of order n, then*

$$\det \mathbf{A} \det \mathbf{B} = \det \mathbf{AB}. \tag{2.10.1}$$

Proof: One result regarding elementary transformations is needed that is not available as yet; it is discussed in the next chapter, although it could be derived completely at this time. By showing the result using 4×4 matrices we indicate the plausibility of the result in general; see Section 3.5 for this result.

We expand the product of the 4×4 matrices **K** and **H**, **K** arbitrary but **H** in a special form, to get

$$(2.10.2)\qquad \begin{bmatrix} k_{11} & k_{12} & k_{13} & k_{14} \\ k_{21} & k_{22} & k_{23} & k_{24} \\ k_{31} & k_{32} & k_{33} & k_{34} \\ k_{41} & k_{42} & k_{43} & k_{44} \end{bmatrix} \begin{bmatrix} 1 & 0 & 0 & 0 \\ 0 & 1 & 0 & 0 \\ c_{31} & c_{32} & 1 & 0 \\ c_{41} & c_{42} & 0 & 1 \end{bmatrix}$$

$$= \begin{bmatrix} k_{11} + k_{13}c_{31} + k_{14}c_{41} & k_{12} + k_{13}c_{32} + k_{14}c_{42} & k_{13} & k_{14} \\ k_{21} + k_{23}c_{31} + k_{24}c_{41} & k_{22} + k_{23}c_{32} + k_{24}c_{42} & k_{23} & k_{24} \\ k_{31} + k_{33}c_{31} + k_{34}c_{41} & k_{32} + k_{33}c_{32} + k_{34}c_{42} & k_{33} & k_{34} \\ k_{41} + k_{43}c_{31} + k_{44}c_{41} & k_{42} + k_{43}c_{32} + k_{44}c_{42} & k_{43} & k_{44} \end{bmatrix}$$

Observe that the effect of multiplying **K** by **H** is to multiply the elements of the third column of **K** by c_{31} and the elements of the fourth column of **K** by c_{41}, and then to add these products to the elements of the first column of **K**. Similarly, the elements of the third column of **K** are multiplied by c_{32} and the elements of the fourth column of **K** are multiplied by c_{42}; these products are then added to the elements of the second column of **K**. According to Theorem 2.6.7, the determinant of the result is the same as the determinant of **K**.

The generalization of this result is that

$$(2.10.3)\qquad \det \mathbf{K} = \det(\mathbf{KH}), \text{ where } \mathbf{H} = \begin{bmatrix} \mathbf{I} & \mathbf{0} \\ \mathbf{C} & \mathbf{I} \end{bmatrix}.$$

Now to proceed with the proof of Theorem 2.10.1 we place the matrices **A** and **B** in the partitioned matrices and expand as follows:

$$(2.10.4)\qquad \begin{bmatrix} \mathbf{B} & -\mathbf{I} \\ \mathbf{0} & \mathbf{A} \end{bmatrix} \begin{bmatrix} \mathbf{I} & \mathbf{0} \\ \mathbf{B} & \mathbf{I} \end{bmatrix} = \begin{bmatrix} \mathbf{0} & -\mathbf{I} \\ \mathbf{AB} & \mathbf{A} \end{bmatrix}.$$

Since **A** and **B** are of order n, so are the other submatrices; the larger matrices are of order $2n$. Since the matrices are equal, the determinant of the left side is equal to the determinant of the right side. Further, the determinant of the left side is the same as the determinant of the first matrix by Eq. (2.10.3). That is,

$$(2.10.5)\qquad \det \begin{bmatrix} \mathbf{B} & -\mathbf{I} \\ \mathbf{0} & \mathbf{A} \end{bmatrix} = \det \begin{bmatrix} \mathbf{0} & -\mathbf{I} \\ \mathbf{AB} & \mathbf{A} \end{bmatrix}.$$

By using the Laplace expansion on the left, we get det **B** det **A** (or det **A** det **B**, since we now have the product of scalars); all other terms are zero because of the zero matrix. Using the Laplace expansion on the right we have

$$(2.10.6)\qquad (-1)^n(-1)^{(1+2+\cdots+n)+(n+1+n+2+\cdots+2n)} \det(\mathbf{AB}) = \det(\mathbf{AB}).$$

That is,

$$(2.10.7)\qquad \det \mathbf{AB} = \det \mathbf{A} \det \mathbf{B},$$

and the theorem is proved. It is left as an exercise for the reader to show that the sign associated with det **AB** in Eq. (2.10.6) is +1.

Example 2.10.1. Verify Theorem 2.10.1 if

$$\mathbf{A} = \begin{bmatrix} 3 & 1 & 4 \\ -1 & 0 & 1 \\ 1 & 2 & 1 \end{bmatrix} \quad \text{and} \quad \mathbf{B} = \begin{bmatrix} 0 & 1 & 3 \\ -5 & 2 & 0 \\ 1 & 2 & 3 \end{bmatrix}.$$

For matrices **A** and **B**, det **A** = −12, det **B** = −21,

$$\mathbf{AB} \begin{bmatrix} -1 & 13 & 21 \\ 1 & 1 & 0 \\ -9 & 7 & 6 \end{bmatrix},$$

and det **AB** = 252. Thus det **A** det **B** = 252 = det **AB**.

Exercises 2.10

1. Verify Theorem 2.10.1 if

$$\mathbf{A} = \begin{bmatrix} 4 & 0 & 0 & 0 \\ 0 & 2 & 0 & 0 \\ 0 & 0 & 1 & 0 \\ 0 & 0 & 0 & -1 \end{bmatrix}, \quad \mathbf{B} = \begin{bmatrix} 1 & 1 & 1 & 1 \\ 1 & 0 & 1 & 1 \\ 1 & 0 & 1 & 0 \\ 0 & 0 & 1 & 0 \end{bmatrix}.$$

2. Prove: det **ABC** = det **A** det **B** det **C**.
3. If

$$\mathbf{A} = \begin{bmatrix} 2 & 1 & 3 \\ -1 & 1 & 2 \\ 1 & 0 & 2 \end{bmatrix} \quad \text{and} \quad \mathbf{B} = \begin{bmatrix} 1 & 0 & 1 \\ 2 & 2 & 1 \\ -3 & 1 & 2 \end{bmatrix},$$

substitute in Eq. (2.10.4) and carry through the steps to arrive at Eq. (2.10.7). Expand the result to verify Theorem 2.10.1.

4. Prove that if **A** is square, $|\mathbf{AA}^*|$ is a real number and furthermore $|\mathbf{AA}^*| \geqq 0$.
5. Show that the sign associated with det **AB** in Eq. (2.10.6) is +1.

2.11.† Cramer's Rule

This section gives two methods for deriving Cramer's[§] rule, which is used for solving systems of equations. (Cramer's rule is discussed more fully in Section 5.3.) Although this method is not essentially a practical computing technique, it is discussed because of the theory involved.

[§] Named after the Swiss mathematician Gabriel Cramer (1704–1752).

We start with a system of n linear equations in n unknowns:

$$
\begin{aligned}
&a_{11}x_1 + a_{12}x_2 + \cdots + a_{1n}x_n = c_1\\
&a_{21}x_1 + a_{22}x_2 + \cdots + a_{2n}x_n = c_2\\
&\cdots\\
&a_{n1}x_1 + a_{n2}x_2 + \cdots + a_{nn}x_n = c_n.
\end{aligned} \tag{2.11.1}
$$

These equations may be written more compactly as

$$\mathbf{A}\mathbf{x} = \mathbf{c} \tag{2.11.2}$$

for which

$$\mathbf{A} = \begin{bmatrix} a_{11} & a_{12} & \cdots & a_{1n} \\ a_{21} & a_{22} & \cdots & a_{2n} \\ \cdots & & & \\ a_{n1} & a_{n2} & \cdots & a_{nn} \end{bmatrix}, \quad \mathbf{x} = \begin{bmatrix} x_1 \\ x_2 \\ \vdots \\ x_n \end{bmatrix}, \quad \text{and} \quad \mathbf{c} = \begin{bmatrix} c_1 \\ c_2 \\ \vdots \\ c_n \end{bmatrix}. \tag{2.11.3}$$

We define the matrix $\mathbf{K}_j$ to be a matrix with the same elements as $\mathbf{A}$ except that the jth column of $\mathbf{A}$ has been replaced by the vector $\mathbf{c}$. That is,

$$\mathbf{K}_j = \begin{bmatrix} a_{11} & a_{12} & \cdots & c_1 & \cdots & a_{1n} \\ a_{21} & a_{22} & \cdots & c_2 & \cdots & a_{2n} \\ \cdots & & & & & \\ a_{n1} & a_{n2} & \cdots & c_n & \cdots & a_{nn} \end{bmatrix}; \tag{2.11.4}$$

the vector $\mathbf{c}$ appears as the jth column.

If none of the x_i are zero and $\det \mathbf{A} \neq 0$ in Eq. (2.11.3), then by applying the theorems of Section 2.6 we can write for x_1

$$\det \mathbf{A} = \begin{vmatrix} a_{11} & a_{12} & \cdots & a_{1n} \\ a_{21} & a_{22} & \cdots & a_{2n} \\ \cdots & & & \\ a_{n1} & a_{n2} & \cdots & a_{nn} \end{vmatrix} \tag{2.11.5}$$

$$= \frac{1}{x_1} \begin{vmatrix} a_{11}x_1 + a_{12}x_2 + \cdots + a_{1n}x_n & a_{12} \cdots a_{1n} \\ a_{21}x_1 + a_{22}x_2 + \cdots + a_{2n}x_n & a_{22} \cdots a_{2n} \\ \cdots & \\ a_{n1}x_1 + a_{n2}x_2 + \cdots + a_{nn}x_n & a_{n2} \cdots a_{nn} \end{vmatrix}$$

$$= \frac{1}{x_1} \det \mathbf{K}_1,$$

or

$$x_1 = \frac{\det \mathbf{K}_1}{\det \mathbf{A}},$$

after replacing the first column by the corresponding values from **c** from Eq. (2.11.1). In a similar manner we get

$$x_j = \frac{\det \mathbf{K}_j}{\det \mathbf{A}}. \tag{2.11.6}$$

for $j = 1, 2, \cdots, n$.

If $x_1 = 0$, say, in Eq. (2.11.5) with $\det \mathbf{A} \neq 0$, it is not difficult to reason that $\det \mathbf{K}_1 = 0$. The case in which $\det \mathbf{A} = 0$ will be discussed more fully later.

We present an alternate method for deriving Cramer's rule by the use of other results of this chapter. Starting again with the system of n linear equations in n unknowns in Eq. (2.11.1) we multiply b)th sides of the first equation by A_{11}, the cofactor of a_{11} in **A** in Eq. (2.11.3). We next multiply both sides of the second equation in Eq. (2.11.1) by $A_{21}, \cdots$, and we multiply the nth equation by A_{n1} and then add the corresponding sides. That is, we have

$$\begin{aligned} a_{11}A_{11}x_1 + a_{12}A_{11}x_2 + \cdots + a_{1n}A_{11}x_n &= c_1A_{11} \\ a_{21}A_{21}x_1 + a_{22}A_{21}x_2 + \cdots + a_{2n}A_{21}x_n &= c_2A_{21} \\ \cdots \\ a_{n1}A_{n1}x_1 + a_{n2}A_{n1}x_2 + \cdots + a_{nn}A_{n1}x_n &= c_nA_{n1}. \end{aligned} \tag{2.11.7}$$

Upon adding corresponding sides of these equations we have

$$\begin{aligned} & x_1(a_{11}A_{11} + a_{21}A_{21} + \cdots + a_{n1}A_{n1}) \\ & + x_2(a_{12}A_{11} + a_{22}A_{21} + \cdots + a_{n2}A_{n1}) \\ & + \cdots \\ & + x_n(a_{1n}A_{11} + a_{2n}A_{21} + \cdots + a_{nn}A_{n1}) \\ = {} & c_1A_{11} + c_2A_{21} + \cdots + c_nA_{n1}. \end{aligned} \tag{2.11.8}$$

From Theorem 2.8.1 the coefficient of x_1 is $\det \mathbf{A}$, and the coefficients of the other x_i are all zero by Theorem 2.8.2. The right side is merely $\det \mathbf{K}_1$ by Eq. (2.11.4). We thus have

$$x_1 \det \mathbf{A} = \det \mathbf{K}_1,$$

or, if $\det \mathbf{A} \neq 0$,

$$x_1 = \frac{\det \mathbf{K}_1}{\det \mathbf{A}}. \tag{2.11.9}$$

In a similar manner we can solve for each x_j, $j = 1, 2, \cdots, n$, if $\det \mathbf{A} \neq 0$. Thus if Eq. (2.11.1) has a solution and $\det \mathbf{A} \neq 0$, the solution is given by

$$x_j = \frac{\det \mathbf{K}_j}{\det \mathbf{A}}. \tag{2.11.10}$$

On the other hand it can be shown that the result in Eq. (2.11.10) actually is a solution under the condition that $\det \mathbf{A} \neq 0$. The verification of this result is left as an exercise for the reader.

The results of this section can be summarized in the following theorem.

Theorem 2.11.1. *For the system of n linear equations in n unknowns, Eq.* (2.11.1), *there exists a solution given by*

$$x_j = \frac{\det \mathbf{K}_j}{\det \mathbf{A}}, \qquad j = 1, 2, \cdots, n, \tag{2.11.11}$$

if $\det \mathbf{A} \neq 0$, *where* $\det \mathbf{K}_j$ *is defined in Eq.* (2.11.4). *The result is known as Cramer's rule.*

Systems of m equations in n unknowns, where $m \neq n$, cannot be solved by Cramer's rule, since det **A** is not defined if **A** is not a square matrix. (This problem will be discussed later.) Further, even though systems of n equations in n unknowns can be solved by Cramer's rule, the method is impractical unless n is small.

Exercises 2.11

1. Use Cramer's rule to solve

$$\begin{aligned} 2x + y + z &= 2 \\ 4x - 2y - 3z &= 0 \\ 6x + 3y - 2z &= 6. \end{aligned}$$

What is the familiar 3-dimensional geometric interpretation of your result?

2. Use Cramer's rule to solve

$$\begin{aligned} (1 - r)x + ry &= 3 \\ rx + (1 - r)y &= 7. \end{aligned}$$

What restrictions must be placed upon r?

3. What information does Cramer's rule give about the solutions of a system of n homogeneous equations in n unknowns?

4. Use Cramer's rule to solve

$$\begin{aligned} x + y &= 7 \\ y + z &= 11 \\ x - z + w &= 0 \\ w + x - y &= -2. \end{aligned}$$

5. Using a method similar to the second method of this section, verify that Eq. (2.11.10) satisfies Eq. (2.11.1).

6. Use Cramer's rule to solve

$$\begin{aligned} 2x - y + 3z &= 0 \\ 5y - 2z + 8 &= 4x \\ 4z + 11 - x &= 9y. \end{aligned}$$

7. Use Cramer's rule to find non-zero solutions for

$$\begin{aligned} x + 3y + z - 2w &= 0 \\ 2x - y - 3z &= 0 \\ 3y + 5z - 6w &= 0. \end{aligned}$$

(Hint: Solve for x, y, and z in terms of w.)

2.12.† *The Sum of Determinants*

At times it is convenient to write a determinant as a sum of determinants, or vice versa. The following theorem gives conditions under which this is possible.

Theorem 2.12.1. *If* $\mathbf{A} = [a_{ij}]$ *and* $\mathbf{B} = [b_{ij}]$ *are square matrices that are identical for all elements except for corresponding elements in the kth row, and if* $\mathbf{C} = [c_{ij}]$, *then det* $\mathbf{A}$ + *det* $\mathbf{B}$ = *det* $\mathbf{C}$ *where* $c_{ij} = a_{ij}$ *except in the kth row in which* $c_{kj} = a_{kj} + b_{kj}$.

Proof: The proof of this theorem follows that used in the proof of Theorem 2.6.7. (See Eq. (2.6.9).) Now det **C** may be written as

$$\begin{aligned} \text{(2.12.1)} \quad \det \mathbf{C} &= \sum_{(j)} (-1)^j a_{1j_1} \cdots a_{(k-1)j_{(k-1)}}(a_{kj_k} + b_{kj_k}) a_{(k+1)j_{(k+1)}} \cdots a_{nj_n} \\ &= \sum_{(j)} (-1)^j a_{1j_1} \cdots a_{nj_n} + \sum_{(j)} (-1)^j a_{1j_1} \cdots b_{kj_k} \cdots a_{nj_n} \\ &= \det \mathbf{A} + \det \mathbf{B}, \end{aligned}$$

since $a_{ij} = b_{ij}$ for all i and j except (perhaps) where $i = k$.

Example 2.12.1. Verify that

$$\begin{vmatrix} 0 & 4 & 2 \\ 2 & 1 & 1 \\ 9 & 6 & 3 \end{vmatrix} + \begin{vmatrix} 0 & 4 & 2 \\ 1 & -2 & 0 \\ 9 & 6 & 3 \end{vmatrix} = \begin{vmatrix} 0 & 4 & 2 \\ 3 & -1 & 1 \\ 9 & 6 & 3 \end{vmatrix}.$$

It is readily verified that the three determinants have values 18, 36, and 54 respectively and that 18 + 36 = 54.

Notice that the addition of determinants is not the same as the addition of matrices; for matrices corresponding elements are added in *all* positions.

Furthermore, matrices need not be square for addition to be defined. For determinants two rows (columns) may be different, but corresponding elements in the other rows (columns) must be the same. This theorem is valuable when it is convenient to write a determinant as a sum of determinants to simplify an expansion.

2.13.† *The Derivative of a Determinant*

If the elements of det **A** are differentiable functions of some variable, x, then $\frac{d}{dx}$ det **A** has meaning, since det **A** is a scalar. Since each of the $n!$ terms in the expansion of det **A** is a product of n factors, the derivative of det **A** is a sum of $n(n!)$ terms:

$$\frac{d}{dx}\det \mathbf{A} = \frac{d}{dx}\sum_{(j)}(-1)^j a_{1j_1}\cdots a_{nj_n} \tag{2.13.1}$$
$$= \sum_{(j)}(-1)^j a'_{1j_1}\cdots a_{nj_n} + \cdots + \sum_{(j)}(-1)^j a_{1j_1}\cdots a'_{nj_n},$$

where the primes indicate differentiation with respect to x.

The final result in Eq. (2.13.1) is merely a sum of determinants; each determinant is the same as det **A** except that the kth row has been replaced by the derivative of the elements in the kth row of det **A**. Thus, using primes to indicate differentiation with respect to x, we can write

$$\frac{d}{dx}\det \mathbf{A} = \begin{vmatrix} a'_{11} & a'_{12} & \cdots & a'_{1n} \\ a_{21} & a_{22} & \cdots & a_{2n} \\ \cdots & & & \\ a_{n1} & a_{n2} & \cdots & a_{nn} \end{vmatrix} + \begin{vmatrix} a_{11} & a_{12} & \cdots & a_{1n} \\ a'_{21} & a'_{22} & \cdots & a'_{2n} \\ \cdots & & & \\ a_{n1} & a_{n2} & \cdots & a_{nn} \end{vmatrix} \tag{2.13.2}$$
$$+ \cdots + \begin{vmatrix} a_{11} & a_{12} & \cdots & a_{1n} \\ a_{21} & a_{22} & \cdots & a_{2n} \\ \cdots & & & \\ a'_{n1} & a'_{n2} & \cdots & a'_{nn} \end{vmatrix}.$$

Example 2.13.1. Find $\frac{d}{dx}$ det **A** if

$$\mathbf{A} = \begin{bmatrix} \cos x & \sin x \\ -\sin x & \cos x \end{bmatrix}.$$

$$\frac{dA}{dx} = \begin{vmatrix} -\sin x & \cos x \\ -\sin x & \cos x \end{vmatrix} + \begin{vmatrix} \cos x & \sin x \\ -\cos x & -\sin x \end{vmatrix} = 0.$$

This is an obvious result, since det **A** = 1.

Example 2.13.2. Find $\frac{dA}{dx}$ if

$$\mathbf{A} = \begin{bmatrix} x & 1 & x^2 \\ e^x & x^2 & 1 \\ 1 & e^x & x \end{bmatrix}.$$

$$\frac{dA}{dx} = \begin{vmatrix} 1 & 0 & 2x \\ e^x & x^2 & 1 \\ 1 & e^x & x \end{vmatrix} + \begin{vmatrix} x & 1 & x^2 \\ e^x & 2x & 0 \\ 1 & e^x & x \end{vmatrix} + \begin{vmatrix} x & 1 & x^2 \\ e^x & x^2 & 1 \\ 0 & e^x & 1 \end{vmatrix}.$$

Note that the determinants in the sum in Eq. (2.13.2) cannot be combined readily into one determinant. Theorem 2.12.1 states that all except one of the rows of determinants to be added must be the same; this is generally not the situation in Eq. (2.13.2).

Exercises 2.13

1. Find $\frac{dA(x)}{dx}$ if

$$\mathbf{A}(x) = \begin{bmatrix} x & 1 & x^2 \\ x+1 & 1 & x^2+2x \\ 1 & 0 & 2x \end{bmatrix}.$$

Observe that two of the determinants in the sum can be combined. Explain your answers.

2. Add a determinant of order n to itself by using the fact that the last $n-1$ rows are the same in both determinants.

3. Perform the addition: $\begin{vmatrix} 1 & 2 & 3 \\ -1 & 0 & 1 \\ 5 & 9 & 6 \end{vmatrix} + \begin{vmatrix} 1 & -1 & 2 \\ 2 & 0 & 0 \\ 3 & 1 & 3 \end{vmatrix}.$

4. (a) Find $\frac{dA}{dx}$ if $A = \begin{vmatrix} \sinh x & e^x \\ \cosh x & e^x \end{vmatrix}$,

(b) Find $\frac{dB}{dx}$ if $B = \begin{vmatrix} x & x^2 & x^3 \\ 1 & 2x & 3x^2 \\ 0 & 2 & 6x \end{vmatrix}$,

(c) Find $\frac{dC}{d\lambda}$ if $C = \begin{vmatrix} 1-\lambda & 2 & 1 \\ 3 & 2-\lambda & 0 \\ 2 & 1 & 3-\lambda \end{vmatrix}.$

3

The Inverse and Rank of a Matrix

3.1. The Adjoint Matrix

In Chapter 1 we considered certain aspects of the inverse of a matrix. However, at that time we were unable to compute the inverse of a matrix except in a few instances. Now, with the ideas from determinant theory at our disposal, we are able to compute the inverse of any matrix that possesses an inverse. In addition, we are able to determine whether or not a matrix has an inverse without actually performing the complete computation.

We already know that only square matrices can have inverses. Throughout our discussion, if matrix $\mathbf{A}$ is to have an inverse (or is thought to have an inverse), we shall assume that $\mathbf{A}$ is square.

We begin by defining the *adjoint matrix* of the square matrix $\mathbf{A}$ as the matrix adj $\mathbf{A}$, where

$$\text{adj } \mathbf{A} = [A_{ij}]' = \begin{bmatrix} A_{11} & A_{21} & \cdots & A_{n1} \\ A_{12} & A_{22} & \cdots & A_{n2} \\ \cdots & & & \\ A_{1n} & A_{2n} & \cdots & A_{nn} \end{bmatrix}, \tag{3.1.1}$$

the element A_{ij} is the cofactor of a_{ij} in $\mathbf{A}$.

Example 3.1.1. Find the adjoint of $\mathbf{A}$ and $\mathbf{B}$ if

$$\mathbf{A} = \begin{bmatrix} 3 & 2 \\ 1 & 5 \end{bmatrix} \quad \text{and} \quad \mathbf{B} = \begin{bmatrix} 1 & 4 & -2 \\ 0 & 2 & 3 \\ 4 & -1 & 1 \end{bmatrix}.$$

From Eq. (3.1.1) we can write

$$\text{adj } \mathbf{A} = \begin{bmatrix} 5 & -2 \\ -1 & 3 \end{bmatrix}, \quad \text{and}$$

$$\text{adj } \mathbf{B} = \begin{bmatrix} \begin{vmatrix} 2 & 3 \\ -1 & 1 \end{vmatrix} & -\begin{vmatrix} 4 & -2 \\ -1 & 1 \end{vmatrix} & \begin{vmatrix} 4 & -2 \\ 2 & 3 \end{vmatrix} \\ -\begin{vmatrix} 0 & 3 \\ 4 & 1 \end{vmatrix} & \begin{vmatrix} 1 & -2 \\ 4 & 1 \end{vmatrix} & -\begin{vmatrix} 1 & -2 \\ 0 & 3 \end{vmatrix} \\ \begin{vmatrix} 0 & 2 \\ 4 & -1 \end{vmatrix} & -\begin{vmatrix} 1 & 4 \\ 4 & -1 \end{vmatrix} & \begin{vmatrix} 1 & 4 \\ 0 & 2 \end{vmatrix} \end{bmatrix}$$

$$= \begin{bmatrix} 5 & -2 & 16 \\ 12 & 9 & -3 \\ -8 & 17 & 2 \end{bmatrix}.$$

3.2. *The Inverse of a Matrix*

From the definition of the adjoint from the preceding section, we can write

$$\text{(3.2.1)} \qquad \mathbf{A}(\text{adj } \mathbf{A}) = (\text{adj } \mathbf{A})\mathbf{A} = \begin{bmatrix} \det \mathbf{A} & 0 & \cdots & 0 \\ 0 & \det \mathbf{A} & \cdots & 0 \\ \cdots & & & \\ 0 & 0 & \cdots & \det \mathbf{A} \end{bmatrix}$$

$$= (\det \mathbf{A})\mathbf{I}$$

by using Theorems 2.8.1 and 2.8.2. Provided that $\det \mathbf{A} \neq 0$, we can divide both sides of Eq. (3.2.1) by $\det \mathbf{A}$:

$$\text{(3.2.2)} \qquad \mathbf{A}\frac{\text{adj } \mathbf{A}}{\det \mathbf{A}} = \frac{\text{adj } \mathbf{A}}{\det \mathbf{A}}\mathbf{A} = \mathbf{I}, \quad \text{or}$$

$$\frac{\text{adj } \mathbf{A}}{\det \mathbf{A}} = \mathbf{A}^{-1},$$

the inverse of the square matrix $\mathbf{A}$. Written out more fully,

$$\text{(3.2.3)} \qquad \mathbf{A}^{-1} = \frac{\text{adj } \mathbf{A}}{\det \mathbf{A}} = \left[\frac{A_{ij}}{A}\right]' = \begin{bmatrix} \frac{A_{11}}{A} & \frac{A_{21}}{A} & \cdots & \frac{A_{n1}}{A} \\ \frac{A_{12}}{A} & \frac{A_{22}}{A} & \cdots & \frac{A_{n2}}{A} \\ \cdots & & & \\ \frac{A_{1n}}{A} & \frac{A_{2n}}{A} & \cdots & \frac{A_{nn}}{A} \end{bmatrix}.$$

Note that $\mathbf{A}^{-1}$ is square since adj $\mathbf{A}$ is square, a result that also follows from Section 1.6. Also we recall from Theorem 1.6.1 that $\mathbf{A}^{-1}$ is a unique matrix.

From the above result, we see that det $\mathbf{A} \neq 0$ is sufficient for $\mathbf{A}^{-1}$ to exist. We now show that this condition is also necessary. Since $\mathbf{A}\mathbf{A}^{-1} = \mathbf{I}$, then

$$\det \mathbf{A} \det \mathbf{A}^{-1} = \det \mathbf{I} = 1. \tag{3.2.4}$$

Thus of necessity det $\mathbf{A} \neq 0$, since otherwise the product would be 0. We combine these two results in the following theorem:

Theorem 3.2.1. *A necessary and sufficient condition that a square matrix* $\mathbf{A}$ *have an inverse is that det* $\mathbf{A} \neq 0$.

Square matrices $\mathbf{A}$ such that det $\mathbf{A} \neq 0$ are *nonsingular*; if det $\mathbf{A} = 0$, then $\mathbf{A}$ is *singular*.

From Eq. (3.2.4) we can state the following:

Theorem 3.2.2. *If the matrix* $\mathbf{A}$ *has an inverse, then*

$$\det \mathbf{A}^{-1} = (\det \mathbf{A})^{-1}. \tag{3.2.5}$$

Note that the symbol -1 on the right refers to the reciprocal of the scalar.

We now consider some examples in which we compute the inverse of a matrix.

Example 3.2.1. Find the inverse of the matrix

$$\mathbf{B} = \begin{bmatrix} 2 & 1 & 2 \\ 1 & 2 & 1 \\ 3 & 1 & 4 \end{bmatrix}.$$

We readily determine that det $\mathbf{B} = 3$. Thus

$$\operatorname{adj} \mathbf{B} = \begin{bmatrix} \begin{vmatrix} 2 & 1 \\ 1 & 4 \end{vmatrix} & -\begin{vmatrix} 1 & 2 \\ 1 & 4 \end{vmatrix} & \begin{vmatrix} 1 & 2 \\ 2 & 1 \end{vmatrix} \\ -\begin{vmatrix} 1 & 1 \\ 3 & 4 \end{vmatrix} & \begin{vmatrix} 2 & 2 \\ 3 & 4 \end{vmatrix} & -\begin{vmatrix} 2 & 2 \\ 1 & 1 \end{vmatrix} \\ \begin{vmatrix} 1 & 2 \\ 3 & 1 \end{vmatrix} & -\begin{vmatrix} 2 & 1 \\ 3 & 1 \end{vmatrix} & \begin{vmatrix} 2 & 1 \\ 1 & 2 \end{vmatrix} \end{bmatrix}$$

$$= \begin{bmatrix} 7 & -2 & -3 \\ -1 & 2 & 0 \\ -5 & 1 & 3 \end{bmatrix}, \quad \text{so}$$

$$\mathbf{B}^{-1} = \begin{bmatrix} 7/3 & -2/3 & -3/3 \\ -1/3 & 2/3 & 0 \\ -5/3 & 1/3 & 3/3 \end{bmatrix}.$$

Example 3.2.2. For what values of x does $\mathbf{H}$ fail to have an inverse if

$$\mathbf{H} = \begin{bmatrix} 1 & 2 & x-2 \\ x & 4 & 0 \\ 2 & x & -3 \end{bmatrix}?$$

Since det $\mathbf{H} = x^3 - 2x^2 - 2x + 4$, det $\mathbf{H} = 0$ for $x = 2, \pm\sqrt{2}$. Thus, by Theorem 3.2.1, $\mathbf{H}$ does not have an inverse for these values of x; $\mathbf{H}^{-1}$ exists for all other x.

Exercises 3.2

1. Find the adjoints of

(a) $\begin{bmatrix} 1 & 2 \\ 3 & 4 \end{bmatrix}$ (b) $\begin{bmatrix} 1 & 2 & -1 \\ 0 & 1 & 0 \\ 1 & 1 & 0 \end{bmatrix}$ (c) $\begin{bmatrix} 1 & 0 & 1 & 2 \\ 0 & 2 & 0 & 1 \\ 0 & 0 & -1 & 1 \\ 0 & 0 & 0 & -2 \end{bmatrix}$

2. Determine the inverse for each of the following matrices that have inverses

(a) $\begin{bmatrix} 2 & 5 \\ 1 & 3 \end{bmatrix}$ (b) $\begin{bmatrix} 4 & 1 & 3 \\ 7 & 2 & 1 \\ 1 & 0 & 5 \end{bmatrix}$ (c) $\begin{bmatrix} 1 & 4 & 1 \\ 2 & 0 & 3 \\ 1 & 2 & 0 \end{bmatrix}$

(d) $\begin{bmatrix} 0 & 1 & 0 & 0 \\ 1 & 0 & 0 & 0 \\ 0 & 0 & 1 & 0 \\ 0 & 0 & 0 & 1 \end{bmatrix}$ (e) $\begin{bmatrix} 0 & 0 & 0 & -1 \\ 0 & 0 & -1 & 0 \\ 0 & -1 & 0 & 0 \\ -1 & 0 & 0 & 0 \end{bmatrix}$

3. If $\mathbf{A}$ is nonsingular, prove that $\mathbf{B} = \mathbf{C}$ if $\mathbf{AB} = \mathbf{AC}$. Explain whether or not $\mathbf{B}$ and $\mathbf{C}$ need to be square.

4. If $\mathbf{A}, \mathbf{B}, \cdots, \mathbf{H}$ are all nonsingular and are of order n, find $(\mathbf{AB} \cdots \mathbf{H})^{-1}$.

5. Show that det $\mathbf{A}^{-1} = (\det \mathbf{A})^{-1}$ for each matrix in exercise 2 that has an inverse.

6. Show that if $\mathbf{B}$ has an inverse, $(\mathbf{B}')^{-1} = (\mathbf{B}^{-1})'$ for those matrices of exercise 2 that have inverses.

7. If $\mathbf{A}$ has an inverse and is symmetric, show that $\mathbf{A}^{-1}$ is also symmetric.

8. If $\mathbf{x}$ and $\mathbf{c}$ are column vectors, under what condition(s) is there a unique $\mathbf{x}$ in $\mathbf{Ax} = \mathbf{c}$? If $\mathbf{A}$ is singular can there exist vector(s) $\mathbf{x}$ satisfying $\mathbf{Ax} = \mathbf{c}$? Give a numerical example to illustrate your answer if $\mathbf{x}$ is a 3-row column vector.

9. If the matrix $\mathbf{A}$ is such that $\mathbf{A}^k = \mathbf{0}$ for some positive integer k, prove that $\mathbf{A}$ is singular.

10. Show that the necessary and sufficient condition that $\mathbf{A}$ be such that $\mathbf{A}^2 = \mathbf{I}$ is that $\mathbf{A} = \mathbf{A}^{-1}$.

11. If we replace $\mathbf{A}^{-1}$ by adj $\mathbf{A}$ in exercise 10, we get the false statement "The matrix $\mathbf{A}$ is such that $\mathbf{A}^2 = \mathbf{I}$ if and only if $\mathbf{A} = \text{adj } \mathbf{A}$." How much can be proven here? Discuss.

12. If $\mathbf{A}$ is nonsingular, prove that $|\text{adj } \mathbf{A}| = |\mathbf{A}|^{n-1}$, where n is the order of $\mathbf{A}$.

13. Prove that the adjoint of adj $\mathbf{A}$ is $|\mathbf{A}|^{n-2} \cdot \mathbf{A}$. This result is true for all $\mathbf{A}$, but we can prove it only for $\mathbf{A}$ nonsingular with the tools at hand.

14. Prove that if $\mathbf{A}$ is such that $\mathbf{A}^2 = \mathbf{A}$ and $\mathbf{A}$ is different from $\mathbf{I}$, then $\mathbf{A}$ is singular. Find some singular matrices of order 2 that satisfy $\mathbf{A}^2 = \mathbf{A}$.

3.3. The Rank of a Matrix

A matrix $\mathbf{A}$ is said to be of *rank* r if and only if the largest nonsingular submatrix of $\mathbf{A}$ is of order r. That is, if there exists a square submatrix of order r whose determinant is not zero, and if all of the submatrices of $\mathbf{A}$ of order greater than r (if there are any) have determinants which are equal to zero, then matrix $\mathbf{A}$ is said to be of rank r.

If $\mathbf{A}$ is of order $m \times n$, the *maximum possible rank of* $\mathbf{A}$ is the smaller of m and n. Thus 2 is the maximum possible rank of a 2×3 matrix. If the rank of $\mathbf{A}$ is the maximum possible rank, then the rank of $\mathbf{A}$ is said to be *full rank*.

It follows from the preceding definition of rank that a matrix $\mathbf{A}$ has rank zero if and only if every element of $\mathbf{A}$ is zero; only the zero matrix has rank zero. Every nonzero matrix has at least one non-zero element, and thus has rank greater than zero.

Example 3.3.1. Determine the rank of the matrix

$$\mathbf{C} = \begin{bmatrix} 2 & 1 & 4 & 4 & 0 \\ 3 & 1 & 2 & 3 & 1 \\ 5 & 2 & 6 & 7 & 1 \\ 1 & 0 & -2 & -1 & 1 \end{bmatrix}.$$

The rank of $\mathbf{C}$ is 2 since the submatrix

$$\begin{bmatrix} 2 & 1 \\ 3 & 1 \end{bmatrix}$$

is nonsingular and all submatrices of order 3 or 4 are singular. The proof of this assertion is rather tedious using only the methods at our disposal thus far. Later methods will be considered by which the rank may be determined without considering all possible submatrices. (The reader might check a few 3rd and 4th order submatrices to see if any are nonsingular.)

Example 3.3.2. From Example 3.2.2. the matrix

$$\mathbf{H}(x) = \begin{bmatrix} 1 & 2 & x-2 \\ x & 4 & 0 \\ 2 & x & -3 \end{bmatrix}$$

is singular for $x = 2$ and $x = \pm\sqrt{2}$. For all other values of x the matrix is nonsingular and its rank is 3. Determine the rank of $\mathbf{H}$ if $x = 2$.

After substituting the value $x = 2$ in $\mathbf{H}(x)$, the submatrix in the lower left-hand corner is nonsingular, so $\mathbf{H}(2)$ is of rank 2.

Exercises 3.3

1. Prove that if matrix $\mathbf{C}_{m,n}$ is of rank k where $k \leqq m \leqq n$, then every submatrix of order $k+1, k+2, \cdots, m$ is singular.

2. Find the ranks of the following matrices.

(a) $\begin{bmatrix} 1 & 2 & 1 & -1 \\ 0 & -1 & -2 & 3 \\ 2 & 3 & 0 & 1 \end{bmatrix}$ (b) $\begin{bmatrix} 1 & 2 & 3 & 4 \\ 0 & 0 & 1 & -1 \\ 0 & 0 & -1 & 1 \\ 0 & 0 & 0 & -1 \end{bmatrix}$

3. Determine the values of x (if any) that will make $\mathbf{G}(x)$ of rank 1; of rank 2; of rank 3; if

$$\mathbf{G}(x) = \begin{bmatrix} x & 2 & x \\ x & x & 2 \\ 2 & x & x \end{bmatrix}.$$

4. Determine the ranks of $\mathbf{A}$, $\mathbf{B}$, $\mathbf{A}+\mathbf{B}$, $\mathbf{A}-\mathbf{B}$, $\mathbf{AB}$, and $\mathbf{BA}$ if

$$\mathbf{A} = \begin{bmatrix} 2 & 1 \\ -3 & 3 \end{bmatrix} \quad \text{and} \quad \mathbf{B} = \begin{bmatrix} -2 & 5 \\ 3 & -3 \end{bmatrix}.$$

Which of the operations of addition, subtraction, or multiplication are you led to believe can give a matrix with rank different from the ranks of the original matrices?

5. Prove the theorem: *If* $\mathbf{A}$ *is an* $n \times n$ *matrix such that det* $\mathbf{A} = 0$, *then the rank of* $\mathbf{A}$ *is less than n.*

3.4. Elementary Row and Column Transformations

As shown in Section 3.3, the task of determining the rank of a matrix can be very lengthy, since a matrix may have many square submatrices. Some methods exist for changing a matrix so that the rank of the resulting matrix is the same as the rank of the original matrix, but the rank of the resulting matrix can be determined more readily. These methods, called *elementary transformations* of a matrix, are of two types. However, to simplify the discussion, these transformations are customarily given as three types. (See number 8 in Exercises 3.4.)

For any matrix **A** of order $m \times n$, an elementary transformation is a transformation of one of the types:

(1) The interchange of two rows (columns) of **A**.

(2) The multiplication of the elements of a row (column) of **A** by the same non-zero scalar k.

(3) The addition of the elements of a row (column) of **A**, after they have been multiplied by the scalar k, to the corresponding elements of another row (column) of **A**.

The inverse of an elementary transformation is the transformation that restores the resulting matrix to the original form of **A**. Note that the inverse of each elementary transformation is a transformation of the same type. For (1) if the same two rows (columns) are again interchanged, the resulting matrix is again **A**. For (2) if the elements of the altered row (column) are multiplied by $1/k$, matrix **A** is again obtained. Finally for (3) if the same row (column) of **A** is multiplied by $-k$ and the result added to the corresponding elements of the other row (column) referred to in (3), **A** is again the resulting matrix. We state these results in the form of a theorem.

Theorem 3.4.1. *Each elementary transformation of a matrix has an inverse that is an elementary transformation of the same type.*

The following theorem is an important result of this section.

Theorem 3.4.2. *The order and rank of a matrix are not altered by an elementary transformation of a matrix.*

Proof: Since rows or columns are not added to **A** or deleted from **A**, the order of **A** is unaltered by any of the elementary transformations.

For a transformation of type (1), the determinants of all the submatrices of **A** are either left unaltered by the interchange of two rows (columns) or multiplied by -1. Hence all zero determinants remain zero, and non-zero determinants remain non-zero. Therefore the rank is unaltered. For example, the rank of

$$\begin{bmatrix} 2 & 1 & 4 \\ 0 & 0 & 0 \\ 3 & 1 & 2 \end{bmatrix}$$

is determined from

$$\begin{bmatrix} 2 & 1 \\ 3 & 1 \end{bmatrix}$$

to be two. If now the second and third rows of the original matrix are interchanged, the submatrix used to determine the rank consists of the same elements as before:

$$\begin{bmatrix} 2 & 1 \\ 3 & 1 \end{bmatrix}.$$

For a transformation of type (2), the determinants of all the submatrices of **A** are either left unaltered by multiplication of a row (column) by $k \neq 0$ or are multiplied by k. Again, all zero determinants remain zero, and all non-zero determinants, remain non-zero. Therefore the rank is unaltered.

It is left as an exercise for the reader to show that a transformation of type (3) does not alter the rank of a matrix.

An important consequence of Theorem 3.4.2 is that the rank of a matrix is not altered by any finite sequence of elementary transformations. Using this fact, we can now determine the rank of a matrix without examining all of the possible submatrices. We write $\mathbf{A} \sim \mathbf{B}$ (read **A** is *equivalent* to **B**) to mean that **A** and **B** have the same order and rank.

Example 3.4.1. Determine the rank of the matrix **C** given in Example 3.3.1.

By applying the elementary transformations one at a time in general, we determine that the rank is 2, an obvious observation in the final matrix. (The reader should make certain that every step is of one of the three types of elementary transformations.)

$$\mathbf{C} = \begin{bmatrix} 2 & 1 & 4 & 4 & 0 \\ 3 & 1 & 2 & 3 & 1 \\ 5 & 2 & 6 & 7 & 1 \\ 1 & 0 & -2 & -1 & 1 \end{bmatrix} \sim \begin{bmatrix} 2 & 1 & 4 & 4 & 0 \\ 3 & 1 & 2 & 3 & 1 \\ 2 & 1 & 4 & 4 & 0 \\ 1 & 0 & -2 & -1 & 1 \end{bmatrix}$$

$$\sim \begin{bmatrix} 2 & 1 & 4 & 4 & 0 \\ 3 & 1 & 2 & 3 & 1 \\ 0 & 0 & 0 & 0 & 0 \\ 1 & 0 & -2 & -1 & 1 \end{bmatrix} \sim \begin{bmatrix} 2 & 1 & 4 & 4 & 0 \\ 2 & 1 & 4 & 4 & 0 \\ 0 & 0 & 0 & 0 & 0 \\ 1 & 0 & -2 & -1 & 1 \end{bmatrix}$$

$$\sim \begin{bmatrix} 2 & 1 & 4 & 4 & 0 \\ 0 & 0 & 0 & 0 & 0 \\ 0 & 0 & 0 & 0 & 0 \\ 1 & 0 & -2 & -1 & 1 \end{bmatrix} \sim \begin{bmatrix} 1 & 1 & 6 & 5 & -1 \\ 0 & 0 & 0 & 0 & 0 \\ 0 & 0 & 0 & 0 & 0 \\ 1 & 0 & -2 & -1 & 1 \end{bmatrix}$$

$$\sim \begin{bmatrix} 0 & 1 & 0 & 0 & 0 \\ 0 & 0 & 0 & 0 & 0 \\ 0 & 0 & 0 & 0 & 0 \\ 1 & 0 & -2 & -1 & 1 \end{bmatrix} \sim \begin{bmatrix} 0 & 1 & 0 & 0 & 0 \\ 0 & 0 & 0 & 0 & 0 \\ 0 & 0 & 0 & 0 & 0 \\ 1 & 0 & 0 & 0 & 0 \end{bmatrix}$$

$$\sim \begin{bmatrix} 0 & 1 & 0 & 0 & 0 \\ 1 & 0 & 0 & 0 & 0 \\ 0 & 0 & 0 & 0 & 0 \\ 0 & 0 & 0 & 0 & 0 \end{bmatrix} \sim \begin{bmatrix} 1 & 0 & 0 & 0 & 0 \\ 0 & 1 & 0 & 0 & 0 \\ 0 & 0 & 0 & 0 & 0 \\ 0 & 0 & 0 & 0 & 0 \end{bmatrix}.$$

Observe in Example 3.4.1 that the matrices are not *equal* but that they all merely have the same order and rank.

As implied by Example 3.4.1, any matrix is equivalent to one of the same order which consists entirely of zeros except for a submatrix I_r, of order r, in the upper left-hand corner. By elementary transformations, either all, or all but one, of the non-zero elements in a row (column) can be reduced to zero. If there is one non-zero element left in a row (column), it can be reduced to a 1 by elementary transformations of type (2); then all of the elements in the column (row) in which it stands can be reduced to zero. By continuing in this manner, $\mathbf{I}_r$ is eventually obtained in the upper left-hand corner. Although an algorithm can be given that will lead to the required result, proceeding by inspection is generally faster unless a computer is used.

A matrix with $\mathbf{I}_r$ in the upper left-hand corner (designated by $\mathbf{R}_r$) is in *normal form*. Any matrix $\mathbf{A}$ can be reduced to normal form by a succession of elementary transformations.

We are now able to state and prove the following theorem.

Theorem 3.4.3. *Two matrices that are equivalent can be transformed from one to the other by a succession of elementary transformations.*

Proof: From the preceding results any matrix $\mathbf{A}$ can be transformed into an equivalent matrix $\mathbf{B}$ that is in normal form. Similarly, if $\mathbf{A} \sim \mathbf{C}$, then $\mathbf{C}$ can be transformed into $\mathbf{B}$. Then, using the transformations that are the inverse of those used in transforming $\mathbf{C}$ into $\mathbf{B}$, $\mathbf{B}$ can be transformed into $\mathbf{C}$. Thus $\mathbf{A} \sim \mathbf{B} \sim \mathbf{C}$; $\mathbf{A}$ can be transformed into $\mathbf{B}$, and $\mathbf{B}$ then transformed into $\mathbf{C}$ by a succession of elementary transformations. Therefore the theorem is proved.

Example 3.4.2. To demonstrate Theorem 3.4.3, show that $\mathbf{A}$ and $\mathbf{C}$ have the same ranks and that $\mathbf{A}$ can be transformed into $\mathbf{C}$ by elementary transformations if

$$\mathbf{A} = \begin{bmatrix} 2 & 1 & 3 \\ 1 & 2 & 0 \end{bmatrix} \quad \text{and} \quad \mathbf{C} = \begin{bmatrix} 1 & 4 & 1 \\ 3 & 2 & 7 \end{bmatrix}.$$

$$\mathbf{A} = \begin{bmatrix} 2 & 1 & 3 \\ 1 & 2 & 0 \end{bmatrix} \sim \begin{bmatrix} 0 & -3 & 3 \\ 1 & 2 & 0 \end{bmatrix} \sim \begin{bmatrix} 0 & -3 & 3 \\ 1 & 0 & 0 \end{bmatrix}$$

$$\sim \begin{bmatrix} 0 & 1 & 0 \\ 1 & 0 & 0 \end{bmatrix} \sim \begin{bmatrix} 1 & 0 & 0 \\ 0 & 1 & 0 \end{bmatrix} \sim \begin{bmatrix} 1 & 0 & 0 \\ 0 & -10 & 0 \end{bmatrix}$$

$$\sim \begin{bmatrix} 1 & 0 & 0 \\ 1 & -10 & 4 \end{bmatrix} \sim \begin{bmatrix} 1 & 4 & 1 \\ 0 & -10 & 4 \end{bmatrix} \sim \begin{bmatrix} 1 & 4 & 1 \\ 3 & 2 & 7 \end{bmatrix} = \mathbf{C}.$$

Exercises 3.4

1. Determine the rank of each of the following matrices.

(a) $\begin{bmatrix} 2 & 1 & 0 \\ 3 & 5 & 1 \\ 1 & 4 & -2 \end{bmatrix}$ (b) $\begin{bmatrix} 0 & 1 & 4 & 3 & 2 \\ 1 & 1 & 3 & -1 & 0 \\ 1 & 2 & 7 & 3 & 2 \end{bmatrix}$ (c) $\begin{bmatrix} 1 & 4 & 1 & 2 \\ 2 & 8 & 2 & 4 \\ -3 & -12 & -3 & -6 \end{bmatrix}$

2. Show that **A** and **B** are equivalent if

$$\mathbf{A} = \begin{bmatrix} 1 & 3 & 7 & 4 \\ 2 & 1 & 6 & 1 \\ 0 & 1 & -3 & 4 \end{bmatrix} \quad \text{and} \quad \mathbf{B} = \begin{bmatrix} 0 & -2 & 1 & 3 \\ 1 & 4 & 0 & 1 \\ 2 & -1 & 0 & 0 \end{bmatrix}.$$

3. Reduce the following matrices to normal form.

(a) $\begin{bmatrix} 2 & 3 \\ 1 & 2 \\ 1 & 4 \\ 0 & 1 \end{bmatrix}$ (b) $[2 \quad 1 \quad 6 \quad 9]$ (c) $\begin{bmatrix} 2 & 1 & 0 & 3 \\ 1 & 4 & 2 & 1 \\ 0 & 1 & 6 & 2 \\ 2 & 1 & 7 & 4 \end{bmatrix}$

(d) $\begin{bmatrix} 5 & 4 & 3 & 2 & 1 \\ 2 & 1 & 4 & 3 & 7 \\ 0 & -1 & 2 & 1 & 4 \\ 1 & 1 & -3 & 6 & 2 \end{bmatrix}$

4. Use elementary transformations to transform **A** to **B**.

(a) $$\mathbf{A} = \begin{bmatrix} 1 & 2 & 1 & 4 \\ 0 & 1 & 1 & -1 \\ 1 & -1 & 0 & 2 \end{bmatrix} \qquad \mathbf{B} = \begin{bmatrix} 1 & 0 & 1 & 0 \\ 0 & 1 & 1 & 1 \\ 0 & 0 & 1 & 1 \end{bmatrix}$$

(b) $$\mathbf{A} = \begin{bmatrix} 1 & 0 & 1 \\ 0 & 1 & 1 \\ 1 & 1 & 0 \end{bmatrix} \qquad \mathbf{B} = \begin{bmatrix} 1 & 2 & 3 \\ 2 & 1 & 3 \\ 3 & 3 & 3 \end{bmatrix}$$

5. For matrices of order 2×4, write all possible matrices in normal form.

6. If $\mathbf{A}_1$ is of rank r_1 and $\mathbf{A}_2$ is of rank r_2, determine the rank of

$$\begin{bmatrix} \mathbf{A}_1 & \mathbf{0} \\ \mathbf{0} & \mathbf{A}_2 \end{bmatrix}.$$

7. (a) Geometrically what is represented by $\det \mathbf{A} = 0$ if

$$\mathbf{A}(x, y) = \mathbf{A} = \begin{bmatrix} x & y & 1 \\ x_1 & y_1 & 1 \\ x_2 & y_2 & 1 \end{bmatrix}$$

and (x_1, y_1) and (x_2, y_2) are two different points in the plane?

(b) What must be the rank of $\mathbf{A}(x_3, y_3)$ if (x_3, y_3) is to lie on the locus in (a)? Why?

8. Show that every elementary transformation of type (1) can be accomplished by applications of elementary transformations of type (2) and (3).

9. Prove that an elementary transformation of type (3) does not alter the rank of a matrix **A**.

3.5. *Elementary Transformation Matrices*

The preceding section described certain transformations on matrices but required a new symbol ($\sim$), since the matrices involved were in general equivalent but not equal. The various elementary transformations can also be accomplished by multiplying by certain matrices called *elementary transformation matrices* or simply *elementary matrices.* These matrices are denoted by $\mathbf{E}_1$, $\mathbf{E}_2$, and $\mathbf{E}_3$; the subscripts correspond to the three types of transformations discussed in Section 3.4. That is,

(1) $\mathbf{E}_1$ is an elementary matrix that interchanges two rows (columns) of **A**.
(2) $\mathbf{E}_2$ is an elementary matrix that multiplies a row (column) of **A** by the non-zero scalar k.
(3) $\mathbf{E}_3$ is an elementary matrix that aids the scalar k times each element in a row (column) to the corresponding element in another row (column).

Since the verification that the elementary matrices $\mathbf{E}_1$, $\mathbf{E}_2$, and $\mathbf{E}_3$ perform the transformations as given is rather lengthy, it is limited here to illustrations using 3×3 matrices. Note that although the elementary transformation matrices are all square, the matrices upon which they operate need not be square.

The interchange of two *rows* of **A** can be accomplished by interchanging the corresponding *rows* of **I** to get the *elementary row matrix* $\mathbf{E}_1$ and then *premultiplying* **A** by $\mathbf{E}_1$. The first and third rows of **A** are interchanged in the following illustration:

$$(3.5.1) \qquad \mathbf{E}_1\mathbf{A} = \begin{bmatrix} 0 & 0 & 1 \\ 0 & 1 & 0 \\ 1 & 0 & 0 \end{bmatrix} \begin{bmatrix} 2 & 1 & 3 \\ 1 & 0 & 2 \\ 4 & 1 & 2 \end{bmatrix} = \begin{bmatrix} 4 & 1 & 2 \\ 1 & 0 & 2 \\ 2 & 1 & 3 \end{bmatrix}.$$

If two *columns* of **I** are interchanged to get the *elementary column matrix* $\mathbf{E}_1$, and **A** is then *postmultiplied* by $\mathbf{E}_1$, the corresponding *columns* of **A** are interchanged.

$$(3.5.2) \qquad \mathbf{A}\mathbf{E}_1 = \begin{bmatrix} 2 & 1 & 3 \\ 1 & 0 & 2 \\ 4 & 1 & 2 \end{bmatrix} \begin{bmatrix} 1 & 0 & 0 \\ 0 & 0 & 1 \\ 0 & 1 & 0 \end{bmatrix} = \begin{bmatrix} 2 & 3 & 1 \\ 1 & 2 & 0 \\ 4 & 2 & 1 \end{bmatrix}.$$

If the elements of a *row* of **I** are multiplied by the non-zero scalar k to get the elementary row matrix $\mathbf{E}_2$, *premultiplying* **A** by $\mathbf{E}_2$ multiplies the elements of the corresponding *row* of $\mathbf{A}$ by k. If the elements of a *column* of $\mathbf{I}$ are multiplied by the non-zero scalar k to get $\mathbf{E}_2$, *postmultiplying* $\mathbf{A}$ by $\mathbf{E}_2$ multiplies the elements of the corresponding *column* of $\mathbf{A}$ by k.

$$\mathbf{E}_2\mathbf{A} = \begin{bmatrix} 1 & 0 & 0 \\ 0 & k & 0 \\ 0 & 0 & 1 \end{bmatrix} \begin{bmatrix} 2 & 1 & 3 \\ 1 & 0 & 2 \\ 4 & 1 & 2 \end{bmatrix} = \begin{bmatrix} 2 & 1 & 3 \\ k & 0 & 2k \\ 4 & 1 & 2 \end{bmatrix} \tag{3.5.3}$$

$$\mathbf{A}\mathbf{E}_2 = \begin{bmatrix} 2 & 1 & 3 \\ 1 & 0 & 2 \\ 4 & 1 & 2 \end{bmatrix} \begin{bmatrix} 1 & 0 & 0 \\ 0 & 1 & 0 \\ 0 & 0 & k \end{bmatrix} = \begin{bmatrix} 2 & 1 & 3k \\ 1 & 0 & 2k \\ 4 & 1 & 2k \end{bmatrix} \tag{3.5.4}$$

If the elements of the ith *row* of $\mathbf{I}$ are multiplied by the scalar k and then the products are added to the corresponding element of the jth *row* to get the elementary row matrix $\mathbf{E}_3$, *premultiplying* $\mathbf{A}$ by $\mathbf{E}_3$ multiplies the elements of the ith *row* by k and adds the products to the corresponding elements on the jth *row*. If the elements of the ith *column* of $\mathbf{I}$ are multiplied by the scalar k and the products are added to the corresponding elements of the jth *column* to get $\mathbf{E}_3$, the elementary column matrix, *postmultiplying* $\mathbf{A}$ by $\mathbf{E}_3$ multiplies the elements of the ith *column* of $\mathbf{A}$ by k and adds the products to the corresponding elements of the jth *column*.

$$\mathbf{E}_3\mathbf{A} = \begin{bmatrix} 1 & 0 & 0 \\ k & 1 & 0 \\ 0 & 0 & 1 \end{bmatrix} \begin{bmatrix} 2 & 1 & 3 \\ 1 & 0 & 2 \\ 4 & 1 & 2 \end{bmatrix} = \begin{bmatrix} 2 & 1 & 3 \\ 2k+1 & k+0 & 3k+2 \\ 4 & 1 & 2 \end{bmatrix} \tag{3.5.5}$$

$$\mathbf{A}\mathbf{E}_3 = \begin{bmatrix} 2 & 1 & 3 \\ 1 & 0 & 2 \\ 4 & 1 & 2 \end{bmatrix} \begin{bmatrix} 1 & 0 & 0 \\ 0 & 1 & 0 \\ k & 0 & 1 \end{bmatrix} = \begin{bmatrix} 2+3k & 1 & 3 \\ 1+2k & 0 & 2 \\ 4+2k & 1 & 2 \end{bmatrix} \tag{3.5.6}$$

Note that the elementary matrices are nonsingular, since they are equivalent to $\mathbf{I}$.

Example 3.5.1. Obtain a matrix equivalent to $\mathbf{B}$ in normal form by premultiplying and postmultiplying $\mathbf{B}$ by elementary matrices if

$$\mathbf{B} = \begin{bmatrix} 2 & 1 & 3 \\ 1 & -4 & 0 \\ 1 & 5 & 3 \end{bmatrix}.$$

The elementary matrices used to accomplish a particular result are not unique, as is shown by the following example. Subscripts are used to indicate different elementary row and column matrices, while superscripts indicate the order in which they are applied. In this example, nine elementary matrices are used, so that by premultiplying and postmultiplying **B** we get

$$\mathbf{E}_1^9\mathbf{E}_3^5\mathbf{E}_3^4\mathbf{E}_3^3\begin{bmatrix}2 & 1 & 3\\ 1 & -4 & 0\\ 1 & 5 & 3\end{bmatrix}\mathbf{E}_3^1\mathbf{E}_3^2\mathbf{E}_2^6\mathbf{E}_2^7\mathbf{E}_3^8$$

$$= \mathbf{E}_1^9\mathbf{E}_3^5\mathbf{E}_3^4\mathbf{E}_3^3\begin{bmatrix}0 & 1 & 3\\ 9 & -4 & 0\\ -9 & 5 & 3\end{bmatrix}\mathbf{E}_3^2\mathbf{E}_2^6\mathbf{E}_2^7\mathbf{E}_3^8$$

$$= \mathbf{E}_1^9\mathbf{E}_3^5\mathbf{E}_3^4\mathbf{E}_3^3\begin{bmatrix}0 & 1 & 0\\ 9 & -4 & 12\\ -9 & 5 & -12\end{bmatrix}\mathbf{E}_2^6\mathbf{E}_2^7\mathbf{E}_3^8 = \mathbf{E}_1^9\mathbf{E}_3^5\mathbf{E}_3^4\begin{bmatrix}0 & 1 & 0\\ 9 & 0 & 12\\ -9 & 5 & -12\end{bmatrix}\mathbf{E}_2^6\mathbf{E}_2^7\mathbf{E}_3^8$$

$$= \mathbf{E}_1^9\mathbf{E}_3^5\begin{bmatrix}0 & 1 & 0\\ 9 & 0 & 12\\ -9 & 0 & -12\end{bmatrix}\mathbf{E}_2^6\mathbf{E}_2^7\mathbf{E}_3^8 = \mathbf{E}_1^9\begin{bmatrix}0 & 1 & 0\\ 9 & 0 & 12\\ 0 & 0 & 0\end{bmatrix}\mathbf{E}_2^6\mathbf{E}_2^7\mathbf{E}_3^8$$

$$= \mathbf{E}_1^9\begin{bmatrix}0 & 1 & 0\\ 1 & 0 & 12\\ 0 & 0 & 0\end{bmatrix}\mathbf{E}_2^7\mathbf{E}_3^8 = \mathbf{E}_1^9\begin{bmatrix}0 & 1 & 0\\ 1 & 0 & 1\\ 0 & 0 & 0\end{bmatrix}\mathbf{E}_3^8 = \mathbf{E}_1^9\begin{bmatrix}0 & 1 & 0\\ 1 & 0 & 0\\ 0 & 0 & 0\end{bmatrix} = \begin{bmatrix}1 & 0 & 0\\ 0 & 1 & 0\\ 0 & 0 & 0\end{bmatrix}.$$

The entire process can be displayed as

$$\begin{bmatrix}0 & 1 & 0\\ 1 & 0 & 0\\ 0 & 0 & 1\end{bmatrix}\begin{bmatrix}1 & 0 & 0\\ 0 & 1 & 0\\ 0 & 1 & 1\end{bmatrix}\begin{bmatrix}1 & 0 & 0\\ 0 & 1 & 0\\ -5 & 0 & 1\end{bmatrix}\begin{bmatrix}1 & 0 & 0\\ 4 & 1 & 0\\ 0 & 0 & 1\end{bmatrix}\begin{bmatrix}2 & 1 & 3\\ 1 & -4 & 0\\ 1 & 5 & 3\end{bmatrix}$$

$$\times\begin{bmatrix}1 & 0 & 0\\ -2 & 1 & 0\\ 0 & 0 & 1\end{bmatrix}\begin{bmatrix}1 & 0 & 0\\ 0 & 1 & -3\\ 0 & 0 & 1\end{bmatrix}\begin{bmatrix}\frac{1}{9} & 0 & 0\\ 0 & 1 & 0\\ 0 & 0 & 1\end{bmatrix}\begin{bmatrix}1 & 0 & 0\\ 0 & 1 & 0\\ 0 & 0 & \frac{1}{12}\end{bmatrix}\begin{bmatrix}1 & 0 & -1\\ 0 & 1 & 0\\ 0 & 0 & 1\end{bmatrix}.$$

An immediate consequence of the definitions of elementary matrices is the following theorem.

Theorem 3.5.1. *Every elementary matrix has an inverse of the same type.*

Proof: The inverse of $\mathbf{E}_1$ is obviously $\mathbf{E}_1$. The inverse of $\mathbf{E}_2$ (recall that $k \neq 0$) is the same as $\mathbf{E}_2$ except that k has been replaced by $1/k$. If $\mathbf{E}_3$ has been obtained from **I** by multiplying the elements of the ith row (column) of **I** by k and adding the resulting products to the corresponding elements in the jth row (column), then $\mathbf{E}_3^{-1}$ is obtained by multiplying the elements of the ith row (column) of **I** by $-k$ and adding the resulting products to the corresponding elements in the jth row (column).

The following three pairs of matrices illustrate elementary matrices and their inverses. Since the inverse of a matrix is unique by Theorem 1.6.1, there is no way of telling whether the operations used to obtain $\mathbf{E}_1$, $\mathbf{E}_2$, and $\mathbf{E}_3$ were on rows or columns. (Indeed, it is not necessary to know.)

$$\mathbf{E}_1 = \begin{bmatrix} 0 & 1 & 0 \\ 1 & 0 & 0 \\ 0 & 0 & 1 \end{bmatrix}, \qquad \mathbf{E}_1^{-1} = \begin{bmatrix} 0 & 1 & 0 \\ 1 & 0 & 0 \\ 0 & 0 & 1 \end{bmatrix} \tag{3.5.7}$$

$$\mathbf{E}_2 = \begin{bmatrix} 1 & 0 & 0 \\ 0 & 3 & 0 \\ 0 & 0 & 1 \end{bmatrix} \qquad \mathbf{E}_2^{-1} = \begin{bmatrix} 1 & 0 & 0 \\ 0 & 1/3 & 0 \\ 0 & 0 & 1 \end{bmatrix} \tag{3.5.8}$$

$$\mathbf{E}_3 = \begin{bmatrix} 1 & 0 & 0 \\ 4 & 1 & 0 \\ 0 & 0 & 1 \end{bmatrix}, \qquad \mathbf{E}_3^{-1} = \begin{bmatrix} 1 & 0 & 0 \\ -4 & 1 & 0 \\ 0 & 0 & 1 \end{bmatrix}. \tag{3.5.9}$$

Exercises 3.5

1. How many different 3×3 elementary matrices of type one (row or column interchange) are there?

2. Do elementary row matrices of type one commute with each other?

3. Do elementary matrices of type two (multiplication of a row or a column by a non-zero scalar) commute with each other?

4. Do elementary matrices of type three commute with each other?

5. Find 4×4 matrices which, when used as left multipliers, accomplish the following:
   (a) multiply the third row by 7.
   (b) interchange the first and fourth rows.
   (c) add 7 times the third row to the second.

6. Find 4×4 elementary matrices which, when used as right multipliers, accomplish the following:
   (a) multiply the second column by 2.
   (b) interchange the first and fourth columns.
   (c) add 7 times the second column to the third.

7. Find matrices $\mathbf{A}_1, \mathbf{A}_2, \cdots$ that will reduce

$$\mathbf{B} = \begin{bmatrix} 1 & 0 & 2 \\ 2 & 1 & 0 \\ 0 & 1 & 1 \end{bmatrix}$$

   to normal form. Display the resulting product as the final result given in Example 3.5.1.

8. If $\mathbf{A} = [a_{ij}]$ is of order 3×4, determine a product of elementary matrices of types $\mathbf{E}_2$ and $\mathbf{E}_3$ that interchanges the first two rows of $\mathbf{A}$. Since these elementary

matrices accomplish the same result as a matrix of type $\mathbf{E}_1$, is their product equal to a matrix of type $\mathbf{E}_1$? Verify by performing the indicated multiplication.

9. (a) Write $\mathbf{C}$ as a product of elementary matrices if

$$\mathbf{C} = \begin{bmatrix} 2 & 0 & 0 \\ 0 & 1 & 0 \\ 1 & 0 & 3 \end{bmatrix}.$$

(b) From the result in (a), determine $\mathbf{C}^{-1}$.

3.6. Properties of Elementary Transformation Matrices

This section considers a few of the important properties and consequences of the use of elementary matrices. These properties are given as theorems.

Theorem 3.6.1. *Any nonsingular matrix may be written as the product of elementary matrices.*

Proof: Since any nonsingular matrix $\mathbf{A}$ is equivalent to the identity matrix $\mathbf{I}$ by the definition of the equivalence, then there exist elementary matrices $\mathbf{B}_i$, $i = 1, 2, \cdots, k$, and $\mathbf{C}_j, j = 1, 2, \cdots, h$, such that

$$(\mathbf{B}_k \cdots \mathbf{B}_2 \mathbf{B}_1)\mathbf{A}(\mathbf{C}_1 \mathbf{C}_2 \cdots \mathbf{C}_h) = \mathbf{I}. \tag{3.6.1}$$

If $\mathbf{D}_i = \mathbf{B}_i^{-1}$ and $\mathbf{F}_j = \mathbf{C}_j^{-1}$, then the matrices $\mathbf{D}_i$, $\mathbf{F}_j$ are also elementary matrices (and are, incidentally, of the same type). Thus, by premultiplying and postmultiplying on both sides of Eq. (3.6.1) by the corresponding inverse matrices, we get

$$\mathbf{A} = (\mathbf{D}_1 \mathbf{D}_2 \cdots \mathbf{D}_k)\mathbf{I}(\mathbf{F}_h \cdots \mathbf{F}_2 \mathbf{F}_1), \tag{3.6.2}$$

and the theorem is proved.

Theorem 3.6.2. *The order and rank of a matrix* $\mathbf{A}$ *are not altered by premultiplying or postmultiplying* $\mathbf{A}$ *by elementary matrices.*

Proof: This theorem is a direct consequence of Theorem 3.4.2, since elementary matrices merely perform the elementary transformations considered in Section 3.4.

The following theorem is obtained immediately from Theorem 3.6.2.

Theorem 3.6.3. *If* $\mathbf{C}$ *is a matrix of any size that has rank* r *that is less than or equal to full rank, and if matrices* $\mathbf{A}$ *and* $\mathbf{B}$ *are nonsingular and are such that the* *various multiplications are defined, then*

(a) $\text{rank}(\mathbf{AC}) = \text{rank } \mathbf{C}$,

(b) $\text{rank}(\mathbf{CB}) = \text{rank } \mathbf{C}$, and

(c) $\text{rank}(\mathbf{ACB}) = \text{rank } \mathbf{C}$.

Proof: Note that the matrix **C** need not be square, but the multiplication must be defined in each case. If **C** has rank r, premultiplying **C** by the nonsingular matrix **A** (the product of elementary matrices) does not alter the rank, by Theorem 3.6.2. Similarly, postmultiplying **C** by **B** does not alter the rank, and postmultiplying **AC** by **B** does not alter the rank. Hence, the products **AC**, **CB**, and **ACB** all have the rank r, the rank of **C**.

Theorem 3.6.4. *If* **A** *is a matrix of rank r, then there exist nonsingular matrices* **P** *and* **Q** *such that*

(3.6.3) $$\mathbf{PAQ} = \mathbf{R}_r,$$

where $\mathbf{R}_r$ *is a matrix of rank r that is in normal form.*

Proof: This theorem is an immediate consequence of Theorem 3.6.2. Matrices **P** and **Q** are chosen so that the product yields $\mathbf{I}_r$ in the upper left-hand corner.

* **Theorem 3.6.5.** *Two matrices,* **A** *and* **B**, *of the same order, are equivalent if and only if* **B** *can be obtained by premultiplying and postmultiplying* **A** *by a finite number of elementary matrices.* (some times used as def of equivalence)

Proof: This theorem is essentially a restatement of Theorem 3.4.3. If **A** and **B** are equivalent and both have rank r, then by Theorem 3.6.4 there exist nonsingular matrices **C**, **D**, **E**, and **F** such that

(3.6.4) $$\mathbf{CAD} = \mathbf{R}_r \quad \text{and} \quad \mathbf{EBF} = \mathbf{R}_r,$$

where $\mathbf{R}_r$ is a matrix of rank r in normal form. Thus

(3.6.5) $$\mathbf{CAD} = \mathbf{EBF} \quad \text{or} \quad \mathbf{E}^{-1}\mathbf{CADF}^{-1} = \mathbf{B}.$$

Since **C**, **D**, **E**, and **F** are nonsingular, they are each products of elementary matrices. The matrices $\mathbf{E}^{-1}\mathbf{C}$ and $\mathbf{DF}^{-1}$ are also products of elementary matrices. Hence, **B** is obtained from **A** by premultiplying and postmultiplying **A** by a finite number of elementary matrices.

Conversely, if there exist nonsingular matrices **P** and **Q** such that

(3.6.6) $$\mathbf{PAQ} = \mathbf{B},$$

then **P** and **Q** do not alter the rank of **A** by multiplication. If **A** is of rank r, **PAQ** is of rank r and so is **B**. Thus **A** and **B** are equivalent.

Theorem 3.6.6. *If* **A** *and* **B** *are any matrices such that* **AB** *is defined, then the rank of* **AB** *is no greater than the rank of either* **A** *or* **B**.

Proof: If **A** is of order $m \times n$ and has rank r, then by Theorem 3.6.4 there exist nonsingular matrices **P** and **Q** such that

$$\mathbf{PAQ} = \mathbf{R}_r \quad \text{or} \quad \mathbf{A} = \mathbf{P}^{-1}\mathbf{R}_r\mathbf{Q}^{-1} \tag{3.6.7}$$

where $\mathbf{R}_r$ is a matrix of rank r in normal form. Thus, if **B** is of order $n \times q$,

$$\mathbf{AB} = \mathbf{P}^{-1}(\mathbf{R}_r\mathbf{Q}^{-1}\mathbf{B}). \tag{3.6.8}$$

Since **P** is nonsingular, $\mathbf{P}^{-1}$ is nonsingular, and, by Theorem 3.6.3, the rank of **AB** is the same as the rank of $\mathbf{R}_r\mathbf{Q}^{-1}\mathbf{B} = \mathbf{R}_r(\mathbf{Q}^{-1}\mathbf{B})$. But $\mathbf{R}_r$ is a matrix whose last $m - r$ rows consist entirely of zero elements; hence, the last $m - r$ rows of $\mathbf{R}_r\mathbf{Q}^{-1}\mathbf{B}$ consist entirely of zero elements. Thus the rank of **AB** is no greater than r, the rank of **A**.

In a similar manner it can be shown that the rank of **AB** is no greater than the rank of **B**, and the theorem is proved.

Theorem 3.6.7. *A nonsingular matrix* **A** *can always be reduced to normal form by elementary row or column transformation matrices only.*

Proof: The normal form for a nonsingular matrix is simply the identity matrix **I**. But since **A** is nonsingular, there exists a nonsingular matrix $\mathbf{A}^{-1}$ such that $\mathbf{A}^{-1}\mathbf{A} = \mathbf{I}$. Since $\mathbf{A}^{-1}$ is the product of elementary row transformation matrices by Theorem 3.6.1, the first part of the theorem is proved.

In a similar manner, by multiplying the nonsingular matrix **A** on the right by $\mathbf{A}^{-1}$ to get $\mathbf{AA}^{-1} = \mathbf{I}$, we see that **A** can be reduced to normal form by elementary column transformation matrices only.

Theorem 3.6.8. *If* **A** *is an* $m \times n$ *matrix of rank* r *and* **X** *is a matrix of order* $n \times p$ *and the product of these matrices is the zero matrix,*

$$\mathbf{AX} = \mathbf{0}, \tag{3.6.9}$$

then (i) *the rank of* **X** *cannot exceed* $n - r$, *and*

(ii) *there exists a matrix* **X** *of rank* $n - r$ *such that Eq.* (3.6.9) *is satisfied.*

Proof: Since **A** is of rank r, by Theorem 3.6.4 there exist nonsingular matrices **P** and **Q** such that

$$\mathbf{PAQ} = \mathbf{R}_r = \begin{bmatrix} \mathbf{I}_{r,r} & \mathbf{0}_{r,n-r} \\ \mathbf{0}_{m-r,r} & \mathbf{0}_{m-r,n-r} \end{bmatrix}. \tag{3.6.10}$$

Then to prove (i), we assume $\mathbf{AX} = \mathbf{0}$ and write

(3.6.11) $$\mathbf{PAQQ}^{-1}\mathbf{X} = \mathbf{0} \quad \text{or} \quad \mathbf{R}_r\,\mathbf{Q}^{-1}\mathbf{X}) = \mathbf{0}.$$

Since $\mathbf{Q}^{-1}$ is nonsingular, $\mathbf{Q}^{-1}\mathbf{X}$ has the same rank as $\mathbf{X}$ by Theorem 3.6.2. If we now let $\mathbf{Q}^{-1}\mathbf{X} = \mathbf{Y}$, then $\mathbf{R}_r\mathbf{Y} = \mathbf{0}$ may be written as

(3.6.12) $$\begin{bmatrix} \mathbf{I}_{r,r} & \mathbf{0}_{r,n-r} \\ \mathbf{0}_{m-r,r} & \mathbf{0}_{m-r,n-r} \end{bmatrix} \begin{bmatrix} \mathbf{Y}_{r,k} & \mathbf{Y}_{r,p-k} \\ \mathbf{Y}_{n-r,k} & \mathbf{Y}_{n-r,p-k} \end{bmatrix} = \mathbf{0},$$

where $0 \leqq k \leqq p$, k an integer. It is obvious that the submatrices $\mathbf{Y}_{r,k}$ and $\mathbf{Y}_{r,p-k}$ must each be zero matrices. Furthermore the submatrices $\mathbf{Y}_{n-r,k}$ and $\mathbf{Y}_{n-r,p-k}$ are each arbitrary. Thus, the rank of $\mathbf{Y}$, and hence the rank of $\mathbf{X}$, cannot be greater than $n - r$, and part (i) is proved.

To prove (ii) we construct an n by p matrix $\mathbf{Y}$, partitioned as the matrix $\mathbf{Y}$ in Eq. (3.6.12) with $k \geqq n - r$, in which $\mathbf{Y}_{r,k}$ and $\mathbf{Y}_{r,p-k}$ are zero submatrices, $\mathbf{Y}_{n-r,k}$ is a submatrix with full rank, and $\mathbf{Y}_{n-r,p-k}$ is arbitrary. From this construction we observe that the matrix $\mathbf{Y}$ has rank $n - r$. Then using $\mathbf{PAQ} = \mathbf{R}_r$ from Eq. (3.6.10), we have that

(3.6.13) $$\mathbf{R}_r\mathbf{Y} = \mathbf{PAQY} = \mathbf{0}.$$

From Eq. (3.6.13) it follows that

(3.6.14) $$\mathbf{AQY} = \mathbf{0},$$

since $\mathbf{P}$ is nonsingular. If we now let $\mathbf{X} = \mathbf{QY}$, then $\mathbf{Y} = \mathbf{Q}^{-1}\mathbf{X}$. Thus $\mathbf{AQQ}^{-1}\mathbf{X} = \mathbf{0}$ or $\mathbf{AX} = \mathbf{0}$, and we have constructed a matrix $\mathbf{X}$ which has the rank $n - r$ (the rank of $\mathbf{Y}$) and is such that $\mathbf{AX} = \mathbf{0}$. Thus part (ii) is proved.

Exercises 3.6

1. (a) Express $\mathbf{B}$ as the product of elementary matrices if

$$\mathbf{B} = \begin{bmatrix} 1 & 0 & 2 \\ 2 & 1 & 0 \\ 0 & 1 & 1 \end{bmatrix}.$$

(b) Use the result of (a) to determine the inverse of $\mathbf{B}$.

2. Reduce the matrix $\mathbf{B}$ in exercise 1 to a triangular matrix by elementary row transformations only.

3. Explain why the rank of $\mathbf{A}$ is 3 but the rank of $\mathbf{C}$ is only 2 after $\mathbf{A}$ is premultiplied by $\mathbf{B}$ in

$$\mathbf{BA} = \begin{bmatrix} 2 & 1 & 0 \\ 1 & 0 & 4 \\ 3 & 2 & -4 \end{bmatrix} \begin{bmatrix} 1 & 3 & 0 & 1 \\ 4 & 1 & 2 & 5 \\ 3 & 2 & 2 & 4 \end{bmatrix} = \begin{bmatrix} 6 & 7 & 2 & 7 \\ 13 & 11 & 8 & 17 \\ -1 & 3 & -4 & -3 \end{bmatrix} = \mathbf{C}.$$

4. If

$$\mathbf{A} = \begin{bmatrix} 2 & 1 & 0 \\ 2 & 3 & 5 \\ 1 & 0 & 4 \end{bmatrix} \quad \text{and} \quad \mathbf{B} = \begin{bmatrix} 2 & 1 & 3 \\ 4 & 1 & 4 \\ 4 & 0 & 2 \end{bmatrix},$$

explain why **A** can be reduced to normal form by elementary column transformations only while **B** cannot.

5. State and prove a theorem for singular matrices analogous to Theorem 3.6.1.

6. Find the **P** and **Q** of Theorem 3.6.4 if

$$\mathbf{A} = \begin{bmatrix} 1 & 4 & -1 & 2 \\ -1 & 2 & 0 & -1 \\ 3 & 0 & -1 & 4 \\ -1 & 8 & -1 & 0 \end{bmatrix}.$$

7. For **A** as in exercise 6, find an **X** of Theorem 3.6.8 of minimum order and maximum rank.

8.* (a) For any matrix **A**, show that $\mathbf{B} = \mathbf{AA}'$ is symmetric.
(b) If **A** is real, describe the elements on the main diagonal.
(c) If **A** is a real $r \times s$ matrix of rank r, and $r \leqq s$, show that **B** is nonsingular.
(d) Show that **B** is singular if **A** has rank less than r.

9.* Prove the theorem: *If* **A** *is a square matrix of order n that has rank r, then there exists a non-zero matrix* **X** *such that* $\mathbf{AX} = \mathbf{0}$ *if and only if* $r < n$.

10.* Prove the theorem: *If* **A** *is an* $m \times n$ *matrix and if* $m < n$, *then there exists a non-zero matrix* **X** *such that* $\mathbf{AX} = \mathbf{0}$.

11.* Prove the theorem: *The rank of* $\mathbf{A} + \mathbf{B}$ *is less than or equal to the rank of* **A** *plus the rank of* **B**.

4

Bilinear and Quadratic Forms

4.1. Linear Forms

This chapter discusses certain types of mathematical expressions called *forms*. The first type of these, covered in this section, is called a *linear form*. A special type of linear form is the *linear homogeneous form*, which is probably the simplest type of form.

For the column vector of n variable scalars x_i, $\mathbf{x} = [x_1 \ x_2 \ \cdots \ x_n]'$, and the row vector of n fixed scalars a_j, $\mathbf{a} = [a_1 \ a_2 \ \cdots \ a_n]$, the *linear homogeneous form* is defined to be the function $f(\mathbf{x})$ where

$$f(\mathbf{x}) = \mathbf{a}\mathbf{x} = [a_1 \quad a_2 \quad \cdots \quad a_n]\begin{bmatrix} x_1 \\ x_2 \\ \vdots \\ x_n \end{bmatrix} = a_1 x_1 + a_2 x_2 + \cdots + a_n x_n. \tag{4.1.1}$$

Equation (4.1.1) may also be written as

$$f(\mathbf{x}) = \sum_{i=1}^{n} a_i x_i. \tag{4.1.2}$$

The function $f(\mathbf{x})$ in Eq. (4.1.1) is linear because the variables x_i appear only to the first degree in each term; it is homogeneous because there is no term present that does not include one of the x_i. Since the product $\mathbf{ax}$ is a scalar product, the result is a scalar.

A *system* of linear forms may be written compactly as

$$\begin{aligned} f_1(\mathbf{x}) &= \mathbf{a}_1\mathbf{x} \\ f_2(\mathbf{x}) &= \mathbf{a}_2\mathbf{x} \\ &\cdots \\ f_m(\mathbf{x}) &= \mathbf{a}_m\mathbf{x} \end{aligned} \tag{4.1.3}$$

where $\mathbf{a}_j = [a_{j1}\ a_{j2}\ \cdots\ a_{jn}]$. The $f_j(\mathbf{x})$ are *linear polynomials* in the n variables x_i. If $f_j(\mathbf{x}) = c_j$, then

$$\begin{aligned} \mathbf{a}_1\mathbf{x} &= c_1 \\ \mathbf{a}_2\mathbf{x} &= c_2 \\ &\cdots \\ \mathbf{a}_m\mathbf{x} &= c_m . \end{aligned} \tag{4.1.4}$$

Equation (4.1.4) may be written still more compactly as

$$\mathbf{Ax} = \mathbf{c}, \tag{4.1.5}$$

where $\mathbf{A} = [a_{ij}]_{m,n}$ and $\mathbf{c} = [c_1\ c_2\ \cdots\ c_m]'$. In other words, Eq. (4.1.5) is nothing more than a system of m linear equations in n unknowns.

Each of the equations in Eq. (4.1.4) for which $c_j \neq 0$ is a *nonhomogeneous equation;* those for which $c_j = 0$ are *homogeneous equations* in the unknowns. Since Cramer's rule (Section 2.11) does not apply unless $m = n$, some other method must be used to solve for the unknown x_i. Even if $m = n$, it may not be possible to use Cramer's rule. (See Theorem 2.11.1.)

One example of a linear form is the following. If a line δ_1 has direction numbers 6, -2, 3, and hence has direction cosines 6/7, $-2/7$, 3/7, then the cosine of the angle θ between δ_1 and a line δ with direction cosines λ, μ, ν, is

$$\cos\theta = \begin{bmatrix} \frac{6}{7} & \frac{-2}{7} & \frac{3}{7} \end{bmatrix} [\lambda\mu\nu]',$$

a linear form in λ, μ, and ν.

Another example of a linear form is the polynomial

$$f(x) = \sum_{i=0}^{n} a_i x^i. \tag{4.1.6}$$

Consider now a system of n equations in n variables x_i, such as Eq. (4.1.5) in which $m = n$. Suppose that we wish to change the variables to y_i by the *nonsingular transformation*

$$\mathbf{x} = \mathbf{By}. \tag{4.1.7}$$

Since the transformation in Eq. (4.1.7) is nonsingular, $\mathbf{B}$ is nonsingular; that is, $\mathbf{B}^{-1}$ exists, and the transformation is reversible:

$$\mathbf{y} = \mathbf{B}^{-1}\mathbf{x}. \tag{4.1.8}$$

Upon substituting Eq. (4.1.7) into Eq. (4.1.5),

$$\mathbf{Ax} = \mathbf{ABy} = \mathbf{c}. \tag{4.1.9}$$

If **B** is chosen to be $\mathbf{A}^{-1}$ (provided **A** is nonsingular), then $\mathbf{y} = \mathbf{c}$ in Eq. (4.1.9), and the vector **x** satisfying Eq. (4.1.5) is readily obtained from Eq. (4.1.7). Note that all multiplications in the preceding discussion are defined.

Example 4.1.1. Change the variables in the system of equations

$$\begin{aligned} x_1 + 5x_2 + 2x_3 &= 7 \\ x_2 + x_3 &= 1 \\ x_1 + 4x_2 + 2x_3 &= 6 \end{aligned}$$

by the transformations

$$\begin{aligned} x_1 &= -2y_1 - 2y_2 + 3y_3 \\ x_2 &= y_1 - y_3 \\ x_3 &= -y_1 + y_2 + y_3 . \end{aligned}$$

Direct substitution yields

$$\begin{aligned} (-2y_1 - 2y_2 + 3y_3) + 5(y_1 - y_3) + 2(-y_1 + y_2 + y_3) &= 7 \\ (y_1 - y_3) + (-y_1 + y_2 + y_3) &= 1 \\ (-2y_1 - 2y_2 + 3y_3) + 4(y_1 - y_3) + 2(-y_1 + y_2 + y_3) &= 6; \end{aligned}$$

collecting like terms,

$$\begin{aligned} (-2 + 5 - 2)y_1 + (-2 + 2)y_2 + (3 - 5 + 2)y_3 &= 7 \\ (1 - 1)y_1 + y_2 + (1 - 1)y_3 &= 1 \\ (-2 + 4 - 2)y_1 + (-2 + 2)y_2 + (3 - 4 + 2)y_3 &= 6, \end{aligned}$$

or

$$\begin{aligned} y_1 + 0y_2 + 0y_3 &= 7 \\ 0y_1 + y_2 + 0y_3 &= 1 \\ 0y_1 + 0y_2 + y_3 &= 6. \end{aligned}$$

This result may be written in matrix form as

$$\begin{bmatrix} 1 & 0 & 0 \\ 0 & 1 & 0 \\ 0 & 0 & 1 \end{bmatrix} \begin{bmatrix} y_1 \\ y_2 \\ y_3 \end{bmatrix} = \begin{bmatrix} 7 \\ 1 \\ 6 \end{bmatrix}.$$

If now in the equations of transformation we make the substitution $y_1 = 7$, $y_2 = 1$, and $y_3 = 6$, we get

$$\begin{aligned} x_1 &= -2 \cdot 7 - 2 \cdot 1 + 3 \cdot 6 = 2 \\ x_2 &= 7 - 6 = 1 \\ x_3 &= -7 + 1 + 6 = 0, \end{aligned}$$

the set of values satisfying the original set of equations.

Alternatively, we can use Eq. (4.1.9):

$$\begin{bmatrix}1 & 5 & 2\\0 & 1 & 1\\1 & 4 & 2\end{bmatrix}\begin{bmatrix}x_1\\x_2\\x_3\end{bmatrix}=\begin{bmatrix}1 & 5 & 2\\0 & 1 & 1\\1 & 4 & 2\end{bmatrix}\begin{bmatrix}-2 & -2 & 3\\1 & 0 & -1\\-1 & 1 & 1\end{bmatrix}\begin{bmatrix}y_1\\y_2\\y_3\end{bmatrix}=\begin{bmatrix}7\\1\\6\end{bmatrix},$$

so that

$$\begin{bmatrix}y_1\\y_2\\y_3\end{bmatrix}=\begin{bmatrix}7\\1\\6\end{bmatrix}.$$

Substituting in Eq. (4.1.7),

$$\begin{bmatrix}x_1\\x_2\\x_3\end{bmatrix}=\begin{bmatrix}-2 & -2 & 3\\1 & 0 & -1\\-1 & 1 & 1\end{bmatrix}\begin{bmatrix}7\\1\\6\end{bmatrix}=\begin{bmatrix}2\\1\\0\end{bmatrix}.$$

In Example 4.1.1, examine the relationship between **A** and **B**. In this example, **B** is chosen in a particular way; in general, **B** is merely required to be nonsingular.

Consider any m and n in $\mathbf{A}_{m,n}\mathbf{x}=\mathbf{c}$ in Eq. (4.1.5). (If $m=n$, **A** may or may not be nonsingular.) By choosing the proper nonsingular matrix **B** in Eq. (4.1.7), the substitution in $\mathbf{x}=\mathbf{By}$ in Eq. (4.1.5) can be written

$$\mathbf{Ax}=\mathbf{ABy}=\mathbf{Dy}=\mathbf{c}, \tag{4.1.10}$$

where, for $n \geq m$,

$$\mathbf{D}=\begin{bmatrix}d_{11} & 0 & \cdots & 0 & 0 & \cdots & 0\\d_{21} & d_{22} & \cdots & 0 & 0 & \cdots & 0\\\cdots & & & & & & \\d_{m1} & d_{m2} & \cdots & d_{mm} & 0 & \cdots & 0\end{bmatrix}, \tag{4.1.11}$$

or, for $n < m$,

$$\mathbf{D}=\begin{bmatrix}d_{11} & 0 & \cdots & 0\\d_{21} & d_{22} & \cdots & 0\\\cdots & & & \\d_{n1} & d_{n2} & \cdots & d_{nn}\\\cdots & & & \\d_{m1} & d_{m2} & \cdots & d_{mn}\end{bmatrix}. \tag{4.1.12}$$

In **D** the elements to the right of each d_{kk} are zero, and the elements d_{kk} are zero or 1. The elements to the left of a $d_{kk}=1$ are all zero, and the elements to the left of a $d_{kk}=0$ may or may not be zero. For example,

$$\mathbf{D}=\begin{bmatrix}1 & 0 & 0 & 0\\0 & 1 & 0 & 0\\2 & 3 & 0 & 0\\0 & 4 & 0 & 0\\1 & 3 & 0 & 4\end{bmatrix}.$$

The definitions given for the elements of **D** in the preceding paragraph are true because **D** results from the postmultiplication of **A** by a **B**, which is chosen as a product of the elementary column matrices (Section 3.5). This choice of **B** satisfies the requirement that **B** be nonsingular. Thus, by Eq. (4.1.10), we can solve for the y_i and hence the x_i. (Note that sometimes no set of the y_i will satisfy $\mathbf{Dy} = \mathbf{c}$, as in Example 4.1.3 below.)

Example 4.1.2. Using the method of the preceding discussion, determine $\mathbf{x}$ such that $\mathbf{Ax} = \mathbf{c}$ if

$$\mathbf{A} = \begin{bmatrix} 1 & 1 & 3 & -1 \\ 0 & 1 & -1 & -1 \\ 1 & -2 & 1 & 1 \end{bmatrix} \quad \text{and} \quad \mathbf{c} = \begin{bmatrix} 1 \\ 0 \\ 3 \end{bmatrix}.$$

We write **B** as a product of elementary matrices that have been chosen so that $\mathbf{AB} = \mathbf{D}$, where **D** is in the form of Eq. (4.1.11) since $n > m$. The matrices in the following product are not elementary matrices but are the products of two or more elementary matrices; the reasoning is obvious.

$$\mathbf{B} = \begin{bmatrix} 1 & -1 & -3 & 1 \\ 0 & 1 & 0 & 0 \\ 0 & 0 & 1 & 0 \\ 0 & 0 & 0 & 1 \end{bmatrix} \begin{bmatrix} 1 & 0 & 0 & 0 \\ 0 & 1 & 1 & 1 \\ 0 & 0 & 1 & 0 \\ 0 & 0 & 0 & 1 \end{bmatrix}$$

$$\times \begin{bmatrix} 1 & 0 & 0 & 0 \\ 0 & 1 & 0 & 0 \\ 0 & 0 & 1 & 0 \\ 1 & -3 & -5 & 1 \end{bmatrix} \begin{bmatrix} 1 & 0 & 0 & 0 \\ 0 & 1 & 0 & 0 \\ 0 & 0 & 0 & 1 \\ 0 & 0 & -1 & 0 \end{bmatrix}$$

$$= \begin{bmatrix} 1 & -1 & 0 & -4 \\ 1 & -2 & -1 & -4 \\ 0 & 0 & 0 & 1 \\ 1 & -3 & -1 & -5 \end{bmatrix}.$$

Then in $\mathbf{ABy} = \mathbf{c}$ we get

$$\mathbf{ABy} = \begin{bmatrix} 1 & 1 & 3 & -1 \\ 0 & 1 & -1 & -1 \\ 1 & -2 & 1 & 1 \end{bmatrix} \begin{bmatrix} 1 & -1 & 0 & -4 \\ 1 & -2 & -1 & -4 \\ 0 & 0 & 0 & 1 \\ 1 & -3 & -1 & -5 \end{bmatrix} \begin{bmatrix} y_1 \\ y_2 \\ y_3 \\ y_4 \end{bmatrix}$$

$$= \begin{bmatrix} 1 & 0 & 0 & 0 \\ 0 & 1 & 0 & 0 \\ 0 & 0 & 1 & 0 \end{bmatrix} \begin{bmatrix} y_1 \\ y_2 \\ y_3 \\ y_4 \end{bmatrix} = \begin{bmatrix} 1 \\ 0 \\ 3 \end{bmatrix},$$

so that $y_1 = 1$, $y_2 = 0$, $y_3 = 3$, and y_4 is arbitrary.

Substituting these results in $\mathbf{x} = \mathbf{B}\mathbf{y}$,

$$\begin{bmatrix} x_1 \\ x_2 \\ x_3 \\ x_4 \end{bmatrix} = \begin{bmatrix} 1 & -1 & 0 & -4 \\ 1 & -2 & -1 & -4 \\ 0 & 0 & 0 & 1 \\ 1 & -3 & -1 & -5 \end{bmatrix} \begin{bmatrix} 1 \\ 0 \\ 3 \\ y_4 \end{bmatrix} = \begin{bmatrix} 1 - 4y_4 \\ -2 - 4y_4 \\ y_4 \\ -2 - 5y_4 \end{bmatrix}.$$

The equations $\mathbf{A}\mathbf{x} = \mathbf{c}$ are thus satisfied, for example, by $[1 \ -2 \ 0 \ -2]'$ when $y_4 = 0$, $[-3 \ -6 \ 1 \ -7]'$ when $y_4 = 1$, and $[5 \ 2 \ -1 \ 3]'$ when $y_4 = -1$.

Example 4.1.3. Using the methods of this section, determine (if possible) a vector $\mathbf{x}$ such that $\mathbf{A}\mathbf{x} = \mathbf{c}$ where

$$\mathbf{A} = \begin{bmatrix} 1 & 2 & -1 \\ 3 & 1 & 2 \\ 4 & 3 & 1 \\ -1 & 3 & -4 \\ 4 & 8 & -4 \end{bmatrix} \quad \text{and} \quad \mathbf{c} = \begin{bmatrix} 1 \\ 2 \\ 1 \\ 3 \\ -1 \end{bmatrix}.$$

For this example, $\mathbf{B}$ is chosen so that $\mathbf{AB} = \mathbf{D}$, where $\mathbf{D}$ is in the form of Eq. (4.1.12) since $n < m$. Thus

$$\mathbf{B} = \begin{bmatrix} 1 & -2 & 1 \\ 0 & 1 & 0 \\ 0 & 0 & 1 \end{bmatrix} \begin{bmatrix} 1 & 0 & 0 \\ 0 & 1 & 1 \\ 0 & 0 & 1 \end{bmatrix} \begin{bmatrix} 1 & 0 & 0 \\ 0 & -1/5 & 0 \\ 0 & 0 & 1 \end{bmatrix} \begin{bmatrix} 1 & 0 & 0 \\ -3 & 1 & 0 \\ 0 & 0 & 1 \end{bmatrix}$$

$$= \begin{bmatrix} -1/5 & 2/5 & -1 \\ 3/5 & -1/5 & 1 \\ 0 & 0 & 1 \end{bmatrix},$$

and $\mathbf{ABy} = \mathbf{c}$ or $\mathbf{Dy} = \mathbf{c}$ becomes

$$\begin{bmatrix} 1 & 2 & -1 \\ 3 & 1 & 2 \\ 4 & 3 & 1 \\ -1 & 3 & -4 \\ 4 & 8 & -4 \end{bmatrix} \begin{bmatrix} -1/5 & 2/5 & -1 \\ 3/5 & -1/5 & 1 \\ 0 & 0 & 1 \end{bmatrix} \begin{bmatrix} y_1 \\ y_2 \\ y_3 \end{bmatrix}$$

$$= \begin{bmatrix} 1 & 0 & 0 \\ 0 & 1 & 0 \\ 1 & 1 & 0 \\ 2 & -1 & 0 \\ 4 & 0 & 0 \end{bmatrix} \begin{bmatrix} y_1 \\ y_2 \\ y_3 \end{bmatrix} = \begin{bmatrix} 1 \\ 2 \\ 1 \\ 3 \\ -1 \end{bmatrix},$$

or

$$\begin{bmatrix} y_1 \\ y_2 \\ y_1 + y_2 \\ 2y_1 - y_2 \\ 4y_1 \end{bmatrix} = \begin{bmatrix} 1 \\ 2 \\ 1 \\ 3 \\ -1 \end{bmatrix}.$$

These results apparently imply that $y_1 = 1$, $y_2 = 2$, and that y_3 is arbitrary. But if these results hold, we also have the impossible results that $y_1 + y_2 = 1$, $2y_1 - y_2 = 3$, and $4y_1 = -1$. The conclusion for this example is that no vector $\mathbf{x}$ exists such that $\mathbf{Ax} = \mathbf{c}$.

Exercises 4.1

1. Write the following sets of equations in the form $\mathbf{Ax} = \mathbf{c}$.

(a) $$\begin{aligned} 2x_1 + 3x_2 &= 7 \\ x_1 - 2x_2 &= 4 \end{aligned}$$ (b) $$\begin{aligned} 2x_1 - 16 &= x_2 + x_3 \\ x_1 - x_2 &= 4 - x_3 \\ x_2 &= x_3 \end{aligned}$$

2. Write Eq. (4.1.6) in the form $\mathbf{ax}$.

3. Change the variables in the system

$$\begin{aligned} x_1 + 2x_2 + 3x_3 &= 4 \\ x_2 - x_3 &= 5 \\ x_1 - x_2 + x_3 &= 6 \end{aligned}$$

by the tranformation

$$\begin{aligned} x_1 &= y_1 + y_2 + y_3 \\ x_2 &= y_1 - y_2 - y_3 \\ x_3 &= y_2 - y_3. \end{aligned}$$

4. Use Eq. (4.1.7) and Eq. (4.1.8) to solve

$$\begin{aligned} x_1 + x_2 + x_3 &= 4 \\ x_1 + 2x_2 - x_3 &= 0 \\ x_1 - x_2 + 3x_3 &= 2. \end{aligned}$$

5. Use Eqs. (4.1.7) and (4.1.8), with either Eq. (4.1.11) or Eq. (4.1.12), to solve (if possible)

(a) $$\begin{aligned} x_1 + 3x_2 + 4x_3 - x_4 &= 7 \\ x_1 - x_3 + x_4 &= 0 \\ x_1 + x_2 + x_3 &= 2, \end{aligned}$$ (b) $$\begin{aligned} x_1 + 4x_2 - x_3 &= -2 \\ 3x_2 + 2x_3 &= 2 \\ 2x_1 + 3x_3 &= 1 \\ 3x_1 + x_2 &= -3. \end{aligned}$$

4.2. *Bilinear Forms*

A *bilinear form* is a polynomial in two sets of variables, $\{x_i\}$ and $\{y_j\}$; it is linear and homogeneous in the variables x_i and also linear and homogeneous in the variables y_j. If $\mathbf{x}' = [x_1\ x_2\ \cdots\ x_n]$, $\mathbf{y} = [y_1\ y_2\ \cdots\ y_m]$, and

$\mathbf{A} = [a_{ij}]_{m,n}$, then the bilinear form $f(\mathbf{y}, \mathbf{x})$ may be written as

$$(4.2.1) \qquad f(\mathbf{y}, \mathbf{x}) = \mathbf{yAx} = [y_1\, y_2 \cdots y_m]\begin{bmatrix} a_{11} & a_{12} & \cdots & a_{1n} \\ a_{21} & a_{22} & \cdots & a_{2n} \\ \cdots & & & \\ a_{m1} & a_{m2} & \cdots & a_{mn} \end{bmatrix}\begin{bmatrix} x_1 \\ x_2 \\ \vdots \\ x_n \end{bmatrix}.$$

The matrix $\mathbf{A}$ is the *matrix of the bilinear form*. Notice that the expanded form of $\mathbf{yAx}$ is a scalar, a sum of products.

Examples of bilinear forms are

$$(4.2.2) \qquad f(\mathbf{y}, \mathbf{x}) = 2y_1x_1 + y_1x_2 + 3y_1x_3 + 5y_2x_1 - y_2x_3, \quad \text{and}$$

$$(4.2.3) \qquad f(\mathbf{y}, \mathbf{x}) = [y_1 \quad y_2]\begin{bmatrix} 1 & 0 \\ 2 & 1 \end{bmatrix}\begin{bmatrix} x_1 \\ x_2 \end{bmatrix} = y_1x_1 + 2y_2x_1 + y_2x_2.$$

The bilinear form Eq. (4.2.1) can be written analogous to the linear form given in Eq. (4.1.5) as

$$(4.2.4) \qquad f(\mathbf{y}, \mathbf{x}) = \sum_{i=1}^{m} \sum_{j=1}^{n} a_{ij}\, y_i x_j.$$

In Eq. (4.2.1), writing the function $f(\mathbf{y}, \mathbf{x})$ as a 1×1 matrix $\mathbf{w}$ instead of a scalar, we have

$$(4.2.5) \qquad \mathbf{yAx} = \mathbf{w}.$$

Taking the transpose of both sides of Eq. (4.2.7), and observing that $\mathbf{w}' = \mathbf{w}$,

$$(4.2.6) \qquad f(\mathbf{y}, \mathbf{x}) = \mathbf{w} = \mathbf{w}' = (\mathbf{yAx})' = \mathbf{x}'\mathbf{A}'\mathbf{y}' = g(\mathbf{x}, \mathbf{y}).$$

That is, the roles of the variables are reversed upon taking the transpose of the matrix of the bilinear form.

Now let us introduce new variables $\mathbf{u}$ and $\mathbf{v}$ to replace $\mathbf{x}$ and $\mathbf{y}$ by

$$(4.2.7) \qquad \mathbf{x} = \mathbf{Qu} \quad \text{and} \quad \mathbf{y} = \mathbf{vP}$$

where $\mathbf{Q}$ and $\mathbf{P}$ are nonsingular matrices. Substituting from Eq. (4.2.7) into Eq. (4.2.5),

$$(4.2.8) \qquad f(\mathbf{y}, \mathbf{x}) = \mathbf{yAx} = \mathbf{vPAQu} = \mathbf{vBu} = g(\mathbf{v}, \mathbf{u}).$$

By Theorem 3.6.4 there exist nonsingular matrices $\mathbf{P}$ and $\mathbf{Q}$ such that $\mathbf{B}$ in Eq. (4.2.8) will be in normal (or *canonical*) form $\mathbf{R}_r$. With such a choice of $\mathbf{P}$ and $\mathbf{Q}$, then

$$(4.2.9) \qquad g(\mathbf{v}, \mathbf{u}) = \mathbf{vR}_r\mathbf{u} = v_1u_1 + v_2u_2 + \cdots + v_ru_r.$$

This is generally a much simpler equation to handle. We summarize the preceding discussion in the following theorem.

Theorem 4.2.1. *There exist nonsingular matrices* **P** *and* **Q** *such that, by the transformations*

$$\mathbf{x} = \mathbf{Qu} \text{ and } \mathbf{y} = \mathbf{vP},$$

every bilinear form $f(\mathbf{y}, \mathbf{x})$ *can be written as*

$$f(\mathbf{y}, \mathbf{x}) = v_1 u_1 + v_2 u_2 + \cdots + v_r u_r = g(v, u),$$

where r is the rank of the matrix of the bilinear form.

The operations of Eq. (4.2.8) are reversible, since

$$(4.2.10)\quad g(\mathbf{v}, \mathbf{u}) = \mathbf{vBu} = \mathbf{v}(\mathbf{PAQ})\mathbf{u} = \mathbf{yP}^{-1}\mathbf{PAQQ}^{-1}\mathbf{x} = \mathbf{yAx} = f(\mathbf{y}, \mathbf{x}).$$

Example 4.2.1. Use the results of Theorem 4.2.1 to simplify

$$f(\mathbf{y}, \mathbf{x}) = 3x_1y_1 + 2x_1y_2 - 4x_1y_3 + 5x_2y_1 + 7x_2y_2 = g(\mathbf{x}, \mathbf{y}).$$

Since **y** has three components and **x** has two,

$$f(\mathbf{y}, \mathbf{x}) = [y_1 \quad y_2 \quad y_3]\begin{bmatrix} 3 & 5 \\ 2 & 7 \\ -4 & 0 \end{bmatrix}\begin{bmatrix} x_1 \\ x_2 \end{bmatrix} = \mathbf{yAx}.$$

This may also be written as

$$g(\mathbf{x}, \mathbf{y}) = [x_1 \quad x_2]\begin{bmatrix} 3 & 2 & -4 \\ 5 & 7 & 0 \end{bmatrix}\begin{bmatrix} y_1 \\ y_2 \\ y_3 \end{bmatrix} = \mathbf{xA'y},$$

where the vectors are the transposes of those in the preceding equation.

If we choose products of elementary matrices for **P** and **Q** (which incidentally are not unique) so that $\mathbf{PAQ} = \mathbf{R}_2$, then

$$\mathbf{P} = \begin{bmatrix} 1 & -1 & 0 \\ -2/11 & 3/11 & 0 \\ 28/11 & -20/11 & 1 \end{bmatrix} \quad \text{and} \quad \mathbf{Q} = \begin{bmatrix} 1 & 2 \\ 0 & 1 \end{bmatrix}.$$

Thus

$$\begin{aligned} f(y, x) &= \mathbf{yAx} = \mathbf{vPAQu} \\ &= [v_1 \quad v_2 \quad v_3]\begin{bmatrix} 1 & -1 & 0 \\ -2/11 & 3/11 & 0 \\ 28/11 & -20/11 & 1 \end{bmatrix}\begin{bmatrix} 3 & 5 \\ 2 & 7 \\ -4 & 0 \end{bmatrix}\begin{bmatrix} 1 & 2 \\ 0 & 1 \end{bmatrix}\begin{bmatrix} u_1 \\ u_2 \end{bmatrix} \\ &= [v_1 \quad v_2 \quad v_3]\begin{bmatrix} 1 & 0 \\ 0 & 1 \\ 0 & 0 \end{bmatrix}\begin{bmatrix} u_1 \\ u_2 \end{bmatrix} \\ &= u_1v_1 + u_2v_2, \end{aligned}$$

a considerably simplified form.

Exercises 4.2

1. Write Eq. (4.2.2) as the product of three matrices.
2. (a) Is $f(\mathbf{y}, \mathbf{x})$ the same as $f(\mathbf{x}', \mathbf{y}')$ in Eq. (4.2.3)?
   (b) For what matrices $\mathbf{A}$ is it true that $f(\mathbf{y}, \mathbf{x}) = f(\mathbf{x}', \mathbf{y}')$?
3. Use Theorem 4.2.1 to simplify the following:
   (a) $f(\mathbf{y}, \mathbf{x}) = x_1y_1 + x_3y_1 - x_1y_2 + 2x_2y_2 + x_2y_3 - x_3y_3$.
   (b) $f(\mathbf{y}, \mathbf{x}) = x_1y_1 + 5x_1y_2 - 4x_1y_3 - 3x_2y_1 - 7x_2y_2 + x_2y_3$.
4. Reduce each of the following to canonical form:
   (a) $f(\mathbf{y}, \mathbf{x}) = 5x_1y_1 + 7x_1y_2 + 4x_1y_3 + 2x_2y_1 - x_2y_2 + 3x_3y_1$.
   (b) $f(\mathbf{y}, \mathbf{x}) = x_1y_2 + 4x_1y_3 - 4x_2y_1 + x_2y_3 - 6x_3y_1 + 6x_3y_2$.

4.3. *Quadratic Forms*

The bilinear forms discussed in Section 4.2 required two sets of variables, $\{x_i\}$ and $\{y_j\}$. If, instead of using two different sets, we use the same set twice (such as a vector and its transpose), we obtain the important and useful homogeneous form called a *quadratic form*. That is, for the column vector $\mathbf{x} = [x_1 \; x_2 \; \cdots \; x_n]'$ and the square matrix $\mathbf{A}$, a quadratic form is defined by

$$(4.3.1) \quad f(\mathbf{x}) = \mathbf{x}'\mathbf{A}\mathbf{x} = [x_1 \quad x_2 \quad \cdots \quad x_n]\begin{bmatrix} a_{11} & a_{12} & \cdots & a_{1n} \\ a_{21} & a_{22} & \cdots & a_{2n} \\ \cdots & & & \\ a_{n1} & a_{n2} & \cdots & a_{nn} \end{bmatrix}\begin{bmatrix} x_1 \\ x_2 \\ \vdots \\ x_n \end{bmatrix}.$$

The expanded quadratic form is a homogeneous polynomial of degree two in the variables x_i. Note that $\mathbf{A}$ must be square for $\mathbf{x}'\mathbf{A}\mathbf{x}$ to be defined.

Simple examples of quadratic forms are the following:

$$(4.3.2) \quad \begin{aligned} f(\mathbf{x}) &= x_1^2 + 3x_1x_2 + 2x_2x_1 + x_2^2 + x_2x_3 + 3x_3x_1 \\ &\quad + x_3x_2 + 2x_3^2 \\ &= [x_1 \quad x_2 \quad x_3]\begin{bmatrix} 1 & 3 & 0 \\ 2 & 1 & 1 \\ 3 & 1 & 2 \end{bmatrix}\begin{bmatrix} x_1 \\ x_2 \\ x_3 \end{bmatrix} = \mathbf{x}'\mathbf{A}\mathbf{x}. \end{aligned}$$

$$(4.3.3) \quad f(\mathbf{x}) = x_1^2 + x_2^2 + x_3^2 = [x_1 \quad x_2 \quad x_3]\begin{bmatrix} 1 & 0 & 0 \\ 0 & 1 & 0 \\ 0 & 0 & 1 \end{bmatrix}\begin{bmatrix} x_1 \\ x_2 \\ x_3 \end{bmatrix} = \mathbf{x}'\mathbf{x}.$$

The quadratic form $f(\mathbf{x})$ of Eq. (4.3.1) may also be written as

$$(4.3.4) \quad f(\mathbf{x}) = \mathbf{x}'\mathbf{A}\mathbf{x} = \sum_{i=1}^{n}\sum_{j=1}^{n} a_{ij}x_ix_j$$

Two examples of quadratic forms taken from analytic geometry are the equation of the ellipse $x^2 + 4y^2 = 1$, which may be expressed as

$$[x \quad y]\begin{bmatrix} 1 & 0 \\ 0 & 4 \end{bmatrix}\begin{bmatrix} x \\ y \end{bmatrix} = 1,$$

and the equation of the degenerate parabola $x^2 - 2xy + y^2 = 1$, which may be written as

$$[x \quad y]\begin{bmatrix} 1 & -1 \\ -1 & 1 \end{bmatrix}\begin{bmatrix} x \\ y \end{bmatrix} = 1.$$

Note that Eq. (4.3.2) includes terms $3x_1x_2$ and $2x_2x_1$ as well as terms x_2x_3 and x_3x_2. The like terms can be combined, so we see that more than one matrix can be associated with a given quadratic form. However, we can associate a unique matrix with a given quadratic form by combining the mixed variable terms and dividing the result into two equal terms. The resulting matrix of the form is a *symmetric matrix*.

Example 4.3.1. Rewrite Eq. (4.3.2) so that the matrix of the form is symmetric.

We write $f(\mathbf{x})$ as 3^2 properly-chosen terms, then write the result in matrix form:

(4.3.5)
$$\begin{aligned} f(\mathbf{x}) &= x_1^2 + \tfrac{5}{2}x_1x_2 + \tfrac{3}{2}x_1x_3 + \tfrac{5}{2}x_2x_1 + x_2^2 + x_2x_3 \\ &\quad + \tfrac{3}{2}x_3x_1 + x_3x_2 + 2x_3^2 \\ &= [x_1 \quad x_2 \quad x_3]\begin{bmatrix} 1 & 5/2 & 3/2 \\ 5/2 & 1 & 1 \\ 3/2 & 1 & 2 \end{bmatrix}\begin{bmatrix} x_1 \\ x_2 \\ x_3 \end{bmatrix}. \end{aligned}$$

Note that the matrix of the form is symmetric.

The method used in Example 4.3.2 can be extended to general quadratic forms by taking like terms of

(4.3.6)
$$\sum_{i=1}^{n}\sum_{j=1}^{n} a_{ij}x_ix_j$$

for $i \neq j$ and writing

(4.3.7)
$$\tfrac{1}{2}(a_{ij} + a_{ji})$$

as the coefficient of x_ix_j and also as the coefficient of x_jx_i. We state this result as a theorem:

Theorem 4.3.1. *The matrix of every quadratic form can always be chosen to be a symmetric matrix.*

With Theorem 4.3.1 at our disposal, henceforth in this book *the matrix of a quadratic form will always be a symmetric matrix.*

Exercises 4.3

1. Since any matrix **A** can be written as the sum of a symmetric matrix **S** and a skew symmetric matrix **K** (as in number 4 of Exercises 1.10), then $\mathbf{A} = \mathbf{S} + \mathbf{K}$ and

$$f(\mathbf{x}) = \mathbf{x}'\mathbf{A}\mathbf{x} = \mathbf{x}'\mathbf{S}\mathbf{x} + \mathbf{x}'\mathbf{K}\mathbf{x}.$$

   By Theorem 4.3.1, $\mathbf{x}'\mathbf{K}\mathbf{x}$ must be zero. Prove by direct means that this is actually the case.

2. Rewrite the following so that the matrix of the form is symmetric:

$$[x_1 \quad x_2 \quad x_3]\begin{bmatrix} 1 & 2 & 0 \\ 0 & 2 & 3 \\ 2 & 5 & 6 \end{bmatrix}\begin{bmatrix} x_1 \\ x_2 \\ x_3 \end{bmatrix}$$

3. Find the matrix of the quadratic form associated with

$$ax^2 + by^2 + cz^2 + 2fyz + 2gzx + 2hxy.$$

4. For the quadratic form

$$\mathbf{x}'\mathbf{A}\mathbf{x} = 3x_1x_3 + 2x^2 + x_2x_4 - 4x_3x_4,$$

   find the matrix **A** of the form and verify that $\mathbf{x}'\mathbf{A}\mathbf{x}$ is symmetric. Find a nonsymmetric matrix **B** such that $\mathbf{x}'\mathbf{A}\mathbf{x} = \mathbf{x}'\mathbf{B}\mathbf{x}$ and verify that $\mathbf{x}'\mathbf{B}\mathbf{x}$ is still symmetric. Explain.

5. Find the matrix of the form and determine its rank for

$$2x_1x_2 + 2x_1x_3 + 2x_2x_3 + 2x_3^2.$$

4.4 *Congruent Matrices*

Consider the change of variables $\mathbf{x} = \mathbf{P}\mathbf{y}$ in the quadratic form $f(\mathbf{x}) = \mathbf{x}'\mathbf{A}\mathbf{x}$, where **A** is symmetric in accordance with Theorem 4.3.1. The result is

$$f(\mathbf{x}) = \mathbf{x}'\mathbf{A}\mathbf{x} = (\mathbf{P}\mathbf{y})'\mathbf{A}(\mathbf{P}\mathbf{y}) = \mathbf{y}'(\mathbf{P}'\mathbf{A}\mathbf{P})\mathbf{y} = \mathbf{y}'\mathbf{B}\mathbf{y} = g(\mathbf{y}). \tag{4.4.1}$$

The relationship of **B** to **A** in Eq. (4.4.1) is not in general the same as in previous cases (such as where **PAQ** was used in Section 4.2), since **P** and its transpose **P′** are involved. If **P** is nonsingular, then **B** is *congruent* to **A** (whether **A** is symmetric or not). In general, a square matrix **B** is said to be congruent to a square matrix **A** of the same order if there exists a nonsingular matrix **P** such that

$$\mathbf{B} = \mathbf{P}'\mathbf{A}\mathbf{P}. \tag{4.4.2}$$

If **A** and **B** are congruent and if **A** is symmetric, then it readily follows from Eq. (4.4.2) that **B** is also symmetric, since

$$\mathbf{B}' = (\mathbf{P}'\mathbf{A}\mathbf{P})' = \mathbf{P}'\mathbf{A}'\mathbf{P} = \mathbf{P}'\mathbf{A}\mathbf{P} = \mathbf{B}. \tag{4.4.3}$$

For congruent matrices **A** and **B**, the matrix **P** in Eq. (4.4.2) is the product of elementary matrices (since it is nonsingular by definition). Since postmultiplying **A** by **P** performs a succession of elementary *column* transformations on **A**, premultiplying **A** by **P′** performs the corresponding elementary *row* transformations on **A**. For example if

$$\mathbf{P} = \begin{bmatrix} 1 & 2 & 0 \\ 0 & 1 & 0 \\ 0 & 0 & 1 \end{bmatrix},$$

postmultiplying **A** by **P** would multiply the first column of **A** by 2 and add it to the second column, while premultiplying **A** by

$$\mathbf{P}' = \begin{bmatrix} 1 & 0 & 0 \\ 2 & 1 & 0 \\ 0 & 0 & 1 \end{bmatrix}$$

would multiply the first row of **A** by 2 and add it to the second row.

If **A** is symmetric, then by the preceding discussion (and by the results of Section 3.6) there exists a nonsingular matrix **P** such that

$$\mathbf{P}'\mathbf{A}\mathbf{P} = \mathbf{D}, \tag{4.4.4}$$

where **D** is a diagonal matrix. That is,

$$(\mathbf{C}_h' \cdots \mathbf{C}_1')\mathbf{A}(\mathbf{C}_1 \cdots \mathbf{C}_h) = (\mathbf{C}_1 \cdots \mathbf{C}_h)'\mathbf{A}(\mathbf{C}_1 \cdots \mathbf{C}_h) = \mathbf{P}'\mathbf{A}\mathbf{P},$$

where the $\mathbf{C}_i$ are elementary matrices.

Although Eq. (4.4.4) may seem obvious theoretically, it may not be so easy to determine the matrix **P** in a particular case. The following two examples illustrate methods for dealing with certain recurring problems; the reader will profit by going through them in detail.

Example 4.4.1. Determine a matrix **P** that will reduce

$$\begin{bmatrix} 0 & 1 \\ 1 & 0 \end{bmatrix}$$

to diagonal form by a congruent transformation. (Note that the given matrix has only zero elements on the main diagonal.) The "obvious" approach is to interchange the columns; however, since rows must also be interchanged, this approach is fruitless. Instead, add the first column (and row) to the second column (and row):

$$\begin{bmatrix} 0 & 1 \\ 1 & 2 \end{bmatrix}.$$

Then add $-\frac{1}{2}$ of the second column (and row) to the first column (and row), to obtain

$$\begin{bmatrix} -1/2 & 0 \\ 0 & 2 \end{bmatrix},$$

a matrix in the desired form. In expanded form this can all be written as

$$\begin{bmatrix} 1 & -1/2 \\ 0 & 1 \end{bmatrix}\begin{bmatrix} 1 & 0 \\ 1 & 1 \end{bmatrix}\begin{bmatrix} 0 & 1 \\ 1 & 0 \end{bmatrix}\begin{bmatrix} 1 & 1 \\ 0 & 1 \end{bmatrix}\begin{bmatrix} 1 & 0 \\ -1/2 & 1 \end{bmatrix}$$

$$= \begin{bmatrix} 1/2 & -1/2 \\ 1 & 1 \end{bmatrix}\begin{bmatrix} 0 & 1 \\ 1 & 0 \end{bmatrix}\begin{bmatrix} 1/2 & 1 \\ -1/2 & 1 \end{bmatrix} = \begin{bmatrix} -1/2 & 0 \\ 0 & 2 \end{bmatrix}.$$

Example 4.4.2. Reduce

$$\begin{bmatrix} 0 & 4 \\ 4 & 5 \end{bmatrix}$$

to diagonal form by a congruent transformation. (Note that this matrix has a zero element on the main diagonal.)

The matrix

$$\mathbf{P} = \begin{bmatrix} 1 & 0 \\ -4/5 & 1 \end{bmatrix}$$

performs the required transformation, since

$$\begin{bmatrix} 1 & -4/5 \\ 0 & 1 \end{bmatrix}\begin{bmatrix} 0 & 4 \\ 4 & 5 \end{bmatrix}\begin{bmatrix} 1 & 0 \\ -4/5 & 1 \end{bmatrix} = \begin{bmatrix} -16/5 & 0 \\ 0 & 5 \end{bmatrix}.$$

How is the element $-4/5$ obtained?

If $\mathbf{A}$ is real, then by a congruent transformation it can be put in the form

$$\mathbf{D} = \begin{bmatrix} d_1 & 0 & 0 & \cdots & 0 \\ 0 & d_2 & 0 & \cdots & 0 \\ 0 & 0 & d_3 & \cdots & 0 \\ \cdots & & & & \\ 0 & 0 & 0 & \cdots & d_n \end{bmatrix}, \tag{4.4.5}$$

where $d_1, d_2, \cdots, d_p$ are all positive, $d_{p+1}, d_{p+2}, \cdots, d_r$ are all negative, and $d_{r+1}, d_{r+2}, \cdots, d_n$ are all zero. Here r is the rank of $\mathbf{D}$, and hence the rank of $\mathbf{A}$.

Example 4.4.3. Choose a nonsingular matrix $\mathbf{P}$ such that the symmetric matrix $\mathbf{A}$ is congruent to a matrix $\mathbf{D}$ in the form given in Eq. (4.4.5), if

$$\mathbf{A} = \begin{bmatrix} 1 & -2 & 1 & -2 \\ -2 & 0 & 3 & -5 \\ 1 & 3 & 2 & 2 \\ -2 & -5 & 2 & -9 \end{bmatrix}.$$

By performing a succession of elementary column transformations (not given in complete detail), a matrix **P** is determined such that **A** is transformed into a matrix **D** by **P′AP**.

$$\mathbf{P} = \begin{bmatrix} 1 & 2 & -1 & 2 \\ 0 & 1 & 0 & 0 \\ 0 & 0 & 1 & 0 \\ 0 & 0 & 0 & 1 \end{bmatrix} \begin{bmatrix} 1 & 0 & 0 & 0 \\ 0 & 1 & 0 & 0 \\ 0 & -5 & 1 & -4 \\ 0 & 0 & 0 & 1 \end{bmatrix} \begin{bmatrix} 1 & 0 & 0 & 0 \\ 0 & 1 & 0 & -1 \\ 0 & 0 & 1 & 0 \\ 0 & 0 & 0 & 1 \end{bmatrix} \begin{bmatrix} 1 & 0 & 0 & 0 \\ 0 & 0 & 1 & 0 \\ 0 & 1 & 0 & 0 \\ 0 & 0 & 0 & 1 \end{bmatrix}$$

$$= \begin{bmatrix} 1 & -1 & 7 & -1 \\ 0 & 0 & 1 & -1 \\ 0 & 1 & -5 & 1 \\ 0 & 0 & 0 & 1 \end{bmatrix}.$$

Thus

$$\mathbf{P'AP} = \begin{bmatrix} 1 & 0 & 0 & 0 \\ -1 & 0 & 1 & 0 \\ 7 & 1 & -5 & 0 \\ -1 & -1 & 1 & 1 \end{bmatrix} \begin{bmatrix} 1 & -2 & 1 & -2 \\ -2 & 0 & 3 & -5 \\ 1 & 3 & 2 & 2 \\ -2 & -5 & 2 & -9 \end{bmatrix} \begin{bmatrix} 1 & -1 & 7 & -1 \\ 0 & 0 & 1 & -1 \\ 0 & 1 & -5 & 1 \\ 0 & 0 & 0 & 1 \end{bmatrix}$$

$$= \begin{bmatrix} 1 & 0 & 0 & 0 \\ 0 & 1 & 0 & 0 \\ 0 & 0 & -29 & 0 \\ 0 & 0 & 0 & 0 \end{bmatrix} = \mathbf{D}.$$

If we continue with Example 4.4.3, we see that the substitution $\mathbf{x} = \mathbf{Py}$ gives

$$f(\mathbf{x}) = \mathbf{x}'\mathbf{Ax} = \mathbf{y}'\mathbf{P}'\mathbf{APy} = \mathbf{y}'\mathbf{Dy}' = y_1^2 + y_2^2 - 29y_3^2 = g(\mathbf{y})$$

The final matrix **D** can be transformed further so that the -29 is replaced by -1. If our scalars are restricted to real numbers, no further simplification is possible.

The following theorems state the results of this section:

Theorem 4.4.1. *For the quadratic form* $\mathbf{x}'\mathbf{Ax}$ *if the matrix* **A** *is of rank r, then there exists a nonsingular matrix* **P** *such that the corresponding quadratic form is equivalent to*

(4.4.6) $\quad g(\mathbf{y}) = d_1 y_1^2 + d_2 y_2^2 + \cdots + d_r y_r^2,\ d_i \neq 0,\ i = 1, 2, \cdots, r,$

under the transformation $\mathbf{x} = \mathbf{Py}$.

Theorem 4.4.2. *If the matrix of the form is real and is of rank r, the corresponding quadratic form is equivalent to*

$$g(\mathbf{y}) = y_1^2 + y_2^2 + \cdots + y_p^2 - y_{p+1}^2 - \cdots - y_r^2. \tag{4.4.7}$$

The integer $p \geq 0$ in Eq. (4.4.7) is called the *index* of the quadratic form; it is the number of positive terms appearing in the simplified quadratic form. The total number of positive and negative terms in Eq. (4.4.7) is the rank r of the matrix of the form. By Theorem 3.4.2, the rank r is not altered by the transformations we are considering; it can be proved that the index is not altered either. That is, the index p of the quadratic form and the rank r of real symmetric matrices are invariant under congruent transformations. The proof of this statement is left as an exercise.

Since there is a unique symmetric matrix associated with a given real quadratic form, and since the rank of a matrix and index of a quadratic form are invariant under congruent transformations, this book will customarily refer both to the rank and index of the matrix of the form, and to the rank and index of the quadratic form itself.

Exercises 4.4

1. Determine a nonsingular matrix $\mathbf{P}$ such that $\mathbf{P'AP}$ is in the form of $\mathbf{D}$ given in Eq. (4.4.5), if

$$\mathbf{A} = \begin{bmatrix} 3 & 0 & 1 & -1 \\ 0 & 0 & -4 & 2 \\ 1 & -4 & 5 & -2 \\ -1 & 2 & -2 & 1 \end{bmatrix}.$$

2. Find the rank and index of $\mathbf{A}$ in exercise 1.

3. Show that the quadratic form

$$f(\mathbf{x}) = x_1^2 + 4x_1x_2 + 6x_1x_3 - x_2^2 + 2x_2x_3 + 4x_3^2$$

is equivalent to

$$g(\mathbf{y}) = y_1^2 + y_2^2,$$

and determine a nonsingular transformation carrying f into g.

4. Show that every nonsingular symmetric matrix is congruent to its inverse.

5. Prove that the index of a quadratic form is not altered by congruent transformations.

6. Prove that if $\mathbf{B}$ is a symmetric matrix such that $\mathbf{B}$ is congruent to $\mathbf{A}$, then $\mathbf{A}$ must necessarily be symmetric.

7. Find the rank and index of the form

$$2x_1x_2 + 2x_1x_3 + 2x_2x_3 + 2x_3^2,$$

determine the nonsingular matrix that will simplify the form, and finally write the simplified quadratic form.

8. For any square matrix $\mathbf{A}$ a quadratic form $\mathbf{x}'\mathbf{A}\mathbf{x}$ is obtained. Demonstrate with a specific matrix of order 3 that the rank of the quadratic form need not be the same as the rank of $\mathbf{A}$.

4.5. *Positive Definite Matrices*

From the discussion of the preceding section, we can classify real quadratic forms using the non-negative integers n, r, and p. The classification of real symmetric matrices is the same as the classification of the corresponding quadratic forms.

For any real symmetric matrix of order n, the rank r can be any integer from zero to n, and the index p of the associated quadratic form can be any integer from zero to r. Hence, although the index may be zero or n, $0 \leq p \leq r \leq n$.

The *canonical representation* of a real quadratic form is given by Eq. (4.4.7);

$$g(\mathbf{y}) = y_1^2 + y_2^2 + \cdots + y_p^2 - y_{p+1}^2 - \cdots - y_r^2. \tag{4.5.1}$$

The matrix of the form is also in canonical form. If $p = n$ (and hence $p = r = n$), the canonical representation of the quadratic form is

$$g(\mathbf{y}) = y_1^2 + y_2^2 + \cdots + y_n^2. \tag{4.5.2}$$

All quadratic forms $g(\mathbf{y})$ are zero when $\mathbf{y} = \mathbf{0}$; this is called the trivial case. A real quadratic form whose value is positive for all non-zero vectors $\mathbf{y}$ is a *positive definite* form, and the matrix of the form is also said to be positive definite or a *positive definite matrix*. Thus if $\mathbf{y}$ is real in Eq. (4.5.2), $g(\mathbf{y})$ is a positive definite form. The canonical form of this matrix is the identity matrix. Since $g(\mathbf{y}) = f(\mathbf{x})$ in Eq. (4.4.1), $f(\mathbf{x})$ is also a positive definite form.

Under the preceding classification, whenever we refer to a quadratic form or the associated matrix of the form we assume that the underlying field is the field of real numbers. (For example, a positive definite matrix is assumed to be a matrix with real elements.)

If $p = n$, then $p = r = n$, and the matrix of the form is nonsingular. If a matrix is in normal form, and $r = n$, the matrix is the identity matrix. Therefore, a positive definite symmetric matrix is congruent to the identity matrix, so that there is a nonsingular matrix $\mathbf{P}$ such that $\mathbf{P}'\mathbf{A}\mathbf{P} = \mathbf{I}$. Conversely, if $\mathbf{A}$ is real and $\mathbf{P}'\mathbf{A}\mathbf{P} = \mathbf{I}$ for some nonsingular matrix $\mathbf{P}$, then $\mathbf{A}$ is a positive definite matrix.

If $p = 0$ but $r = n$, then

$$g(\mathbf{y}) = -y_1^2 - y_2^2 - \cdots - y_n^2. \tag{4.5.3}$$

Here the canonical representation of the quadratic forms is such that each coefficient is -1. Note that the rank of the matrix of the form is n, so that the matrix is nonsingular; the quadratic form in this case is a *negative definite* quadratic form. The matrix of the form is also negative definite; it is congruent to $-\mathbf{I}$. Note that $g(\mathbf{y})$ is zero only for $\mathbf{y} = \mathbf{0}$ for positive and negative definite quadratic forms.

If $r = n$ but $0 < p < n$, no special name is attached in general to the quadratic form.

If $r < n$ and $p = r$, we get

(4.5.4) $$g(\mathbf{y}) = y_1^2 + y_2^2 + \cdots + y_r^2;$$

this form is *positive semidefinite*. The canonical form of the matrix for positive semidefinite matrices is the normal form.

If $r < n$ and $p = 0$, we get the *negative semidefinite* form

(4.5.5) $$g(\mathbf{y}) = -y_1^2 - y_2^2 - \cdots - y_r^2.$$

This form is never positive for any real vector $\mathbf{y}$, although it may be zero for non-zero vectors $\mathbf{y}$. Again the corresponding matrix of the form is negative semidefinite.

Finally, a symmetric matrix $\mathbf{A}$ and the associated quadratic form are *non-negative definite* if they are either positive definite or positive semidefinite.

Exercises 4.5

1. Show that $x_1^2 - 2x_1x_2 + x_2^2 + x_3^2$ is a positive semidefinite quadratic form.
2. Let $g(\mathbf{x})$ range over all possible non-zero canonical representations of the quadratic forms for $n = 3$. Describe the locus of $g(\mathbf{x}) = 1$.
3. (a) Show that if $Ax_1^2 + 2Bx_1x_2 + Cx_2^2$ is positive definite or negative definite, then $Ax^2 + 2Bx + C = 0$ has imaginary roots.

   (b) Show that
$$\begin{bmatrix} A & B \\ B & C \end{bmatrix}$$
   is positive definite or negative definite, if
$$\begin{vmatrix} A & B \\ B & C \end{vmatrix} > 0.$$

   (c) Show that
$$\begin{bmatrix} A & B \\ B & C \end{bmatrix}$$
   is positive or negative semidefinite, if
$$\begin{vmatrix} A & B \\ B & C \end{vmatrix} = 0.$$

4. Verify that a negative semidefinite form may be zero for non-zero vectors.

5. Determine a nonsingular matrix **P** such that **P′AP** is in canonical form if **A** is

(a) $\begin{bmatrix} 0 & 0 & 1 \\ 0 & 1 & 0 \\ 1 & 0 & 0 \end{bmatrix}$, (b) $\begin{bmatrix} 0 & 0 & 1 \\ 0 & 1 & 0 \\ 1 & 0 & 1 \end{bmatrix}$, (c) $\begin{bmatrix} 1 & 0 & 1 \\ 0 & 1 & 0 \\ 1 & 0 & 1 \end{bmatrix}$.

4.6. *Positive Definite Matrices Continued*

This section includes several additional theorems on positive definite matrices, and considers in more detail some of the consequences of the results of Section 4.5. Note that matrices classified as positive definite, negative definite, positive semidefinite, negative semidefinite, or non-negative definite are always real.

Since a positive definite matrix **A** is congruent to the identity matrix, there exists a matrix **B** such that $\mathbf{B}'\mathbf{AB} = \mathbf{I}$. Thus

$$\det \mathbf{B}'\mathbf{AB} = \det \mathbf{B}' \det \mathbf{A} \det \mathbf{B} = 1,$$

or

$$\det \mathbf{A} = 1/(\det \mathbf{B})^2, \tag{4.6.1}$$

since $\det \mathbf{B}' = \det \mathbf{B}$. Since the right side of Eq. (4.6.1) is positive, $\det \mathbf{A} > 0$. This result is stated as a theorem:

Theorem 4.6.1. *If* **A** *is a positive definite matrix, then det* **A** *is a positive number.*

Example 4.6.1. Verify that **A** is a positive definite matrix but that **B** is not, where

$$\mathbf{A} = \begin{bmatrix} 2 & 1 \\ 1 & 2 \end{bmatrix}, \quad \text{and} \quad \mathbf{B} = \begin{bmatrix} 1 & 1 \\ 1 & -1 \end{bmatrix}.$$

Note that, although Theorem 4.6.1 gives a *necessary* condition that a matrix be positive definite, the condition is not sufficient. (See Example 4.6.2 below.) Since $\det \mathbf{A} = 3$, **A** can be positive definite; since $\det \mathbf{B} = -2$, **B** cannot be. Although we could reduce each matrix to canonical form, we proceed somewhat differently so as to stay closer to the basic idea behind positive definiteness. Thus

$$\mathbf{x}'\mathbf{Ax} = 2(x_1^2 + x_1x_2 + x_2^2) = (x_1 + x_2)^2 + x_1^2 + x_2^2,$$

and so $\mathbf{x}'\mathbf{Ax} > 0$ for any $\mathbf{x} \neq 0$. Similarly,

$$\mathbf{x}'\mathbf{Bx} = x_1^2 + 2x_1x_2 - x_2^2 = (x_1 + x_2)^2 - 2x_2^2,$$

which can be negative for a properly chosen **x**. Therefore, **B** is not a positive definite matrix.

Since the matrix of a quadratic form is symmetric, and the rank and index of a matrix are invariant under nonsingular transformations, we can state the following theorem:

Theorem 4.6.2. *If* $\mathbf{A}$ *is any positive definite (semidefinite) matrix of a quadratic form and if* $\mathbf{B}$ *is any nonsingular matrix, then* $\mathbf{B'AB}$ *is also positive definite (semidefinite).*

The following theorem permits us to construct positive definite matrices readily:

Theorem 4.6.3. *A necessary and sufficient condition that* $\mathbf{A}$ *be a positive definite matrix is that there exists a nonsingular matrix* $\mathbf{B}$ *such that* $\mathbf{A} = \mathbf{B'B}$.

Proof: If $\mathbf{A} = \mathbf{B'B}$, observe first that $\mathbf{A}$ is symmetric, since $\mathbf{A'} = (\mathbf{B'B})' = \mathbf{B'B} = \mathbf{A}$. Second, $\mathbf{A}$ is nonsingular, since $\mathbf{B}$ and $\mathbf{B'}$ are both nonsingular. Third, $\det \mathbf{A} = \det \mathbf{B'} \det \mathbf{B} = (\det \mathbf{B})^2 > 0$ in accordance with Theorem 4.6.1. These conditions are all necessary for $\mathbf{A}$ to be positive definite, but are not sufficient. However, since $\mathbf{A} = \mathbf{B'B}$,

$$(\mathbf{B'})^{-1}\mathbf{A}\mathbf{B}^{-1} = (\mathbf{B}^{-1})'\mathbf{A}\mathbf{B}^{-1} = \mathbf{I};$$

that is, $\mathbf{A}$ is congruent to $\mathbf{I}$. The associated quadratic form is obviously positive definite. Therefore, $\mathbf{A}$ is a positive definite matrix.

On the other hand if $\mathbf{A}$ is a positive definite matrix, then $r = n$, and $\mathbf{A}$ is congruent to the identity matrix $\mathbf{I}$. That is, there exists a nonsingular matrix $\mathbf{C}$ such that

$$\mathbf{C'AC} = \mathbf{I} \qquad \text{or} \qquad \mathbf{A} = (\mathbf{C'})^{-1}\mathbf{C}^{-1} = (\mathbf{C}^{-1})'\mathbf{C}^{-1}.$$

If we let $\mathbf{B} = \mathbf{C}^{-1}$, the theorem is proved.

Theorem 4.6.4. *If* $\mathbf{A}$ *is a positive definite matrix, then every principal minor of* $\mathbf{A}$ *is positive.*

Proof: Let $q = \mathbf{x'Ax}$ be the quadratic form associated with $\mathbf{A}$. Now $q > 0$ for all non-zero vectors $\mathbf{x}$, even if some of the elements of $\mathbf{x}$ are zero; if q_i is the value of q when $x_i = 0$ in $\mathbf{x}$, we still have $q_i > 0$ as long as $\mathbf{x} \neq \mathbf{0}$. Note that having $x_i = 0$ is equivalent to deleting the ith row and column of $\mathbf{A}$. Since this argument can be repeated for $i = 1, 2, \cdots, n$, every principal minor of $\mathbf{A}$ of order $n - 1$ is positive by Theorem 4.6.1.

By repeating the argument using $2, 3, \cdots, k, \cdots, n - 1$ zeros in $\mathbf{x}$, with $\mathbf{x} \neq \mathbf{0}$, the same result is obtained if the corresponding k rows and columns of $\mathbf{A}$ are deleted. Thus, the principal minors of order $n - k$ are all positive, concluding the proof.

Note in particular that if $k = n - 1$, then $a_{ii} > 0$ for $i = 1, 2, \cdots, n$. That is, if one element on the principal diagonal is not positive, the matrix is not positive definite.

Example 4.6.2. Prove or disprove that

$$\mathbf{A} = \begin{bmatrix} 1 & 6 & 2 \\ 6 & 2 & 3 \\ 2 & 3 & -1 \end{bmatrix}$$

is a positive definite matrix.

The matrix $\mathbf{A}$ is not positive definite by Theorem 4.6.4 because the element -1 lies on the principal diagonal. Note, however, that $\det \mathbf{A} = 89 > 0$. This shows that Theorem 4.6.1 does not give a sufficient condition that a matrix be positive definite.

Examining this example further, we see that if

$$\mathbf{B} = \begin{bmatrix} 0 & 1 & 0 \\ 1 & -12/11 & 0 \\ 3 & -14/11 & 1 \end{bmatrix}, \quad \text{then} \quad \mathbf{B}'\mathbf{A}\mathbf{B} = \begin{bmatrix} 11 & 0 & 0 \\ 0 & -89/11 & 0 \\ 0 & 0 & -1 \end{bmatrix};$$

the rank is 3, but the index is only 1. Hence $\mathbf{A}$ is not positive definite.

As a final observation, recall that $\mathbf{x}'\mathbf{A}\mathbf{x}$ must be positive for *all* vectors $\mathbf{x} \neq \mathbf{0}$. If we choose $\mathbf{x} = [0\ 0\ 1]'$ then $\mathbf{x}'\mathbf{A}\mathbf{x} = -1$; again, $\mathbf{A}$ is not positive definite.

Although we cannot obtain a quadratic form if $\mathbf{A}$ is not square, still $\mathbf{A}'\mathbf{A}$ and $\mathbf{A}\mathbf{A}'$ are both defined and in fact are symmetric matrices. (See number 3 in Exercises 4.6, below.) We can thus prove the following theorem:

Theorem 4.6.5. *If* $\mathbf{A}$ *is an* $m \times n$ *matrix with rank* n *where* $n < m$, *then* $\mathbf{A}'\mathbf{A}$ *is a positive definite matrix and* $\mathbf{A}\mathbf{A}'$ *is a positive semidefinite matrix.*

Proof: The product $\mathbf{A}'\mathbf{A}$ is a symmetric matrix of order n. The quadratic form for $\mathbf{A}'\mathbf{A}$ is

$$\text{(4.6.2)} \quad \mathbf{x}'\mathbf{A}'\mathbf{A}\mathbf{x} = (\mathbf{x}'\mathbf{A}')(\mathbf{A}\mathbf{x}) = (\mathbf{A}\mathbf{x})'(\mathbf{A}\mathbf{x}) = \mathbf{y}'\mathbf{y} = y_1^2 + y_2^2 + \cdots + y_n^2,$$

if we let $\mathbf{y} = \mathbf{A}\mathbf{x}$. By Theorem 3.6.8 the rank of $\mathbf{x}$ cannot exceed $n - n = 0$ for $\mathbf{A}\mathbf{x} = \mathbf{0}$, since $\mathbf{A}$ is of rank n. That is, the only vector that would make $\mathbf{y}$ the zero vector in $\mathbf{y} = \mathbf{A}\mathbf{x}$, and thus $\mathbf{x}'\mathbf{A}'\mathbf{A}\mathbf{x} = 0$ in Eq. (4.6.2), is $\mathbf{x} = \mathbf{0}$. Hence, $\mathbf{A}'\mathbf{A}$ is a positive definite matrix, since the final result is obviously positive for any nonzero vector $\mathbf{y}$.

Similarly, since $\mathbf{A}\mathbf{A}'$ is of order m and $n < m$, $\mathbf{A}\mathbf{A}'$ is positive semidefinite.

If $m = n$ in Theorem 4.6.5, then by Theorem 4.6.3 $\mathbf{A}'\mathbf{A} = \mathbf{A}\mathbf{A}'$, and is positive definite immediately.

Corollary 4.6.1. *If* $\mathbf{A}$ *is an* $m \times n$ *matrix of rank* r, *then* $\mathbf{A}'\mathbf{A}$ *and* $\mathbf{A}\mathbf{A}'$ *are each congruent to a matrix* $\mathbf{R}_r$ *in normal form of appropriate size.*

Exercises 4.6

1. Determine which, if any, of the following matrices are positive definite.

(a) $\begin{bmatrix} 2 & 1 & -1 \\ 1 & 1 & 4 \\ -1 & 4 & 3 \end{bmatrix}$, (b) $\begin{bmatrix} 1 & 2 & 1 \\ 2 & -1 & 3 \\ 1 & 3 & -1 \end{bmatrix}$, (c) $\begin{bmatrix} 1 & 2 & 1 \\ 2 & 2 & 2 \\ 1 & 2 & 1 \end{bmatrix}$, (d) $\begin{bmatrix} 2 & 1 & 2 \\ 1 & 2 & 1 \\ 2 & 1 & 3 \end{bmatrix}$.

2. Determine the rank and index of (a), (b), (c), (d) in exercise 1.

3. If

$$\mathbf{A} = \begin{bmatrix} 2 & 1 & 3 \\ 1 & 2 & 2 \end{bmatrix},$$

verify by expanding that both $\mathbf{A'A}$ and $\mathbf{AA'}$ are symmetric, but that $\mathbf{A'A} \neq \mathbf{AA'}$. Then prove in general that $\mathbf{A'A}$ and $\mathbf{AA'}$ are both symmetric. When can the two products be equal?

4. Prove that if $\mathbf{A}$ is a positive semidefinite matrix, then every principal minor of $\mathbf{A}$ is positive or zero.

5. Prove that if $\mathbf{A}$ is the matrix of a quadratic form of rank r, then $\mathbf{A}$ has at least one non-zero principal minor of order r.

6. Prove that if $\mathbf{A}$ is of order $m \times n$ and of rank r that is less than full rank, then $\mathbf{A'A}$ and $\mathbf{AA'}$ are positive semidefinite.

7. If $\mathbf{A}$ is an $m \times n$ matrix of rank n and $\mathbf{B}$ is any $m \times n$ matrix, then prove that $\mathbf{A'A} + \mathbf{B'B}$ is symmetric and positive definite.

5

Linear Vector Spaces

5.1. Linear Dependence and Independence

Consider the set of n-dimensional row vectors $\{\mathbf{x}_1, \mathbf{x}_2, \cdots, \mathbf{x}_m\}$ whose elements are scalars from a field $\mathscr{F}$; i.e.,

(5.1.1) $$\mathbf{x}_i = [x_{i1}\ x_{i2} \cdots x_{in}], \qquad i = 1, 2, \cdots, m.$$

Such a set of m vectors is *linearly dependent* over $\mathscr{F}$ provided that there exists a set of m scalars from $\mathscr{F}$, $\{c_1, c_2, \cdots, c_m\}$, not all zero, such that

(5.1.2) $$c_1\mathbf{x}_1 + c_2\mathbf{x}_2 + \cdots + c_m\mathbf{x}_m = \mathbf{0}.$$

If the m vectors are not linearly dependent, they are *linearly independent.* In that instance, the only set of scalars in $\mathscr{F}$, $\{c_1, c_2, \cdots, c_m\}$, for which Eq. (5.1.2) holds is $c_1 = c_2 = \cdots = c_m = 0$. Corresponding definitions of linear dependence and linear independence apply to column vectors, matrices, and functions in general.

Example 5.1.1. Show that vectors $\mathbf{x}_1 = [2\ \ -1\ \ 0]$ and $\mathbf{x}_2 = [-4\ \ 2\ \ 0]$ are linearly dependent.

Since $\mathbf{x}_2 = -2\mathbf{x}_1$, scalars $c_1 = 2$ and $c_2 = 1$ are such that $c_1\mathbf{x}_1 + c_2\mathbf{x}_2 = \mathbf{0}$. Thus $\mathbf{x}_1$ and $\mathbf{x}_2$ are linearly dependent.

Example 5.1.2. Show that the vectors $\mathbf{u}_1 = [3\ \ 2\ \ 1]$, $\mathbf{u}_2 = [2\ \ 0\ \ 2]$, $\mathbf{u}_3 = [0\ \ 1\ \ 1]$, and $\mathbf{u}_4 = [2\ \ 1\ \ -1]$ are linearly dependent.

For these vectors to be linearly dependent we must have

(5.1.3) $$c_1\mathbf{u}_1 + c_2\mathbf{u}_2 + c_3\mathbf{u}_3 + c_4\mathbf{u}_4 = \mathbf{0},$$

or, from the definition of equality of matrices (and hence of vectors),

$$\begin{aligned} 3c_1 + 2c_2 + 0c_3 + 2c_4 &= 0, \\ 2c_1 + 0c_2 + c_3 + c_4 &= 0, \\ c_1 + 2c_2 + c_3 - c_4 &= 0. \end{aligned}$$

Two possible sets of non-zero scalars that satisfy Eq. (5.1.3) are $c_1 = -2$, $c_2 = 1$, $c_3 = 2$, $c_4 = 2$, and $c_1 = 4$, $c_2 = -2$, $c_3 = -4$, $c_4 = -4$. (Note that there are four 3-dimensional vectors, so that $m > n$.) Therefore, the vectors are linearly dependent.

Example 5.1.3. Determine whether or not the vectors $\mathbf{v}_1 = [1 \ 0 \ 2 \ 1]$, $\mathbf{v}_2 = [0 \ 2 \ 1 \ -1]$, $\mathbf{v}_3 = [0 \ 3 \ 0 \ 1]$, and $\mathbf{v}_4 = [2 \ 1 \ 2 \ 0]$ are linearly dependent.

The four vectors are linearly independent. Using Cramer's rule (or elementary substitutions), the only set of scalars c_1, c_2, c_3, c_4 satisfying

$$\begin{aligned} c_1 + 2c_4 &= 0 \\ 2c_2 + 3c_3 + c_4 &= 0 \\ 2c_1 + c_2 + 2c_4 &= 0 \\ c_1 - c_2 + c_3 &= 0 \end{aligned}$$

is $c_1 = c_2 = c_3 = c_4 = 0$.

The sum

$$\mathbf{y} = c_1\mathbf{x}_1 + c_2\mathbf{x}_2 + \cdots + c_m\mathbf{x}_m, \tag{5.1.4}$$

where the c's are scalars from a field $\mathscr{F}$, is a *linear combination* of the n-dimensional vectors $\mathbf{x}_1, \mathbf{x}_2, \cdots, \mathbf{x}_m$. With linear dependence, one vector can be written as a linear combination of the other vectors. (With linear independence, this is impossible.) For example, if one of the c_i in Eq. (5.1.2) is not zero, say $c_1 \neq 0$, then

$$\mathbf{x}_1 = -\frac{1}{c_1}(c_2\mathbf{x}_2 + \cdots + c_m\mathbf{x}_m); \tag{5.1.5}$$

$\mathbf{x}_1$ *depends* on the other vectors $\mathbf{x}_i$. Thus we can state the following theorem:

Theorem 5.1.1. *If m vectors are linearly dependent, at least one of them can always be expressed as a linear combination of the others.*

By the definition of linear dependence, the zero vector is always linearly dependent with any other vector $\mathbf{x}$, since

$$c_1\mathbf{0} + c_2\mathbf{x} = \mathbf{0} \quad \text{for} \quad c_1 \neq 0 \quad \text{and} \quad c_2 = 0. \tag{5.1.6}$$

Theorem 5.1.2. *If there are s vectors, $s \le m$, in the set of m vectors $\{\mathbf{x}_1, \mathbf{x}_2, \cdots, \mathbf{x}_m\}$ that are linearly dependent, then the entire set of m vectors is linearly dependent.*

Proof: Assume that the s linearly dependent vectors in the set are $\mathbf{x}_1, \mathbf{x}_2, \cdots, \mathbf{x}_s$. This implies that

$$c_1\mathbf{x}_1 + c_2\mathbf{x}_2 + \cdots + c_s\mathbf{x}_s = \mathbf{0}, \tag{5.1.7}$$

and not all c's are zero. The equation

$$c_1\mathbf{x}_1 + c_2\mathbf{x}_2 + \cdots + c_s\mathbf{x}_s + c_{s+1}\mathbf{x}_{s+1} + \cdots + c_m\mathbf{x}_m = \mathbf{0} \tag{5.1.8}$$

is satisfied if $c_{s+1} = c_{s+2} = \cdots = c_m = 0$, since at least one c_i, $i = 1, 2, \cdots, s$, is not zero. Hence, the entire set of m vectors is linearly dependent.

Theorem 5.1.3. *If the m vectors $\mathbf{x}_1, \mathbf{x}_2, \cdots, \mathbf{x}_m$ are linearly independent, while the set of $m + 1$ vectors $\{\mathbf{x}_1, \mathbf{x}_2, \cdots, \mathbf{x}_m, \mathbf{x}_{m+1}\}$ is linearly dependent, then $\mathbf{x}_{m+1}$ is expressible as a linear combination of $\mathbf{x}_1, \mathbf{x}_2, \cdots, \mathbf{x}_m$.*

The proof of this theorem is left as an exercise.

Section 1.11 showed how a matrix could be expressed in terms of row or column vectors. The $m \times n$ matrix having the m n-dimensional vectors $\mathbf{x}_1, \mathbf{x}_2, \cdots, \mathbf{x}_m$ as rows,

$$\begin{bmatrix} \mathbf{x}_1 \\ \mathbf{x}_2 \\ \vdots \\ \mathbf{x}_m \end{bmatrix} = \begin{bmatrix} [x_{11} & x_{12} & \cdots & x_{1n}] \\ [x_{21} & x_{22} & \cdots & x_{2n}] \\ \cdots & & & \\ [x_{m1} & x_{m2} & \cdots & x_{mn}] \end{bmatrix}, \tag{5.1.9}$$

is the *matrix of the vectors.*

Theorem 5.1.4. *A necessary and sufficient condition for the m n-dimensional vectors $\mathbf{x}_1, \mathbf{x}_2, \cdots, \mathbf{x}_m$ to be linearly dependent is that the rank r of the matrix of the vectors be less than the number of vectors m; that is, $r < m$.*

Proof: The proof of the necessary part of this theorem is not too difficult and is left as an exercise. The proof of the sufficient part is given below. The theorem states that the rank r of the matrix of the vectors, say $\mathbf{A}$, is less than the number of vectors: $r < m$. For convenience, assume that the rank of $\mathbf{A}$ is determined by the first r columns of $\mathbf{A}$, so that there is a non-zero determinant of order n in the first r columns. (Assuming otherwise merely makes the explanation more lengthy.)

By an interchange of vectors the rank of $\mathbf{A}$ is not changed; the rank of $\mathbf{E}_1\mathbf{A}$ is the same as the rank of $\mathbf{A}$, where $\mathbf{E}_1$ is the product of elementary row transformation matrices. Thus, by a proper choice of $\mathbf{E}_1$, the matrix in the upper left-hand corner is a nonsingular submatrix of order r.

By Theorem 3.6.7 we can perform elementary row transformations (say $\mathbf{E}_2$) on $\mathbf{E}_1\mathbf{A}$, such that

$$\mathbf{E}_2\mathbf{E}_1\mathbf{A} = \begin{bmatrix} \mathbf{I}_{r,r} & \mathbf{B}_{r,n-r} \\ \mathbf{C}_{m-r,r} & \mathbf{D}_{m-r,n-r} \end{bmatrix}.$$

By further elementary row transformations (say $\mathbf{E}_3$) the matrix $\mathbf{C}$ can be made to be zero. Then from $\mathbf{E}_3\mathbf{E}_2\mathbf{E}_1\mathbf{A}$ we see that $\mathbf{D}$ must also be a zero matrix, since otherwise the rank of $\mathbf{A}$ would be greater than r. Thus, by elementary row transformations only, the last $m - r$ rows can all be made to be zero. In other words, the last $m - r$ rows of $\mathbf{E}_1\mathbf{A}$ are linear combinations of the first r rows. Therefore, the entire set of row vectors is linearly dependent.

Theorem 5.1.5. *If the rank of the matrix of the m n-dimensional vectors, $\mathbf{x}_1, \mathbf{x}_2, \cdots, \mathbf{x}_m$, is r, and $r \leqq m$, then there exists a subset of r of these vectors that are linearly independent, while each of the remaining $m - r$ vectors is expressible as a linear combination of these r vectors.*

Proof: Assume that the rank of the matrix of the vectors in Eq. (5.1.9) is r, where $r \leqq m$ obviously. By elementary row operations of the first type (row interchanges), a matrix of vectors with the same rank r is obtained that has r linearly independent vectors in the first r rows. If the first r vectors were not linearly independent, then one of them could be expressed as a linear combination of the other $r - 1$, so that the rank of the matrix would be less than r. Thus there exist r vectors that are linearly independent. Furthermore, the other $m - r$ vectors are expressible as a linear combination of the first r; otherwise, choosing an additional vector from the last $m - r$ vectors as row $r + 1$ would make the rank of the matrix more than r.

Theorem 5.1.6. *For m n-dimensional vectors $\mathbf{x}_1, \mathbf{x}_2, \cdots, \mathbf{x}_m$, if $m > n$ then the m vectors are always linearly dependent.*

Proof: This result follows immediately from Theorem 5.1.5, since the maximum rank of the matrix of the vectors is n.

The preceding discussion dealt with the linear dependence and independence of *vectors*. If the word *vectors* is replaced in the discussion in this section by the words *matrices*, *equations*, or *functions*, then the statements, definitions, and theorems (except Theorems 5.1.4, 5.1.5, and 5.1.6, which deal with a matrix of vectors) hold equally well, with perhaps some minor obvious changes in sentence structure. For example, the set of functions of x $\{f_1, f_2, \cdots, f_m\}$ is *linearly dependent* over $\mathscr{F}$ provided that there exists a set of m scalars from $\mathscr{F}$ $\{c_1, c_2, \cdots, c_m\}$, not all zero, such that

$$c_1 f_1 + c_2 f_2 + \cdots + c_m f_m = 0. \tag{5.1.10}$$

If the m functions are not linearly dependent, they are *linearly independent.*

Throughout the remainder of this book we shall assume that the definitions of linear dependence and linear independence, as well as Theorems 5.1.1, 5.1.2, and 5.1.3, apply to matrices, functions, and equations as they do to vectors.

Example 5.1.4. Show that the functions x, e^x, xe^x, and $(2 - 3x)e^x$ are linearly dependent.

The sum $c_1 x + c_2 e^x + c_3 xe^x + c_4(2 - 3x)e^x$ can be rewritten as $c_1 x + (c_2 + 2c_4)e^x + (c_3 - 3c_4)xe^x$. Thus, any set of c's such that $c_1 = 0$, $c_2 = -2c_4$, and $c_3 = 3c_4$ meets the condition that the functions be linearly dependent. For example, two sets of c's that are not all zero are $\{0, -2, 3, 1\}$ and $\{0, 2, -3, -1\}$; any one set is sufficient to show linear dependence.

Example 5.1.5. Show that the equations

$$\begin{aligned} 2x + 3y \phantom{{}+3z} &= 4, \\ x - y + 3z &= 1, \\ 3x + 7y - 3z &= 7 \end{aligned}$$

are linearly dependent.

We first rewrite the equations as

$$\begin{aligned} \Phi_1 &\equiv 2x + 3y \phantom{{}-3z} - 4 = 0, \\ \Phi_2 &\equiv x - y + 3z - 1 = 0, \\ \Phi_3 &\equiv 3x + 7y - 3z - 7 = 0, \end{aligned}$$

and ask if there are c's, not all zero, such that

$$c_1 \Phi_1 + c_2 \Phi_2 + c_3 \Phi_3 \equiv 0.$$

This requires that

$$\begin{aligned} 2c_1 + c_2 + 3c_3 &= 0, \\ 3c_1 - c_2 + 7c_3 &= 0, \\ 3c_2 - 3c_3 &= 0, \\ -4c_1 - c_2 - 7c_3 &= 0. \end{aligned}$$

Any set of values $\{-2k, k, k\}$, k a scalar, will satisfy these equations.

Example 5.1.6. Show that the matrices **A**, **B**, and **C** are linearly independent if

$$\mathbf{A} = \begin{bmatrix} 2 & 0 \\ 1 & 3 \end{bmatrix}, \quad \mathbf{B} = \begin{bmatrix} 0 & 1 \\ 1 & 0 \end{bmatrix}, \quad \text{and} \quad \mathbf{C} = \begin{bmatrix} 1 & 1 \\ 0 & 1 \end{bmatrix}.$$

For $c_1\mathbf{A} + c_2\mathbf{B} + c_3\mathbf{C} = \mathbf{0}$ we must have

$$\begin{aligned} 2c_1 \qquad + c_3 &= 0, \\ c_2 + c_3 &= 0, \\ c_1 + c_2 \qquad &= 0, \\ 3c_1 \qquad + c_3 &= 0. \end{aligned}$$

From the first and last of these equations we see that $c_1 = c_3 = 0$ and from the second that $c_2 = 0$ also. Thus the matrices are linearly independent.

Exercises 5.1

1. Prove Theorem 5.1.3.
2. Complete the proof of Theorem 5.1.4.
3. For each of the following sets of vectors, show either that it is a linearly dependent set or that it is a linearly independent set.

   (a) $\{[2 \;\; 1 \;\; 2],\ [1 \;\; 2 \;\; 0],\ [-1 \;\; 1 \;\; 2]\}$
   (b) $\{[2 \;\; 1 \;\; 2],\ [1 \;\; 2 \;\; 0],\ [1 \;\; -1 \;\; 2]\}$
   (c) $\{[2 \;\; 0 \;\; 0],\ [0 \;\; 2 \;\; 0],\ [0 \;\; 0 \;\; 2],\ [1 \;\; 2 \;\; 3]\}$
   (d) $\{[0 \;\; 1 \;\; 0 \;\; 1],\ [1 \;\; -1 \;\; 0 \;\; 2],\ [1 \;\; 0 \;\; 0 \;\; 3]\}$
   (e) $\{[1 \;\; 0 \;\; 0 \;\; 0],\ [0 \;\; 1 \;\; 0 \;\; 0],\ [1 \;\; 1 \;\; 0 \;\; 0],\ [0 \;\; 0 \;\; 0 \;\; 1]\}$

4. For each of the vectors in exercise 3(e), find which vectors depend on the others. Write each such vector as a linear combination of the others.
5. For each of the following matrices, find the rank r, find r linearly independent rows, and write the other rows as linear combinations of these r rows.

   (a) $\begin{bmatrix} 1 & 2 & 0 \\ 0 & 1 & 0 \\ 2 & 0 & 1 \\ 3 & 4 & 5 \end{bmatrix}$ (b) $\begin{bmatrix} 1 & 2 & -1 & 0 \\ 0 & 1 & 1 & 2 \\ 2 & 3 & -1 & -2 \\ 1 & 4 & 1 & 4 \end{bmatrix}$

6. Verify that $\cos 2t$, $\sin 2t$, and $\cos(2t - a)$ are linearly dependent by presenting c's such that Eq. (5.1.10) is satisfied.
7. Determine whether the following equations are linearly dependent or independent.

$$\begin{aligned} 2x - \;\; y + \;\; z &= 3 \\ x + \;\; y - 2z &= 4 \\ -x + 2y + \;\; z &= 5 \end{aligned}$$

5.2. *Linear Vector Spaces*

Section 1.8 defined n-dimensional row and column vectors as $1 \times n$ and $n \times 1$ matrices respectively. In this book, unless we need to specify row vectors or column vectors, we merely use the term vector. The elements of the vectors and matrices can be any scalars (including complex numbers or complex-valued functions), even though the elements in our examples are generally real numbers (and usually integers).

In some instances the field from which the elements are chosen is important. For example, in Sections 4.4 and 4.5 in dealing with real quadratic forms and positive definite forms (and others), the elements are chosen from $\mathcal{F}_r$, the real number field. Whenever the elements must come from a particular field, the field will be specified.

The *n-dimensional vector space* over $\mathcal{F}$ is defined as the set of all n-dimensional vectors (row or column) for a fixed positive integer n whose elements are chosen from a field $\mathcal{F}$. This vector space is designated by $V_n(\mathcal{F})$, or simply by V_n if there is no question about the field from which the elements are chosen. Thus all n-dimensional row vectors $\mathbf{x}_i = [x_{i1}\ x_{i2}\ \cdots\ x_{in}]$ form an n-dimensional vector space V_n, and the set of all n-dimensional column vectors $\mathbf{y}_i = [y_{1i}\ y_{2i}\ \cdots\ y_{ni}]'$ forms another n-dimensional vector space V_n.

Under the definition of addition of vectors, with scalar elements chosen from a field $\mathcal{F}$, the following theorem follows readily from the definition of a linear space given in Section A.3. It is left as an exercise for the reader to verify that the defining properties for a linear space are satisfied and thus prove this theorem.

Theorem 5.2.1. *The n-dimensional vector space over $\mathcal{F}$ is a linear space.*

We now consider certain *linear subspaces* of the n-dimensional vector space over $\mathcal{F}$. That is, we want to consider a subspace of V_n which is a linear space with the addition and scalar multiplication defined as in V_n. Any linear subspace of V_n is called a *linear vector space* and is designated by V. The following theorem gives conditions under which a subset of V_n is a subspace of V_n.

Theorem 5.2.2. *A subset V of V_n is a linear vector space if the following two conditions are satisfied:*

(a) *If $\mathbf{x}$ is any vector in V, and c is any scalar in $\mathcal{F}$, then $c\mathbf{x}$ is also a vector in V.*

(b) *If $\mathbf{x}$ and $\mathbf{y}$ are any two vectors in V, then $\mathbf{x} + \mathbf{y}$ is also a vector in V.*

Proof: For a linear space, the vectors in the subset V must form an Abelian group under addition. The closure property is satisfied by condition (b). From the definition of the addition of matrices (and hence vectors), the associative and commutative properties are satisfied. The zero vector is an element of every linear vector space (since $\mathbf{x} + (-1)\mathbf{x} = \mathbf{0}$), and it is identity element under addition. The inverse under addition for any vector in the linear vector space is $(-1)\mathbf{x} = -\mathbf{x}$. Thus the vectors of a linear vector space form an Abelian group under addition.

Next conditions (1) through (5) of Eq. (A.3.1) must be satisfied. These are:
(1) $m\mathbf{x} = \mathbf{x}m$ must be an element of the set,
(2) $(m + n)\mathbf{x} = m\mathbf{x} + n\mathbf{x}$,
(3) $m(\mathbf{x} + \mathbf{y}) = m\mathbf{x} + m\mathbf{y}$,
(4) $m(n\mathbf{x}) = (mn)\mathbf{x} = (nm)\mathbf{x} = n(m\mathbf{x})$, and
(5) $1\mathbf{x} = \mathbf{x}$.

Condition (1) follows from condition (a) of the theorem, and conditions (2) through (5) are direct consequences of operations with scalars and matrices and of the definition of a linear vector space. Therefore, conditions (a) and (b) of Theorem 5.2.2 are sufficient for V to form a linear vector space (and hence a subspace of V_n).

Example 5.2.1. Consider the system of m homogeneous linear equations in n unknowns,

$$\begin{aligned} a_{11}x_1 + a_{12}x_2 + \cdots + a_{1n}x_n &= 0,\\ a_{21}x_1 + a_{22}x_2 + \cdots + a_{2n}x_n &= 0,\\ \cdots &\\ a_{m1}x_1 + a_{m2}x_2 + \cdots + a_{mn}x_n &= 0, \end{aligned} \tag{5.2.1}$$

or simply $\mathbf{Ax} = \mathbf{0}$ where the a_{ij} are from a field $\mathscr{F}$. A solution of $\mathbf{Ax} = \mathbf{0}$ requires a vector $\mathbf{c} = [c_1 \ c_2 \ \cdots \ c_n]'$, whose elements are in $\mathscr{F}$, such that

$$a_{i1}c_1 + a_{i2}c_2 + \cdots + a_{in}c_n = 0 \quad \text{for} \quad i = 1, 2, \cdots, m. \tag{5.2.2}$$

Prove that all such vectors $\mathbf{c}$ define a linear vector space over $\mathscr{F}$.

For vectors $\mathbf{c}$ that are solutions of Eq. (5.2.1) and for any scalar b in $\mathscr{F}$, $\mathbf{Ac} = \mathbf{0}$ and also $\mathbf{A}(b\mathbf{c}) = b(\mathbf{Ac}) = \mathbf{0}$, so condition (a) of Theorem 5.2.2 is satisfied. For vectors $\mathbf{c}$ and $\mathbf{d}$ satisfying $\mathbf{Ax} = \mathbf{0}$, condition (b) of Theorem 5.2.2 is satisfied because

$$\mathbf{A}(\mathbf{c} + \mathbf{d}) = \mathbf{Ac} + \mathbf{Ad} = \mathbf{0}$$

(from the distributive law for matrices). Thus the vectors that are solutions of $\mathbf{Ax} = \mathbf{0}$ define a linear vector space.

Theorem 5.2.3. *If* $\mathbf{x}_1, \mathbf{x}_2, \cdots, \mathbf{x}_m$ *are* m *vectors whose elements belong to* $\mathscr{F}$, *the set of all linear combinations*

$$c_1\mathbf{x}_1 + c_2\mathbf{x}_2 + \cdots + c_m\mathbf{x}_m, \tag{5.2.3}$$

for c_i *in* $\mathscr{F}$, *is a linear vector space.*

Proof: If $\mathbf{y}_1$ is a vector of the form of Eq. (5.2.3), then $b\mathbf{y}_1$ is also a vector of the same type for any b in $\mathscr{F}$, since the c_i in Eq. (5.2.3) have merely been replaced by bc_i. If $b_1\mathbf{x}_1 + b_2\mathbf{x}_2 + \cdots + b_m\mathbf{x}_m$ is a vector of the type of Eq. (5.2.3), then

$$\begin{aligned} &(c_1\mathbf{x}_1 + c_2\mathbf{x}_2 + \cdots + c_m\mathbf{x}_m) + (b_1\mathbf{x}_1 + b_2\mathbf{x}_2 + \cdots + b_m\mathbf{x}_m)\\ &= (c_1 + b_1)\mathbf{x}_1 + (c_2 + b_2)\mathbf{x}_2 + \cdots + (c_m + b_m)\mathbf{x}_m \end{aligned}$$

is also of the same type. Thus the two conditions for a linear vector space are satisfied, and the theorem is proved.

The vectors $\mathbf{x}_1, \mathbf{x}_2, \cdots, \mathbf{x}_m$ of Theorem 5.2.3 *span* or *generate* the linear vector space $\{\sum c_i \mathbf{x}_i\}$. That is, any vector in the space can be obtained by a finite sum of vectors. Note that the m vectors need not be linearly independent.

Theorem 5.2.4. *If the rank of the matrix of the vectors* $\mathbf{x}_1, \mathbf{x}_2, \cdots, \mathbf{x}_m$ *that span the vector space* V *is* r, *then there are* r *linearly independent vectors in the set such that every vector of* V *can be expressed uniquely as a linear combination of these* r *vectors.*

This theorem is essentially a restatement of Theorem 5.1.5, except for the *unique* representation of vectors of V. The proof of this part of the theorem is left as an exercise.

The r linearly independent vectors of Theorem 5.2.4 that span V form a *basis* of the linear vector space V; they are a *basis set of vectors* for the linear vector space V. That is, such a set of r vectors is sufficient to generate every other vector of the space. A set of basis vectors is not unique for a linear vector space V.

Example 5.2.2. Show that the set of vectors {[0 1 0], [0 0 1]}, as well as the set of vectors {[0 2 1], [0 1 3]}, spans the linear vector space V consisting of all 3-dimensional vectors whose first element is 0, so that each set forms a basis for V.

Any vector $[0\ a\ b]$ of V can be obtained from the first set, because

$$[0 \quad a \quad b] = a[0 \quad 1 \quad 0] + b[0 \quad 0 \quad 1].$$

For the second set,

$$[0 \quad 2 \quad 1] = 2[0 \quad 1 \quad 0] + 1[0 \quad 0 \quad 1], \quad \text{and}$$
$$[0 \quad 1 \quad 3] = 1[0 \quad 1 \quad 0] + 3[0 \quad 0 \quad 1],$$

so

$$\begin{aligned}[0 \quad a \quad b] &= c[0 \quad 2 \quad 1] + d[0 \quad 1 \quad 3] \\ &= c\{2[0 \quad 1 \quad 0] + 1[0 \quad 0 \quad 1]\} \\ &\quad + d\{1[0 \quad 1 \quad 0] + 3[0 \quad 0 \quad 1]\}.\end{aligned}$$

Thus

$$a = 2c + d \quad \text{and}$$
$$b = c + 3d,$$

or

$$c = -b/5 + 3a/5 \quad \text{and}$$
$$d = -a/5 + 2b/5.$$

Thus every vector of V can be obtained from either set of basis vectors. Furthermore, since [0 1 0] is not a multiple of [0 0 1], and, since [0 2 1] is not a multiple of [0 1 3], the vectors in each set are linearly independent vectors. The rank of the matrix of the vectors in each instance is 2, since

$$\begin{bmatrix} 0 & 1 & 0 \\ 0 & 0 & 1 \end{bmatrix} \quad \text{and} \quad \begin{bmatrix} 0 & 2 & 1 \\ 0 & 1 & 3 \end{bmatrix}$$

each have rank 2.

Theorem 5.2.5. *If the linear vector space V is spanned by a set of m n-dimensional vectors, and if the matrix of these vectors is of rank r, then any set of $r + 1$ vectors of V is linearly dependent.*

Proof: If $r + 1$ vectors of V were linearly independent, then the rank of the matrix of these vectors would be $r + 1$ instead of r. Since this is contrary to Theorem 5.1.5, no more than r vectors can be linearly independent. Thus any set of $r + 1$ vectors must be linearly dependent.

If the rank of the matrix of the n-dimensional vectors $\mathbf{x}_1, \mathbf{x}_2, \cdots, \mathbf{x}_m$ over $\mathscr{F}$ is r, then the vector space V spanned by these vectors is of *dimension* r, or the *order* of the linear vector space is r. By Theorem 5.2.4, the dimension of a linear vector space is unique; it is precisely the maximum number of linearly independent vectors in the space.

Since it can be shown (number 1 of Exercises 5.2) that $V_n(\mathscr{F})$ is a linear vector space over $\mathscr{F}$, and since the set of n n-dimensional vectors $\mathbf{e}_1 = [1 \ 0 \ \cdots \ 0]$, $\mathbf{e}_2 = [0 \ 1 \ \cdots \ 0]$, $\cdots$, $\mathbf{e}_n = [0 \ 0 \ \cdots \ 1]$ is linearly independent, the set $\mathbf{e}_1, \mathbf{e}_2, \cdots, \mathbf{e}_n$ can be chosen as a basis for V_n. These n basis vectors clearly span V_n because any vector of V_n can be written as a linear combination of them.

Exercises 5.2

1. Prove that $V_n(\mathscr{F})$ is a linear vector space over $\mathscr{F}$.
2. Prove that every vector of a linear vector space V can be expressed *uniquely* as a linear combination of the r linearly independent vectors that span V. That is, prove the last part of Theorem 5.2.4.
3. Find a set of vectors which span the solution set of

$$\text{(a)}\quad \begin{aligned} x + 3y + z &= 0 \\ x - 2y \qquad &= 0 \\ 5y + z &= 0 \end{aligned} \qquad\qquad \text{(b)}\quad \begin{aligned} x + 3y - w &= 0 \\ x - \quad z + w &= 0 \\ x + \ y \qquad &= 0 \end{aligned}$$

4. Find r linearly independent vectors that span the space of the rows of

$$\begin{bmatrix} 1 & 2 & 0 & 1 \\ -1 & 0 & 2 & 1 \\ 1 & 4 & 2 & 2 \\ 0 & 2 & 2 & 1 \\ 1 & 8 & 6 & 4 \end{bmatrix}.$$

5. Find a basis for the space spanned by the rows of

$$\begin{bmatrix} 1 & \pi & 0 & \pi \\ 2 & \sqrt{3} & 0 & \sqrt{3} \\ 0 & 0 & 1 & 0 \\ 2\sqrt{3} & 3 & 3 & 3 \end{bmatrix}.$$

6. Show that the Pauli spin matrices and the identity matrix are linearly independent. (See number 4 of Exercises 1.4.) Do they form a basis for 2×2 matrices over the complex number field?

5.3. Cramer's Rule

In Section 2.11 we derived Cramer's rule by two methods. Since we can now determine the inverse of a matrix, we consider a third method by which this rule may be derived, before considering the general case of m equations in n unknowns.

We write our system of n linear equations in n unknowns in matrix notation as

(5.3.1) $$\mathbf{Ax} = \mathbf{c},$$

where $\mathbf{A}$ is a nonsingular matrix of order n, and $\mathbf{x}$ and $\mathbf{c}$ are column vectors. Since $\mathbf{A}$ is nonsingular, it has an inverse, and we can write

(5.3.2) $$\mathbf{x} = \mathbf{A}^{-1}\mathbf{c} = \frac{\text{adj } \mathbf{A}}{\det \mathbf{A}}\,\mathbf{c}.$$

Substituting $\mathbf{x} = \mathbf{A}^{-1}\mathbf{c}$ into Eq. (5.3.1), we get

(5.3.3) $$\mathbf{AA}^{-1}\mathbf{c} = \mathbf{Ic} = \mathbf{c},$$

thus, the $\mathbf{x}$ given by Eq. (5.3.2) satisfies Eq. (5.3.1).

In expanded form Eq. (5.3.2) is

(5.3.4) $$\begin{bmatrix} x_1 \\ x_2 \\ \vdots \\ x_n \end{bmatrix} = \frac{1}{\det \mathbf{A}} \begin{bmatrix} A_{11} & A_{21} & \cdots & A_{n1} \\ A_{12} & A_{22} & \cdots & A_{n2} \\ \cdots & & & \\ A_{1n} & A_{2n} & \cdots & A_{nn} \end{bmatrix} \begin{bmatrix} c_1 \\ c_2 \\ \vdots \\ c_n \end{bmatrix}$$

$$= \frac{1}{\det \mathbf{A}} \begin{bmatrix} c_1 A_{11} + c_2 A_{21} + \cdots + c_n A_{n1} \\ c_1 A_{12} + c_2 A_{22} + \cdots + c_n A_{n2} \\ \cdots \\ c_1 A_{1n} + c_2 A_{2n} + \cdots + c_n A_{nn} \end{bmatrix}.$$

This means that

(5.3.5) $$x_i = \frac{1}{\det \mathbf{A}}(c_1 A_{1i} + c_2 A_{2i} + \cdots + c_n A_{ni}) = \frac{\det \mathbf{K}_i}{\det \mathbf{A}},$$

where $\mathbf{K}_i$ is defined by Eq. (2.11.4). Observe that this result is precisely the same as that obtained in Section 2.11.

We now prove the following uniqueness theorem:

Theorem 5.3.1 *A system of n equations in n unknowns has a unique solution if the rank of the coefficient matrix is n.*

Proof: By Eq. (5.3.3), the vector $\mathbf{x}$ in Eq. (5.3.2) is a solution of $\mathbf{Ax} = \mathbf{c}$. Assume that there is a second solution, $\mathbf{y}$, so that

$$\mathbf{Ax} = \mathbf{c} \qquad \text{and also} \qquad \mathbf{Ay} = \mathbf{c}.$$

By the equality of matrices $\mathbf{Ax} = \mathbf{Ay}$; since $\mathbf{A}$ is nonsingular, $\mathbf{x} = \mathbf{y}$ and $\mathbf{x}$ is unique.

If the vector $\mathbf{c}$ in Eq. (5.3.1) is the zero vector, then the equation is *homogeneous*, and the system is a *system of linear homogeneous equations.* If at least one of the elements in $\mathbf{c}$ is non-zero, then $\mathbf{Ax} = \mathbf{c}$ is *nonhomogeneous*, and the system is a *system of linear nonhomogeneous equations.*

The equation $\mathbf{Ax} = \mathbf{0}$ always has the *trivial solution* $\mathbf{x} = \mathbf{0}$ whether $\mathbf{A}$ is singular or nonsingular. That is, a system of homogeneous linear equations always has the trivial solution. The preceding theorem shows that $\mathbf{x} = \mathbf{0}$ is the *only* solution if $\mathbf{A}$ is nonsingular. The next section considers possible nontrivial solutions to $\mathbf{Ax} = \mathbf{0}$ if $\mathbf{A}$ is singular.

Exercises 5.3

1. Solve the system of equations

$$\begin{aligned} 7x + 6y + 4z &= 6 \\ 4x - 3y - z &= 0 \\ -5x - 4y + z &= 7 \end{aligned}$$

by the method described in this section.

2. Show that $\mathbf{y} = [6 \ \ -2 \ \ -2]'$ and also $\mathbf{x} = [-3 \ \ 1 \ \ 1]'$ are nontrivial solutions of $\mathbf{Ax} = \mathbf{0}$ if

$$\mathbf{A} = \begin{bmatrix} 1 & 2 & 1 \\ 3 & -1 & 10 \\ 2 & 3 & 3 \end{bmatrix}.$$

3. Solve $\mathbf{Ax} = \mathbf{c}$ if

$$\mathbf{A} = \begin{bmatrix} 2 & 1 & 2 \\ 1 & 2 & 3 \\ 3 & 1 & 2 \end{bmatrix}$$

and if

(a) $\mathbf{c}' = [1 \ \ 0 \ \ 2]$, (b) $\mathbf{c}' = [0 \ \ 4 \ \ -2]$, (c) $\mathbf{c} = \mathbf{0}$.

4. Use Cramer's rule to solve for three of the unknowns in terms of the fourth in

$$\begin{aligned} 3x + y - z + w &= 1 \\ x + y + 3z - 2w &= 6 \\ 3y + z - 2w &= 0. \end{aligned}$$

Find two sets of values of the unknowns to show that the solution is not unique.

5.4. Systems of Linear Equations

Sections 2.11 and 5.3 showed how a system of n linear equations in n unknowns $\mathbf{Ax} = \mathbf{c}$ could be solved for a unique vector $\mathbf{x}$ that satisfied the equation, provided that $\mathbf{A}$ is nonsingular, by using Cramer's rule. We now consider the various cases arising when we have m equations in n unknowns with $m \neq n$, or when $\mathbf{A}$ is singular when $m = n$.

If the system of equations

$$\mathbf{A}_{m,n}\mathbf{x} = \mathbf{c} \tag{5.4.1}$$

has solutions, all such solutions can be obtained by the method of *successive elimination*. This method consists of eliminating various unknown x_i's of the vector $\mathbf{x}$ in turn, so that some of the x_i's can be written in terms of the others. Although this method (from elementary algebra) uses no matrix theory as such, we could prove by using it that the system of Eq. (5.4.1) has either

(5.4.2)
(i) no solutions,
(ii) one and only one solution, or
(iii) infinitely many solutions.

Note that if Eq. (5.4.1) has more than one solution, it cannot have a finite number of different solutions.

Section 4.1 gave examples of the possibilities of Eq. (5.4.2): Example 4.1.1 illustrates (ii), Example 4.1.2 illustrates (iii), and Example 4.1.3 illustrates (i).

The matrix $\mathbf{A}_{m,n}$ in Eq. (5.4.1) is called the *matrix of the coefficients*. The matrix of order $m \times (n+1)$

$$\mathbf{M} = \begin{bmatrix} a_{11} & a_{12} & \cdots & a_{1n} & c_1 \\ a_{21} & a_{22} & \cdots & a_{2n} & c_2 \\ \cdots \\ a_{m1} & a_{m2} & \cdots & a_{mn} & c_m \end{bmatrix} \tag{5.4.3}$$

that is obtained by adjoining one more column to $\mathbf{A}$, the vector $\mathbf{c}$, is called the *augmented matrix* $\mathbf{M}$.

Theorem 5.4.1. *A necessary and sufficient condition that a set of m linear equations in n unknowns, Eq.* (5.4.1), *be solvable is that the rank of the coefficient matrix* $\mathbf{A}$ *be equal to the rank of the augmented matrix* $\mathbf{M}$.

Proof: If we write $\mathbf{A}$ as a matrix of column vectors

$$\mathbf{A} = [\mathbf{v}_1 \quad \mathbf{v}_2 \quad \cdots \quad \mathbf{v}_n], \tag{5.4.4}$$

where $\mathbf{v}_i' = [a_{1i} \; a_{2i} \; \cdots \; a_{mi}]$, then Eq. (5.4.1) can be written as

$$x_1\mathbf{v}_1 + x_2\mathbf{v}_2 + \cdots + x_n\mathbf{v}_n = \mathbf{c}. \tag{5.4.5}$$

If r is the rank of $\mathbf{A}$, it follows from Theorems 5.2.4 and 5.2.5 that exactly r of the vectors $\mathbf{v}_i$ are linearly independent. In addition, every vector of the linear vector space V that is spanned by the $\mathbf{v}_i$'s is expressible as a linear combination of these r vectors. Consequently, if the vector $\mathbf{c}$ belongs to v, then the augmented matrix $\mathbf{M}$ must have rank r. That is, $\mathbf{A}$ and $\mathbf{M}$ must have the same rank for there to be a set of x_i's satisfying Eq. (5.4.5).

Conversely, if the rank of $\mathbf{M}$ is r (the rank of $\mathbf{A}$), then the vector $\mathbf{c}$ belongs to V (see Theorem 5.1.4), the linear vector space spanned by the $\mathbf{v}_i$'s. Therefore, Eq. (5.4.1) is solvable; there exists a set of x_i's such that Eq. (5.4.5) is satisfied.

Observe that the preceding theorem is an existence theorem; it does not provide an algorithm telling us how to determine vectors $\mathbf{x}$ satisfying Eq. (5.4.1) in the same manner as Cramer's rule did for a nonsingular coefficient matrix. It merely tells us that if $\mathbf{A}$ and $\mathbf{M}$ have different ranks, we need not look for solutions. Although the method of successive elimination always works, the following method may be easier to apply.

After determining that the coefficient matrix $\mathbf{A}$ and the augmented matrix $\mathbf{M}$ have the same rank r, $r \leqq n$, rewrite the m equations as

$$\begin{aligned} g_1(\mathbf{x}) &\equiv a_{11}x_1 + a_{12}x_2 + \cdots + a_{1n}x_n - c_1 = 0, \\ g_2(\mathbf{x}) &\equiv a_{21}x_1 + a_{22}x_2 + \cdots + a_{2n}x_n - c_2 = 0, \\ &\cdots \\ g_m(\mathbf{x}) &\equiv a_{m1}x_1 + a_{m2}x_2 + \cdots + a_{mn}x_n - c_m = 0. \end{aligned} \tag{5.4.6}$$

or

$$G(\mathbf{x}) = \begin{bmatrix} g_1(\mathbf{x}) \\ \cdots \\ g_m(\mathbf{x}) \end{bmatrix} = \mathbf{My} = \mathbf{0}, \quad \text{where} \tag{5.4.7}$$

$$\mathbf{y} = \begin{bmatrix} \mathbf{x} \\ \hline -\mathbf{I}_1 \end{bmatrix}.$$

We then seek a system of equations equivalent to Eq. (5.4.6) but in simplified form, such as one in which all of the coefficients of the x_i in some equations are equal to zero except one, say x_k. *Equivalent systems of equations* are systems of equations that have identical sets of solutions. The following theorem enables us to obtain a simplified system of equations:

Theorem 5.4.2. *Any vector* $\mathbf{y}$ *satisfying* $\mathbf{My} = \mathbf{0}$ *of Eq.* (5.4.7) *also satisfies the equivalent system of equations* $\mathbf{HMy} = \mathbf{0}$, *where* $\mathbf{H}$ *is any nonsingular matrix for which the multiplication is defined.*

Proof: Any vector **y** satisfying Eq. (5.4.7) will also satisfy $\mathbf{EMy} = \mathbf{0}$ where **E** is any elementary matrix. Similarly, if **H** is any nonsingular matrix, and hence the product of elementary matrices, then $\mathbf{HMy} = \mathbf{0}$ also gives an equivalent system of equations.

Since multiplying **M** on the left by **H** in $\mathbf{HMy} = \mathbf{0}$ performs row transformations only on **M**, the set of equations in Eq. (5.4.6) is probably altered, but the set of vectors **x** satisfying one system satisfies the other. Specifically if

$$\mathbf{H} = \begin{bmatrix} 1 & 0 & & \cdots & & 0 \\ 0 & 1 & & \cdots & & 0 \\ \cdots \\ \lambda_1 & \lambda_2 & \cdots & \lambda_k & \cdots & \lambda_m \\ \cdots \\ 0 & 0 & & \cdots & & 1 \end{bmatrix},$$

where the λ_i are scalars in the kth row and $\lambda_k \neq 0$, we have the system of equations

$$\begin{aligned} & g_1(\mathbf{x}) = 0, \\ & g_2(\mathbf{x}) = 0, \\ & \cdots \\ & \lambda_1 g_1(\mathbf{x}) + \cdots + \lambda_k g_k(\mathbf{x}) + \cdots + \lambda_m g_m(\mathbf{x}) = 0, \\ & \cdots \\ & g_m(\mathbf{x}) = 0, \end{aligned} \tag{5.4.8}$$

which is equivalent to the system in Eq. (5.4.6). Note that if $\lambda_k = 0$ the new system may not be equivalent to the old one.

Even if the $g_i(\mathbf{x})$ of Eq. (5.4.6) are considered as expressions in **x** in general instead of as linear expressions in the components of **x**, then the solutions of $g_1(\mathbf{x}) = 0, \cdots, g_m(\mathbf{x}) = 0$ are still the same as the solutions of the set of equations corresponding to Eq. (5.4.8).

If we write Eq. (5.4.6) as $\mathbf{Ax} = \mathbf{c}$, then, in a manner similar to that used in Section 4.1, we can premultiply **A** by a nonsingular matrix **B** such that the product $\mathbf{BA} = \mathbf{D}$ is in one of the forms

$$\mathbf{D} = \begin{bmatrix} d_{11} & d_{12} & \cdots & d_{1m} & \cdots & d_{1n} \\ 0 & d_{22} & \cdots & d_{2m} & \cdots & d_{2n} \\ \cdots \\ 0 & 0 & \cdots & d_{mm} & \cdots & d_{mn} \end{bmatrix} \quad \text{if} \quad n \geqq m, \quad \text{or} \tag{5.4.9}$$

$$\mathbf{D} = \begin{bmatrix} d_{11} & d_{12} & \cdots & d_{1n} \\ 0 & d_{21} & \cdots & d_{2n} \\ \cdots \\ 0 & 0 & \cdots & d_{nn} \\ 0 & 0 & \cdots & 0 \\ \cdots \\ 0 & 0 & \cdots & 0 \end{bmatrix} \quad \text{if} \quad n < m. \tag{5.4.10}$$

In **D** the elements below each d_{kk} are all zero and the elements d_{kk} are zero or one. We can stop at this point, or we can continue to premultiply by elementary row transformation matrices to get a matrix **D** with elements above a $d_{kk} = 1$ that are all zero; the elements above a $d_{kk} = 0$ may or may not be zero.

Since premultiplying **A** by a nonsingular matrix **B** performs elementary row operations on **A**, premultiplying on both sides of $\mathbf{Ax} = \mathbf{c}$ performs the same row operations on **c**. If $\mathbf{Ax} = \mathbf{c}$ has a solution (that is, if the ranks of the coefficient matrix **A** and the augmented matrix **M** are the same in accordance with Theorem 5.4.1), then $\mathbf{BAx} = \mathbf{Dx} = \mathbf{Bc}$. Solutions for the equations can be found readily.*

Example 5.4.1. Solve the following system of equations.

$$\begin{aligned} x + \ y + z - u + \ v &= 1 \\ y - z + u - 4v &= 0 \\ 2x \qquad + z \qquad + 2v &= 3 \\ x + 2y \qquad\qquad - 3v &= 1. \end{aligned}$$

The coefficient matrix clearly has rank 3, and the augmented matrix **M** also had rank 3; thus the system has solutions. If **B** is chosen as a product of elementary matrices $\mathbf{B}_1, \mathbf{B}_2, \cdots, \mathbf{B}_5$ such that $\mathbf{B} = \mathbf{B}_5 \cdots \mathbf{B}_2 \mathbf{B}_1$, where

$$\mathbf{B}_1 = \begin{bmatrix} 1 & 0 & 0 & 0 \\ 0 & 1 & 0 & 0 \\ -2 & 0 & 1 & 0 \\ 0 & 0 & 0 & 1 \end{bmatrix}, \quad \mathbf{B}_2 = \begin{bmatrix} 1 & 0 & 0 & 0 \\ 0 & 1 & 0 & 0 \\ 0 & 0 & 1 & 0 \\ -1 & 0 & 0 & 1 \end{bmatrix},$$

$$\mathbf{B}_3 = \begin{bmatrix} 1 & 0 & 0 & 0 \\ 0 & 1 & 0 & 0 \\ 0 & 2 & 1 & 0 \\ 0 & 0 & 0 & 1 \end{bmatrix}, \quad \mathbf{B}_4 = \begin{bmatrix} 1 & 0 & 0 & 0 \\ 0 & 1 & 0 & 0 \\ 0 & 0 & 1 & 0 \\ 0 & -1 & 0 & 1 \end{bmatrix},$$

$$\mathbf{B}_5 = \begin{bmatrix} 1 & 0 & 0 & 0 \\ 0 & 1 & 0 & 0 \\ 0 & 0 & -1/3 & 0 \\ 0 & 0 & 0 & 1 \end{bmatrix},$$

$$\text{then} \quad \mathbf{BA} = \begin{bmatrix} 1 & 0 & 0 & 0 \\ 0 & 1 & 0 & 0 \\ 2/3 & -2/3 & -1/3 & 0 \\ -1 & -1 & 0 & 1 \end{bmatrix} \begin{bmatrix} 1 & 1 & 1 & -1 & 1 \\ 0 & 1 & -1 & 1 & -4 \\ 2 & 0 & 1 & 0 & 2 \\ 1 & 2 & 0 & 0 & -3 \end{bmatrix}$$

$$= \begin{bmatrix} 1 & 1 & 1 & -1 & 1 \\ 0 & 1 & -1 & 1 & -4 \\ 0 & 0 & 1 & -4/3 & 8/3 \\ 0 & 0 & 0 & 0 & 0 \end{bmatrix} = \mathbf{D}$$

*The procedure described here is referred to as the *Gaussian elimination process* or *Gauss reduction*, named after the German mathematician Karl Friedrich Gauss (1777–1855).

$$\text{and}\quad \mathbf{Dx} = \mathbf{Bc} = \begin{bmatrix} 1 & 0 & 0 & 0 \\ 0 & 1 & 0 & 0 \\ 2/3 & -2/3 & -1/3 & 0 \\ -1 & -1 & 0 & 1 \end{bmatrix} \begin{bmatrix} 1 \\ 0 \\ 3 \\ 1 \end{bmatrix} = \begin{bmatrix} 1 \\ 0 \\ -1/3 \\ 0 \end{bmatrix}.$$

Thus we have an equivalent system of equations

$$\begin{aligned} x + y + z - \quad u + \quad v &= 1 \\ y - z + \quad u - \quad 4v &= 0 \\ z - 4/3u + 8/3v &= -1/3. \end{aligned}$$

For an arbitrary choice of u and v, values for x, y, and z are readily determined. For instance, if $u = 3$ and $v = 1$, then $z = 1$, $y = 2$, and $x = 0$.

Using Theorem 5.4.2, we can simplify the method for finding solutions to the system of equations in Eq. (5.4.6). We first reorder the equations in Eq. (5.4.6) so that the matrix of the coefficients of the x_i for the first r equations is of rank r, using the proper matrix $\mathbf{H}$ in Theorem 5.4.2. Thus, the following system of equations is equivalent to Eq. (5.4.6) (the primes merely indicate a rearrangement of equations):

$$\begin{aligned} g_1'(\mathbf{x}) &\equiv a_{11}'x_1 + a_{12}'x_2 + \cdots + a_{1n}'x_n - c_1' = 0, \\ g_2'(\mathbf{x}) &\equiv a_{21}'x_1 + a_{22}'x_2 + \cdots + a_{2n}'x_n - c_2' = 0, \\ &\cdots \\ g_r'(\mathbf{x}) &\equiv a_{r1}'x_1 + a_{r2}'x_2 + \cdots + a_{rn}'x_n - c_r' = 0, \\ &\cdots \\ g_m'(\mathbf{x}) &\equiv a_{m1}'x_1 + a_{m2}'x_2 + \cdots + a_{mn}'x_n - c_m' = 0; \end{aligned} \tag{5.4.11}$$

the rank of the coefficient matrix in Eq. (5.4.11) is determined by the first r equations.

The augmented matrix for Eq. (5.4.11) then becomes

$$\mathbf{M}' = \begin{bmatrix} a_{11}' & a_{12}' & \cdots & a_{1n}' & c_1' \\ a_{21}' & a_{22}' & \cdots & a_{2n}' & c_2' \\ \cdots \\ a_{r1}' & a_{r2}' & \cdots & a_{rn}' & c_r' \\ a_{r+1,1}' & a_{r+1,2}' & \cdots & a_{r+1,n}' & c_{r+1}' \\ \cdots \\ a_{m1}' & a_{m2}' & \cdots & a_{mn}' & c_m' \end{bmatrix}, \quad \text{or} \tag{5.4.12}$$

$$\mathbf{M}' = \begin{bmatrix} \mathbf{u}_1 \\ \mathbf{u}_2 \\ \cdots \\ \mathbf{u}_r \\ \mathbf{u}_{r+1} \\ \cdots \\ \mathbf{u}_m \end{bmatrix}$$

when written as a column vector of row vectors $\mathbf{u}_i$. Since the rank of $\mathbf{M}$ (and hence of $\mathbf{M}'$, which is not the transpose of $\mathbf{M}$) is r, the first r vectors $\mathbf{u}_1, \mathbf{u}_2, \cdots, \mathbf{u}_r$ are linearly independent. Then, by Theorem 5.1.5, the final $m - r$ vectors $\mathbf{u}_{r+1}, \cdots \mathbf{u}_m$ are expressible as linear combinations of the first r vectors.

This result from Eq. (5.4.12) implies in Eq. (5.4.11) that there exist constants c_{ij} such that

$$g_j'(\mathbf{x}) = c_{1j} g_1'(\mathbf{x}) + c_{2j} g_2'(\mathbf{x}) + \cdots + c_{rj} g_r'(x) \tag{5.4.13}$$

for $j = r + 1, r + 2, \cdots, m$. If a vector $\mathbf{x}$ satisfies the first r equations of Eq. (5.4.11), it also satisfies the final $m - r$ equations. That is, the system of equations in Eq. (5.4.6) is equivalent to the system consisting of the first r equations of Eq. (5.4.11), since the two systems have identical sets of solutions.

The final step is to determine a vector $\mathbf{x}$ that satisfies Eq. (5.4.11), and hence Eq. (5.4.6). We rewrite the first r equations of Eq. (5.4.11) so that terms involving r of the unknown x_i's (the determinant of whose coefficients is different from zero) are on the left, and the remaining terms are on the right. We then use Cramer's rule to solve for the r unknown x_i's in terms of the remaining $n - r$ unknowns.

Unless the coefficient matrix and the augmented matrix have the same rank, no solution is possible. If these matrices have the same rank and if $n = r$, then one solution is obtained; if $n > r$, an infinite number of solutions result. These observations are all in accordance with Eq. (5.4.2).

Example 5.4.2. First determine whether the following system of equations has a solution. If it does have a solution, determine all possible solutions.

$$\begin{aligned} x_1 + x_2 + x_3 + 2x_4 &= 4 \\ 2x_1 + 3x_2 + x_3 + 3x_4 &= 7 \\ x_2 - x_3 - x_4 &= -1 \\ x_1 + 2x_2 + x_4 &= 3. \end{aligned}$$

Both the matrix of the coefficients $\mathbf{A}$ and the augmented matrix $\mathbf{M}$ have rank 2, where

$$\mathbf{A} = \begin{bmatrix} 1 & 1 & 1 & 2 \\ 2 & 3 & 1 & 3 \\ 0 & 1 & -1 & -1 \\ 1 & 2 & 0 & 1 \end{bmatrix} \quad \text{and} \quad \mathbf{M} = \begin{bmatrix} 1 & 1 & 1 & 2 & 4 \\ 2 & 3 & 1 & 3 & 7 \\ 0 & 1 & -1 & -1 & -1 \\ 1 & 2 & 0 & 1 & 3 \end{bmatrix}.$$

Thus solutions exist for the system of equations. Since $r = 2$, and since the submatrix

$$\begin{bmatrix} 1 & 1 \\ 2 & 3 \end{bmatrix}$$

in the upper left-hand corner of **A** is nonsingular, we use only the first two equations, and rewrite them as

$$x_1 + x_2 = 4 - x_3 - 2x_4$$
$$2x_1 + 3x_2 = 7 - x_3 - 3x_4 .$$

By Cramer's rule,

$$x_1 = 5 - 2x_3 - 3x_4 .$$
$$x_2 = -1 + x_3 + x_4 .$$

For each pair of values for x_3 and x_4, values for x_1 and x_2 are obtained, so there is an infinite set of 4-dimensional vectors **x** that satisfy the system of equations.

Exercises 5.4

1. Determine if the following systems of equations have solutions, and, if so, find all possible solutions.

(a)
$$\begin{aligned} x_1 + x_2 + x_3 &= 4 \\ x_1 - x_2 - x_3 &= 7 \end{aligned}$$

(b)
$$\begin{aligned} x_1 + x_2 + x_3 &= 4 \\ x_1 - x_2 - x_3 &= 7 \\ 3x_1 + x_2 + x_3 &= 15 \\ x_1 + 3x_2 + 3x_3 &= 1 \end{aligned}$$

(c)
$$\begin{aligned} x_1 + x_2 &= 5 \\ x_2 + x_3 &= 7 \\ x_1 + x_3 &= 9 \end{aligned}$$

(d)
$$\begin{aligned} x_1 + x_2 + x_3 &= 4 \\ 2x_1 - x_3 &= 0 \\ 3x_1 + x_2 &= 2 \end{aligned}$$

(e)
$$\begin{aligned} x_1 + x_2 + x_3 &= 0 \\ x_1 - x_2 + 2x_3 - x_4 &= 1 \\ 2x_1 + 3x_3 - x_4 &= 2 \\ x_1 + x_3 + x_4 &= 1 \end{aligned}$$

2. Prove the theorem: *If the coefficient matrix of a system of n linear equations in n unknowns has rank n, then the system has a solution.*

3. Verify the assertion in the paragraph following Eq. (5.4.8) for the pairs of equations:

(a) $g_1(\mathbf{x}) \equiv x_1^2 + x_2^2 - 4 = 0$ and $g_2(\mathbf{x}) \equiv x_1^2 - 3x_2^2 = 0$, using $\lambda_1 = 1$, $\lambda_2 = -1$.

(b) $g_1(\mathbf{x}) \equiv 4x_1^2 + 9x_2^2 - 36 = 0$ and $g_2(\mathbf{x}) \equiv 9x_1^2 + 4x_2^2 - 36 = 0$, using $\lambda_1 = 1$, $\lambda_2 = -1$.

Make a sketch in the x_1x_2-plane and explain the results in each case.

4. Prove the theorem: *If the system* $\mathbf{Ax} = \mathbf{b}$ *has a solution and* **A** *and* **b** *are real, then the solution* **x** *is real.*

5.5. Systems of Linear Homogeneous Equations

Consider the system of linear homogeneous equations

$$\begin{aligned} a_{11}x_1 + a_{12}x_2 + \cdots + a_{1n}x_n &= 0 \\ a_{21}x_1 + a_{22}x_2 + \cdots + a_{2n}x_n &= 0 \\ \cdots \\ a_{m1}x_1 + a_{m2}x_2 + \cdots + a_{mn}x_n &= 0, \end{aligned} \tag{5.5.1}$$

where the a_{ij} are known scalars from some field $\mathscr{F}$. The system Eq. (5.5.1) may be written more compactly as

$$\mathbf{Ax} = \mathbf{0}, \tag{5.5.2}$$

where $\mathbf{x}$ is the unknown n-dimensional vector. By Theorem 5.4.1 the system has a solution, since the ranks of the coefficient matrix and of the augmented matrix are necessarily the same.

The *trivial solution*, the vector $\mathbf{x} = [0 \ 0 \ \cdots \ 0]'$, clearly satisfies *any* system of homogeneous equations $\mathbf{Ax} = \mathbf{0}$. This section specifies the conditions under which nontrivial solutions exist, and provides methods by which such nontrivial solutions can be found.

The system of equations in Eq. (5.5.1) is the same as that in Example 5.2.1. As proved there, the vectors that are solutions of $\mathbf{Ax} = \mathbf{0}$ define a linear vector space. This vector space is denoted by S and is the *solution space* of the set of equations in Eq. (5.5.1).

The *dimension* of the vector space S is equal to the maximum number of linearly independent vectors in the space. From Theorem 3.6.8 if $\mathbf{A}$ is an $m \times n$ matrix of rank r, and if $\mathbf{X}$ is an $n \times q$ matrix such that

$$\begin{bmatrix} a_{11} & a_{12} & \cdots & a_{1n} \\ a_{21} & a_{22} & \cdots & a_{2n} \\ \cdots \\ a_{m1} & a_{m2} & \cdots & a_{mn} \end{bmatrix} \begin{bmatrix} x_{11} & x_{12} & \cdots & x_{1q} \\ x_{21} & x_{22} & \cdots & x_{2q} \\ \cdots \\ x_{n1} & x_{n2} & \cdots & x_{nq} \end{bmatrix} = \begin{bmatrix} 0 & 0 & \cdots & 0 \\ 0 & 0 & \cdots & 0 \\ \cdots \\ 0 & 0 & \cdots & 0 \end{bmatrix}, \tag{5.5.3}$$

or simply

$$\mathbf{AX} = \mathbf{0}, \tag{5.5.4}$$

then the rank of $\mathbf{X}$ cannot exceed $n - r$. Furthermore, a matrix $\mathbf{X}$ of rank $n - r$ exists such that Eq. (5.5.4) is satisfied. Since the matrix $\mathbf{X}$ consists of q column vectors $\mathbf{x}_i$,

$$\mathbf{X} = \begin{bmatrix} x_{11} & x_{12} & \cdots & x_{1q} \\ x_{21} & x_{22} & \cdots & x_{2q} \\ \cdots \\ x_{n1} & x_{n2} & \cdots & x_{nq} \end{bmatrix} = [\mathbf{x}_1 \ \ \mathbf{x}_2 \ \ \cdots \ \ \mathbf{x}_q], \tag{5.5.5}$$

each of these vectors is a solution of $\mathbf{Ax} = \mathbf{0}$. Since each column of $\mathbf{X}$ belongs to the solution space S, S has dimension $n - r$. (See Section 5.2.)

Thus, the $n-r$ linearly independent vectors of S provide a basis for the solution space. In summary, if $\mathbf{A}$ is an $m \times n$ matrix having rank r, there exists an $n \times q$ matrix $\mathbf{X}$ having $n-r$ linearly independent column vectors, and the solution space has dimension $n-r$.

For the system of homogeneous equations in Eq. (5.5.4) the solution vectors $\mathbf{x}_i$ constitute a vector space called the *null space* of $\mathbf{A}$. The dimension of this space is $n-r$, the *nullity* of $\mathbf{A}$.

If S is a linear vector space whose elements are solutions of the set of linear homogeneous equations in Eq. (5.5.1), a *basis* of the solution space S is a *fundamental system of solutions* of $\mathbf{Ax}=\mathbf{0}$; every other solution is a linear combination of these solutions.

If the coefficient matrix $\mathbf{A}$ of Eq. (5.5.1) has rank r, then $n-r$ linearly independent solutions exist for this system of equations. Precisely r of the equations are linearly independent;* the remaining $m-r$ equations are linear combinations of the r linearly independent equations.

Thus, to solve the system of equations $\mathbf{Ax}=\mathbf{0}$, we consider r linearly independent equations and proceed in a manner analogous to that used in Section 5.4. (See Example 5.4.1 in particular. Example 5.5.1, at the end of this section, also illustrates the method.)

If $r=n$, then $n-r=0$, so that a basis for the solution space S would have no non-trivial vectors. In this instance, the fundamental system of solutions consists of the unique vector, the zero vector.

For $r<n$, we assign arbitrary values from $\mathscr{F}$ to $x_{r+1}, x_{r+2}, \cdots, x_n$ and then solve for $x_1, x_2, \cdots, x_r$ in terms of $x_{r+1}, \cdots, x_n$. Using primes to denote particular elements of the vectors, the $n-r$ solutions are

$$\begin{array}{l} [x_1' \quad \cdots \quad x_r' \quad x_{r+1}' \quad \cdots \quad x_n']' \\ [x_1'' \quad \cdots \quad x_r'' \quad x_{r+1}'' \quad \cdots \quad x_n'']' \\ \cdots \\ [x_1^{(n-r)} \quad \cdots \quad x_r^{(n-r)} \quad x_{r+1}^{(n-r)} \quad \cdots \quad x_n^{(n-r)}]'. \end{array} \tag{5.5.6}$$

The arbitrary values assigned successively to $x_{r+1}, \cdots, x_n$ to give Eq. (5.5.6) can clearly be chosen (in infinitely many ways) so that the determinant

$$\begin{vmatrix} x_{r+1}' & \cdots & x_n' \\ \cdots & & \\ x_{r+1}^{(n-r)} & \cdots & x_n^{(n-r)} \end{vmatrix} \tag{5.5.7}$$

is different from zero. Thus the $n-r$ solutions of Eq. (5.5.6) are linearly independent; the set of solutions constitutes a fundamental system of solutions of Eq. (5.5.1), or a basis of the solution space.

The following theorems are consequences of the preceding discussion:

*Recall that the same types of definitions apply for linear dependence and independence of functions or equations as those given in Section 5.1 for vectors. Note in particular the paragraphs after Theorem 5.1.6.

Theorem 5.5.1. *Let* $\mathbf{A}\mathbf{x} = \mathbf{0}$ *be a set of m homogeneous linear equations in n unknowns whose coefficient matrix* $\mathbf{A}$ *is of rank r. If* $r = n$, *the set of equations possesses only the trivial solution* $\mathbf{x} = \mathbf{0}$. *If* $r < n$, *there exist* $n - r$ *linearly independent solutions such that every solution of the solution space is expressible as a linear combination of them.*

Theorem 5.5.2. *A set of m homogeneous linear equations in n unknowns* $\mathbf{A}\mathbf{x} = \mathbf{0}$ *has a nontrivial solution if and only if the coefficient matrix* $\mathbf{A}$ *has rank r such that* $r < n$.

This theorem follows immediately from Theorem 5.5.1. If $m < n$, a set of homogeneous linear equations always possesses a nontrivial solution, because the rank of the coefficient matrix must then be less than n.

Theorem 5.5.3. *A set of n homogeneous linear equations in n unknowns has nontrivial solutions if and only if the determinant of the coefficient matrix is equal to zero.*

This theorem also follows from Theorem 5.5.1. Consider n homogeneous linear equations in n unknowns. If the coefficient matrix is nonsingular, Cramer's rule applies; the unique solution is the trivial solution. If the coefficient matrix is singular, Theorem 5.5.3 applies instead.

Example 5.5.1. Determine the number of linearly independent vector solutions, the number of linearly independent equations, and all nontrivial solutions, for the system of linear homogeneous equations

$$\begin{aligned}
f_1(\mathbf{x}) &\equiv x_1 + x_2 - x_4 + x_5 = 0,\\
f_2(\mathbf{x}) &\equiv 3x_2 - x_3 - 2x_4 + 3x_5 = 0,\\
f_3(\mathbf{x}) &\equiv 2x_1 - x_2 + x_3 - x_5 = 0,\\
f_4(\mathbf{x}) &\equiv x_1 - 2x_2 + x_3 + x_4 - 2x_5 = 0.
\end{aligned}$$

Since the rank of the coefficient matrix for this system of equations is 2, there are $5 - 2 = 3$ linearly independent vectors; all solutions can be expressed in terms of them. Also, since $r = 2$ there are two linearly independent equations; the other equations are linear combinations of these two. Since $f_2(\mathbf{x})$ is not a multiple of $f_1(\mathbf{x})$, these are two linearly independent equations. The reader can verify that

$$f_3(\mathbf{x}) = 2f_1(\mathbf{x}) - f_2(\mathbf{x})$$

and

$$f_4(\mathbf{x}) = f_1(\mathbf{x}) - f_2(\mathbf{x}).$$

To solve for nontrivial solutions for the system of equations, rewrite the the first two (or use any two linearly independent ones) as

$$\begin{aligned} x_1 + x_2 &= x_4 - x_5 \\ 3x_2 &= x_3 + 2x_4 - 3x_5, \end{aligned}$$

or

$$\begin{aligned} x_2 &= 1/3(x_3 + 2x_4 - 3x_5) \\ x_1 &= 1/3(-x_3 + x_4). \end{aligned}$$

Then arbitrary choices for x_3, x_4, and x_5, yield values x_1 and x_2. Three possible vector solutions are $[0\ -1\ 1\ 1\ 2]'$, $[1\ 1\ 0\ 3\ 1]'$, and $[-1\ 2\ 4\ 1\ 0]'$. Since

$$c_1 \begin{bmatrix} 0 \\ -1 \\ 1 \\ 1 \\ 2 \end{bmatrix} + c_2 \begin{bmatrix} 1 \\ 1 \\ 0 \\ 3 \\ 1 \end{bmatrix} + c_3 \begin{bmatrix} -1 \\ 2 \\ 4 \\ 1 \\ 0 \end{bmatrix} = \begin{bmatrix} 0 \\ 0 \\ 0 \\ 0 \\ 0 \end{bmatrix}$$

only if $c_1 = c_2 = c_3 = 0$, the vectors are linearly independent, and can serve as a basis for the solution space for the system of equations. Any other vector satisfying the system of equations must be a linear combination of the three basis vectors.

Exercises 5.5

1. For each of the following systems of equations determine
   (i) the number of linearly independent vector solutions.
   (ii) the number of linearly independent equations.
   (iii) all non-trivial solutions (for those systems possessing non-trivial solutions).

(a)
$$\begin{aligned} x_1 + x_2 + x_3 &= 0 \\ 3x_1 + x_2 - 3x_3 &= 0 \\ x_1 - 2x_3 &= 0 \\ 2x_1 + x_2 - x_3 &= 0 \end{aligned}$$

(b)
$$\begin{aligned} x + 3y + z &= 0 \\ x - 2y &= 0 \\ 5y + z &= 0 \end{aligned}$$

(c)
$$\begin{aligned} x_1 + 3x_2 - x_4 &= 0 \\ x_1 - x_3 + x_4 &= 0 \\ x_1 + x_2 &= 0 \end{aligned}$$

(d)
$$\begin{aligned} x + 2y + u &= 0 \\ -x + 2z + u &= 0 \\ x + 4y + 2z + 2u &= 0 \\ 2y + 2z + u &= 0 \\ x + 8y + 6z + 4u &= 0 \end{aligned}$$

2. Show that **A** is singular if

$$\mathbf{A} = \begin{bmatrix} 2 & 2 & 4 \\ 1 & 2 & 3 \\ 3 & -3 & 0 \end{bmatrix}.$$

Determine a nonzero singular matrix **B** such that $\mathbf{AB} = \mathbf{0}$.

3. Find a matrix $\mathbf{X}$ of rank 2 such that $\mathbf{AX} = \mathbf{0}$ if

$$\mathbf{A} = \begin{bmatrix} 1 & 2 & 3 \\ 2 & 4 & 6 \\ 2 & 4 & 6 \end{bmatrix}.$$

5.6. *Nonhomogeneous Systems of Equations*

Section 5.4 showed how to solve a nonhomogeneous system of equations for which the rank of the augmented matrix is the same as the rank of the matrix of the coefficients. In general, there can be many solutions. Using the results of Section 5.5, we can now determine how many solutions there are and what form they take.

For linear differential equations, the general solution of a nonhomogeneous differential equation consists of the sum of a particular solution of the equation and the general solution of the corresponding homogeneous equation. The set of functions $\{f(x)\}$ forms a linear space upon which the differential operator $D = d/dx$ acts linearly. Similarly, for the equation

$$\mathbf{Ax} = \mathbf{c},$$

a matrix $\mathbf{A}$ acts linearly upon the linear space V_n, and the following theorem holds:

Theorem 5.6.1. *Let* $\mathbf{y}$ *be a solution of the equation*

$$\mathbf{Ax} = \mathbf{c}, \tag{5.6.1}$$

where $\mathbf{A}$ *has rank* r, *and let* $\mathbf{x}_1, \cdots, \mathbf{x}_{n-r}$ *be* $n - r$ *linearly independent solutions of the corresponding homogeneous equation*

$$\mathbf{Ax} = \mathbf{0}. \tag{5.6.2}$$

Then every solution of Eq. (5.6.1) *is of the form*

$$\mathbf{x} = \mathbf{y} + c_1\mathbf{x}_1 + c_2\mathbf{x}_2 + \cdots + c_{n-r}\mathbf{x}_{n-r}. \tag{5.6.3}$$

Conversely, every vector of the form of Eq. (5.6.3) *is a solution of Eq.* (5.6.1).

Proof: Suppose $\mathbf{x}$ is a solution of Eq. (5.6.1). Since $\mathbf{y}$ is also a solution,

$$\mathbf{A}(\mathbf{x} - \mathbf{y}) = \mathbf{Ax} - \mathbf{Ay} = \mathbf{c} - \mathbf{c} = \mathbf{0}.$$

Hence $\mathbf{x} - \mathbf{y}$ is a solution of the corresponding homogeneous equation; by Theorem 5.5.1 it must be of the form

$$\mathbf{x} - \mathbf{y} = c_1\mathbf{x}_1 + c_2\mathbf{x}_2 + \cdots + c_{n-r}\mathbf{x}_{n-r}, \quad \text{or}$$
$$\mathbf{x} = \mathbf{y} + c_1\mathbf{x}_1 + c_2\mathbf{x}_2 + \cdots + c_{n-r}\mathbf{x}_{n-r}.$$

Conversely, suppose that

$$\mathbf{x} = \mathbf{y} + c_1\mathbf{x}_1 + \cdots + c_{n-r}\mathbf{x}_{n-r}.$$

Substituting this $\mathbf{x}$ in Eq. (5.6.1) gives

$$\mathbf{Ax} = \mathbf{A}(\mathbf{y} + c_1\mathbf{x}_1 + \cdots + c_{n-r}\mathbf{x}_{n-r})$$
$$= \mathbf{Ay} + c_1\mathbf{Ax}_1 + \cdots + c_{n-r}\mathbf{Ax}_{n-r} = \mathbf{c} + \mathbf{0} + \cdots + \mathbf{0} = \mathbf{c}.$$

Therefore, $\mathbf{x}$ is a solution, the *general solution*; $\mathbf{y}$ is a *particular solution.*

In geometric terms, the solution space of the homogeneous equation Eq. (5.6.2) is a hyperplane which passes through the origin of V_n. The set of solutions of the nonhomogeneous equation Eq. (5.6.1) is not a linear space, because it is not closed under addition or under scalar multiplication. It is a hyperplane that is displaced from the origin by the vector $\mathbf{y}$.

Example 5.6.1. Solve the system of equations:

$$\begin{aligned} x + y + z &= 6, \\ -x + y - 2z &= -5, \\ 2y - z &= 1. \end{aligned} \tag{5.6.4}$$

Since the coefficient matrix and the augmented matrix both have rank two, a solution exists. Since the first two equations are linearly independent, we need only consider these two in finding a particular solution. Assigning a convenient value to z, say $z = 0$, yields

$$\begin{aligned} x + y &= 6, \quad \text{and} \\ -x + y &= -5. \end{aligned} \tag{5.6.5}$$

The solution of Eq. (5.6.5) is $x = 11/2$, $y = 1/2$, either by Cramer's rule or by inspection. Thus one particular solution of Eq. (5.6.4) is $(x, y, z) = (11/2, 1/2, 0)$.

The homogeneous equations corresponding to Eq. (5.6.4) are

$$\begin{aligned} x + y + z &= 0, \\ -x + y - 2z &= 0, \\ 2y - z &= 0. \end{aligned} \tag{5.6.6}$$

Following the method of Section 5.5, adding the first equation to the second yields

$$\begin{aligned} x + y + z &= 0, \\ 2y - z &= 0, \\ 2y - z &= 0, \end{aligned}$$

and then subtracting the second equation from the third yields

$$\begin{aligned} x + y + z &= 0 \\ 2y - z &= 0 \\ 0 &= 0. \end{aligned}$$

Since there are three unknowns and the rank of the coefficient matrix is two, there is $3 - 2 = 1$ linearly independent solution. Assigning 2 as a convenient value to z, $y = 1$ and $x = -3$. Therefore the general solution of Eq. (5.6.6) is

$$(x, y, z) = c(-3, 1, 2),$$

and the general solution of Eq. (5.6.4) is

$$(x, y, z) = (11/2, 1/2, 0) + c(-3, 1, 2). \tag{5.6.7}$$

Note that (11/2, 1/2, 0) is not the only particular solution. One which does not include fractions can be found by a judicious choice of c in Eq. (5.6.7). For instance, if $c = 1/2$, then (4, 1, 1) is a particular solution of Eq. (5.6.4); the general solution then becomes

$$(x, y, z) = (4, 1, 1) + c(-3, 1, 2). \tag{5.6.8}$$

Exercises 5.6

1. Use the methods of this section to find the general solutions to the following systems of equations. Express the solutions in the form of Eq. (5.6.3).

(a) $\begin{aligned} x + y + z + v &= 2 \\ x - y + z \quad &= -2 \end{aligned}$

(b) $\begin{aligned} x + y - z &= 1 \\ x + 2y + 3z &= 6 \\ 2x + 3y + 2z &= 7 \\ 4x + 5y \quad &= 9 \\ x \quad - 5z &= -4 \end{aligned}$

(c) $\begin{aligned} x + 2y \quad - v &= 2 \\ x + 3y - z + v &= 1 \\ x \quad - 2z + 3v &= 0 \\ 2y + z - 2v &= 2 \end{aligned}$

(d) $\begin{aligned} x - 2y - z &= 0 \\ x + y + z &= 4 \\ x + 2y + 2z &= 6 \end{aligned}$

2. Draw a sketch exhibiting the graphs of the following sets of equations. Include the solution vectors.

(a) $\begin{aligned} x + y &= 5 \\ x - y &= -1 \end{aligned}$

(b) $\begin{aligned} x + 2y &= 5 \\ 2x + 4y &= 10 \end{aligned}$

(c) $\begin{aligned} x \quad &= 2 \\ x + y + z &= 6 \\ 3x + y + z &= 10 \end{aligned}$

3. If $\mathbf{x}_1$ and $\mathbf{x}_2$ are vector solutions of $\mathbf{Ax} = \mathbf{c}$, explain why $a\mathbf{x}_1 + b\mathbf{x}_2$ with $ab \neq 0$ is not also a solution. When would the sum be a solution?

5.7.† *The Rank of the Product of Matrices*

Although this section generally deals with the rows of a matrix (considered as row vectors), it applies equally to the columns of the matrix (as column vectors).

If an $m \times n$ matrix $\mathbf{A}$ with $m \leqq n$ is of rank r, and if $r = m$, then the row vectors of $\mathbf{A}$ are linearly independent. If they were not, some of the rows would be linear combinations of the others; the rank would then be less than m. However, if $r < m$, then the rows are linearly dependent, and $m - r$ of the rows can be expressed as linear combinations of r linearly independent rows.

Applying the preceding argument to columns instead of rows, yields similar results. If $\mathbf{A}$ is square, so that $m = n$, we can state the following theorem.

Theorem 5.7.1. *If* $\mathbf{A}$ *is a square matrix with rank* r*, then* $\mathbf{A}$ *has* r *linearly independent row vectors and* r *linearly independent column vectors.*

Note that this theorem holds even if $\mathbf{A}$ is nonsingular.

By Theorem 3.6.6, the rank of the product of matrices $\mathbf{A}$ and $\mathbf{B}$ cannot exceed the rank of either $\mathbf{A}$ or $\mathbf{B}$. That is, the rank of $\mathbf{A}$ is not increased by multiplying by $\mathbf{B}$, even if $\mathbf{B}$ has its maximum possible rank. This establishes an upper bound for the rank of the product.

A possible lower bound for the rank of the product of nonzero matrices is zero. A sharper lower bound on the rank of the product of square matrices is given by:

Theorem 5.7.2. *If matrices* $\mathbf{A}$ *and* $\mathbf{B}$ *are each of order* $n \times n$ *and have ranks* r *and* s *respectively, and if the product* $\mathbf{AB}$ *has rank* q*, then* $q \geqq r + s - n$.

Proof: By Theorem 3.6.4, nonsingular matrices $\mathbf{P}$ and $\mathbf{Q}$ can be chosen so that

$$\mathbf{PAQ} = \mathbf{R}_r.$$

Since $\mathbf{P}$ is nonsingular, the rank q of $\mathbf{AB}$ is the same as the rank of $\mathbf{PAB}$. The rank of $\mathbf{PA}(\mathbf{QQ}^{-1})\mathbf{B} = (\mathbf{PAQ})(\mathbf{Q}^{-1}\mathbf{B}) = \mathbf{R}_r\mathbf{B}_1$ is also q. But $\mathbf{B}_1$ has rank s, the same rank as $\mathbf{B}$, since $\mathbf{Q}^{-1}$ is nonsingular. Since $\mathbf{R}_r$ has nonzero elements only in the first r rows, the rank q of $\mathbf{R}_r\mathbf{B}_1$ (and hence of $\mathbf{AB}$) is equal to the rank of the first r rows of $\mathbf{B}_1$. That is, in these r rows there are $r - q$ linearly dependent vectors, by Theorem 5.1.5. But considering all of the rows of $\mathbf{B}$, there are $n - s$ dependent rows. Since the number of dependent rows in $\mathbf{B}_1$ is no greater than the number of dependent rows in $\mathbf{B}$,

$$r - q \leqq n - s. \tag{5.7.1}$$

From this,

$$q \geqq r + s - n. \tag{5.7.2}$$

The quantity $r + s - n$ in Eq. (5.7.2) may sometimes be a negative integer. This, of course, does not imply that q can be negative, since the rank of a matrix is always a non-negative integer.

Note that Theorem 5.7.2 deals with square matrices. (How can the theorem be applied if one or both matrices in a product are not square?) Note also that the theorem does not definitely determine the rank of a product of matrices in general; it merely gives a lower bound for the rank, while Theorem 3.6.6 gives an upper bound.

Exercises 5.7

1. (a) Without expanding, find the rank of the product of matrices **A** and **B** if

$$\mathbf{A} = \begin{bmatrix} 2 & 1 & -1 \\ 1 & 0 & 3 \\ 3 & 2 & -5 \end{bmatrix} \quad \text{and} \quad \mathbf{B} = \begin{bmatrix} 0 & 1 & 2 \\ 1 & 0 & 3 \\ 2 & 3 & 0 \end{bmatrix}.$$

   (b) Explain why the rank can be definitely determined in this particular example.

2. (a) If **A** is a 3×5 matrix and **B** is a 5×2 matrix, show how Theorem 5.7.2 can be applied.
   (b) For matrices with orders given in (a), give a numerical example to show that the rank of the product can be the maximum possible rank.
   (c) Give a specific example for such matrices as in (a) to show that the lower bound for the rank of the product can be attained.

3. For each matrix in exercise 1, find r linearly independent (a) rows and (b) columns, and show that the other rows (columns) are linear combinations of these r rows (columns).

4. Work exercise 3 using the matrix

$$\begin{bmatrix} -2 & 6 & 2 & 0 & 4 \\ 7 & -7 & -1 & 2 & -4 \\ 0 & 7 & 3 & 1 & 5 \\ 5 & 6 & 4 & 3 & 5 \\ 8 & -3 & 1 & 3 & -1 \end{bmatrix}.$$

5. Prove the theorem: *If* **A** *is real and* $\mathbf{A'A} = \mathbf{0}$, *then* $\mathbf{A} = \mathbf{0}$.

6. State and prove the theorem corresponding to exercise 5 if **A** is complex.

7. Prove the theorem: *If* **A** *and* **B** *are square and* $\mathbf{AB} = \mathbf{0}$, *then* $\mathbf{A} = \mathbf{0}$ *or* $\mathbf{B} = \mathbf{0}$ *or both* **A** *and* **B** *are singular.*

Linear Transformations and The Characteristic Equation

6.1. Linear Homogeneous Transformations

Chapter 4 considered certain nonsingular transformations in connection with bilinear and quadratic forms. Such transformations may be thought of either as "moving" vectors in a fixed coordinate system or as fixed vectors in a "moving" coordinate system.

First, consider a fixed coordinate system. Then the equation

$$\mathbf{z} = \mathbf{A}\mathbf{x} \tag{6.1.1}$$

may be thought of as "moving" $\mathbf{x}$ to $\mathbf{z}$; in other words, $\mathbf{x}$ is transformed into $\mathbf{z}$ by the *linear homogeneous transformation of matrix* $\mathbf{A}$.

If the transformation $\mathbf{z} = \mathbf{A}\mathbf{x}$ of Eq. (6.1.1) transforms $\mathbf{x}_1$ into $\mathbf{z}_1$ and $\mathbf{x}_2$ into $\mathbf{z}_2$, then

(a) $k\mathbf{x}_1$ is transformed into $k\mathbf{z}_1$ for every scalar k, and

(b) $k\mathbf{x}_1 + h\mathbf{x}_2$ is transformed into $k\mathbf{z}_1 + h\mathbf{z}_2$ for any scalars k and h.

These results follow directly from the multiplication of scalars and matrices and from the distributive law for matrix multiplication. Properties (a) and (b) are the properties that make the transformation *linear*. The transformation is *homogeneous* because the origin transforms into itself. The transformation

$$\mathbf{z} = \mathbf{A}\mathbf{x} + \mathbf{a},\ \mathbf{a} \neq \mathbf{0},$$

is a *nonhomogeneous* transformation.

For transformations such as Eq. (6.1.1) in general, the matrix $\mathbf{A}$ may be singular or nonsingular; the *transformation* is *singular* or *nonsingular* depending on whether $\mathbf{A}$ is singular or nonsingular. If the transformation in Eq.

(6.1.1) is nonsingular, then two distinct vectors **z** correspond to two distinct vectors **x**. Conversely, a nonsingular matrix **A** uniquely determines the transformation Eq. (6.1.1).

If **x** is transformed into **z** by **C** and if **z** is transformed into **y** by **D**, i.e., $\mathbf{z} = \mathbf{Cx}$ and $\mathbf{y} = \mathbf{Dz}$, then

(6.1.2) $$\mathbf{y} = \mathbf{D}(\mathbf{Cx}) = (\mathbf{DC})\mathbf{x}.$$

The transformation of **x** into **y** by the matrix (**DC**) is called the *product of the transformations* $\mathbf{z} = \mathbf{Cx}$ and $\mathbf{y} = \mathbf{Dz}$. Note that if **C** and **D** are both nonsingular, then the product is also nonsingular. This result is stated as a theorem.

Theorem 6.1.1. *If the vector* **x** *is transformed into the vector* **z** *under the linear homogeneous transformation* $\mathbf{z} = \mathbf{Cx}$, *and if* **z** *is transformed into the vector* **y** *under the linear homogeneous transformation* $\mathbf{y} = \mathbf{Dz}$, *then* **x** *is transformed into* **y** *by the transformation matrix* **DC**.

If the transformation $\mathbf{z} = \mathbf{Cx}$ is nonsingular, then **C** has an inverse, so that the transformation $\mathbf{x} = \mathbf{C}^{-1}\mathbf{z}$, called the *inverse transformation*, carries the vector **z** back into the vector **x**.

Thus transformations (represented by matrices) might be thought of as "moving" vectors from place to place.

Example 6.1.1. Find the image (the vector resulting from a transformation) of [1 2 3]′ under the transformation associated with

$$\begin{bmatrix} 1 & 1 & 1 \\ 1 & 0 & -1 \\ 2 & 1 & 1 \end{bmatrix}.$$

Let $\mathbf{z} = [z_1 \ z_2 \ z_3]'$ be the image. Then

$$\mathbf{z} = \begin{bmatrix} 1 & 1 & 1 \\ 1 & 0 & -1 \\ 2 & 1 & 1 \end{bmatrix} \begin{bmatrix} 1 \\ 2 \\ 3 \end{bmatrix} = \begin{bmatrix} 6 \\ -2 \\ 7 \end{bmatrix}.$$

Example 6.1.2. Find the matrix of the transformation T_1T_2 if

the matrix of T_1 is $\begin{bmatrix} 1 & 0 & 0 \\ 0 & 1 & 1 \\ 0 & 1 & -1 \end{bmatrix}$ and of T_2 is $\begin{bmatrix} 2 & 0 & 0 \\ 1 & 1 & 0 \\ 1 & 1 & 1 \end{bmatrix}$.

The matrix is

$$\begin{bmatrix} 1 & 0 & 0 \\ 0 & 1 & 1 \\ 0 & 1 & -1 \end{bmatrix} \begin{bmatrix} 2 & 0 & 0 \\ 1 & 1 & 0 \\ 1 & 1 & 1 \end{bmatrix} = \begin{bmatrix} 2 & 0 & 0 \\ 2 & 2 & 1 \\ 0 & 0 & -1 \end{bmatrix}.$$

The preceding transformations can also be viewed as moving the coordinate system and leaving the vectors alone. Consider the n-dimensional vector space over $\mathscr{F}$, $V_n(\mathscr{F})$. Section 5.2 (and especially number 1 of Exercises 5.2) showed that the whole space V_n is a linear vector space over $\mathscr{F}$. Let U be a basis for V_n, where U consists of the vectors

$$\mathbf{u}_1 = [1 \quad 0 \quad \cdots \quad 0]', \quad \mathbf{u}_2 = [0 \quad 1 \quad \cdots \quad 0]', \cdots, \quad \mathbf{u}_n = [0 \quad 0 \quad \cdots \quad 1]'.$$

The vectors of U are *elementary vectors over* $\mathscr{F}$. Then, for an arbitrary vector $\mathbf{y}$ in V_n, where $\mathbf{y}' = [y_1 \ y_2 \ \cdots \ y_n]$,

$$\mathbf{y} = \sum_{j=1}^{n} y_j \mathbf{u}_j = y_1\mathbf{u}_1 + y_2\mathbf{u}_2 + \cdots + y_n\mathbf{u}_n. \tag{6.1.3}$$

Now let T be a second basis for V_n defined by the n-dimensional vectors over $\mathscr{F}$,

$$\mathbf{t}_j = [a_{1j} a_{2j} \cdots a_{nj}]', j = 1, 2, \cdots, n. \tag{6.1.4}$$

Since the vectors $\mathbf{t}_j$ are linearly independent, the matrix of the vectors is nonsingular; det $[a_{ij}] \neq 0$. Thus for any vector $\mathbf{x}$ in V_n there are scalars z_j such that

$$\mathbf{x} = \sum_{j=1}^{n} z_j \mathbf{t}_j. \tag{6.1.5}$$

The vector $[z_1 \ z_2 \ \cdots \ z_n]'$ gives the *coordinates of* $\mathbf{x}$ *with respect to the basis* T.

A vector having one set of coordinates with respect to a given basis usually has a different set of coordinates with respect to a different basis. The zero vector has coordinates $[0 \ 0 \ \cdots \ 0]'$ with respect to any basis.

If $\mathbf{x}$ has coordinates $[x_1 \ x_2 \ \cdots \ x_n]'$ with respect to the U basis and coordinates $[z_1 \ z_2 \ \cdots \ z_n]'$ with respect to the T basis, then

$$\mathbf{x} = \sum_{i=1}^{n} x_i \mathbf{u}_i = \sum_{j=1}^{n} z_j \mathbf{t}_j. \tag{6.1.6}$$

But, since the two bases U and T are each composed of sets of linearly independent vectors in V_n, there exist scalars c_{ij} such that

$$\mathbf{u}_i = \sum_{j=1}^{n} c_{ij} \mathbf{t}_j, \qquad i = 1, 2, \cdots, n, \tag{6.1.7}$$

with det $[c_{ij}] \neq 0$. From Eqs. (6.1.6) and (6.1.7),

$$\mathbf{x} = \sum_{j=1}^{n} z_j \mathbf{t}_j = \sum_{i=1}^{n} x_i \left(\sum_{j=1}^{n} c_{ij} \mathbf{t}_j \right) = \sum_{j=1}^{n} \left(\sum_{i=1}^{n} c_{ij} x_i \right) \mathbf{t}_j, \tag{6.1.8}$$

and thus

$$z_j = \sum_{i=1}^{n} c_{ij} x_i, \qquad j = 1, 2, \cdots, n, \tag{6.1.9}$$

and det $[c_{ij}] \neq 0$. Stated as a theorem:

Theorem 6.1.2. *If an arbitrary vector* $\mathbf{x}$ *in* V_n *has coordinates* $[x_1\ x_2\ \cdots\ x_n]'$ *with respect to the U basis and coordinates* $[z_1\ z_2 \cdots z_n]'$ *with respect to the T basis, then the two sets of coordinates are connected by a nonsingular linear homogeneous relation Eq.* (6.1.9).

Equation (6.1.9) can be interpreted as defining a transformation of coordinates from one basis in V_n to another, where the two bases are related by Eq. (6.1.7). That is, the sets of coordinates $[x_1\ x_2\ \cdots\ x_n]'$ and $[z_1\ z_2\ \cdots\ z_n]'$ related by Eq. (6.1.9) are *two sets of coordinates* for the *same vector* with respect to the two bases U and T related by Eq. (6.1.7).

Example 6.1.3. The sets of vectors $\{[1\ 0\ 0]', [0\ 1\ 1]', [0\ 1\ -1]'\}$ and $\{[1\ 1\ 0]', [1\ 0\ -1]', [1\ -1\ 1]'\}$ are two bases for V_3. Find the matrix $[c_{ij}]$ connecting them.

In Eq. (6.1.7) let $\mathbf{u}_1 = [1\ 0\ 0]'$, $\mathbf{u}_2 = [0\ 1\ 1]'$, $\mathbf{u}_3 = [0\ 1\ -1]'$; $\mathbf{t}_1 = [1\ 1\ 0]'$, $\mathbf{t}_2 = [1\ 0\ -1]'$, and $\mathbf{t}_3 = [1\ -1\ 1]'$. Then

$$\mathbf{u}_1 = c_{11}[1\quad 1\quad 0]' + c_{12}[1\quad 0\quad -1]' + c_{13}[1\quad -1\quad 1]'$$

or

$$\begin{aligned} 1 &= c_{11} + c_{12} + c_{13} \\ 0 &= c_{11} \qquad\ \ - c_{13} \\ 0 &= \qquad - c_{12} + c_{13} \end{aligned}$$

from which it follows that $c_{11} = c_{12} = c_{13} = 1/3$. Similarly $c_{21} = 1$, $c_{22} = -1$, $c_{23} = 0$, $c_{31} = c_{32} = 1/3$, and $c_{33} = -2/3$. Hence,

$$[c_{ij}] = \begin{bmatrix} 1/3 & 1/3 & 1/3 \\ 1 & -1 & 0 \\ 1/3 & 1/3 & -2/3 \end{bmatrix}.$$

Example 6.1.4. The basis $\{[1\ 0\ 0]', [1\ 1\ 0]', [1\ 1\ 1]'\}$ is to be transformed by the matrix

$$\begin{bmatrix} 1 & -1 & 0 \\ 0 & 1 & -1 \\ 0 & 0 & 1 \end{bmatrix}.$$

Find the new basis.

From $\mathbf{Cx} = \mathbf{z}$,

$$\begin{bmatrix} 1 & -1 & 0 \\ 0 & 1 & -1 \\ 0 & 0 & 1 \end{bmatrix}\begin{bmatrix} 1 \\ 0 \\ 0 \end{bmatrix} = \begin{bmatrix} 1 \\ 0 \\ 0 \end{bmatrix},$$

$$\begin{bmatrix} 1 & -1 & 0 \\ 0 & 1 & -1 \\ 0 & 0 & 1 \end{bmatrix}\begin{bmatrix} 1 \\ 1 \\ 0 \end{bmatrix} = \begin{bmatrix} 0 \\ 1 \\ 0 \end{bmatrix}, \quad \text{and}$$

$$\begin{bmatrix} 1 & -1 & 0 \\ 0 & 1 & -1 \\ 0 & 0 & 1 \end{bmatrix} \begin{bmatrix} 1 \\ 1 \\ 1 \end{bmatrix} = \begin{bmatrix} 0 \\ 0 \\ 1 \end{bmatrix}.$$

The new basis is $\{[1\ 0\ 0]', [0\ 1\ 0]', [0\ 0\ 1]'\}$.

Exercises 6.1

1. Determine the images of $\mathbf{x}$ and $\mathbf{y}$ under each of the transformations $\mathbf{A}$ and $\mathbf{B}$ if

$$\mathbf{x}' = [1\ \ 0\ \ 1], \qquad \mathbf{y}' = [-1\ \ 4\ \ 1],$$

$$\mathbf{A} = \begin{bmatrix} 1 & 2 & 0 \\ 2 & 1 & 0 \\ 1 & 1 & 1 \end{bmatrix}, \qquad \mathbf{B} = \begin{bmatrix} 2 & 2 & 7 \\ 2 & 1 & 2 \\ 0 & 1 & -3 \end{bmatrix}.$$

2. (a) Find the matrix that transforms the basis $\{[1\ 0\ 0]', [0\ 1\ 0]', [0\ 0\ 1]'\}$ to the basis $\{[1\ 2\ 3]', [0\ 1\ 2]', [0\ 0\ 1]'\}$.
   (b) Find the matrix that transforms the basis $\{[1\ 2\ 3]', [0\ 1\ 2]', [0\ 0\ 1]'\}$ to the basis $\{[1\ 0\ 0]', [0\ 1\ 0]', [0\ 0\ 1]'\}$.

3. Transform the vector $[x_1\ x_2]'$ by the matrix

$$\begin{bmatrix} \cos\theta & \sin\theta \\ -\sin\theta & \cos\theta \end{bmatrix}.$$

   Describe geometrically the transformation associated with this matrix.

6.2. *Change of Basis*

Consider the linear homogeneous transformation

$$\mathbf{y} = \mathbf{A}\mathbf{x}, \tag{6.2.1}$$

where $\mathbf{x}$ and $\mathbf{y}$ are vectors belonging to V_n. Section 6.1 showed how such vectors can be represented with respect to different bases. Generally, if $\mathbf{x}$ has coordinates $[x_1\ x_2\ \cdots\ x_n]'$ with respect to the basis T, it will have different coordinates $[x_1'\ x_2'\ \cdots\ x_n']$ with respect to a different basis W. Then, by Theorem 6.1.2, a nonsingular matrix $\mathbf{C}$ exists such that

$$[x_1\ \ x_2\ \ \cdots\ \ x_n]' = \mathbf{C}[x_1'\ \ x_2'\ \ \cdots\ \ x_n']'. \tag{6.2.2}$$

Similarly, if $\mathbf{y}$ has coordinates $[y_1\ y_2\ \cdots\ y_n]'$ with respect to the basis T and coordinates $[y_1'\ y_2'\ \cdots\ y_n']'$ with respect to the basis W, then

$$[y_1\ \ y_2\ \ \cdots\ \ y_n]' = \mathbf{C}[y_1'\ \ y_2'\ \ \cdots\ \ y_n']'. \tag{6.2.3}$$

Substituting from Eqs. (6.2.2) and (6.2.3) into Eq. (6.2.1):

$$\mathbf{C}[y_1' \quad y_2' \quad \cdots \quad y_n']' = \mathbf{AC}[x_1' \quad x_2' \quad \cdots \quad x_n']',$$

or

$$[y_1' \quad y_2' \quad \cdots \quad y_n']' = \mathbf{C}^{-1}\mathbf{AC}[x_1' \quad x_2' \quad \cdots \quad x_n']'. \tag{6.2.4}$$

If Eq. (6.2.1) is rewritten as

$$[y_1 \quad y_2 \quad \cdots \quad y_n]' = \mathbf{A}[x_1 \quad x_2 \quad \cdots \quad x_n]' \tag{6.2.5}$$

and then compared to Eq. (6.2.4), they clearly represent the *same transformation* with respect to *different bases.* Rewriting these transformations as

$$\mathbf{y} = (\mathbf{C}^{-1}\mathbf{AC})\mathbf{x} \qquad \text{and} \qquad \mathbf{y} = \mathbf{Ax}, \tag{6.2.6}$$

they become two *different transformations* with respect to the *same basis.* As a consequence, the transformations in Eq. (6.2.6), and hence their matrices, are *similar.* The matrix $\mathbf{C}^{-1}\mathbf{AC}$ is the *transform of* $\mathbf{A}$ *by* $\mathbf{C}$. Note that the definition of similar matrices does *not* mean that $\mathbf{A}$ and $\mathbf{C}^{-1}\mathbf{AC}$ transform a given vector into the same vector.

Example 6.2.1. Let

$$\mathbf{A} = \begin{bmatrix} 1 & 0 & 1 \\ 0 & 1 & 1 \\ 0 & 0 & 1 \end{bmatrix}$$

represent a transformation T, and let

$$\mathbf{C} = \begin{bmatrix} 1 & 0 & 0 \\ 1 & 1 & 0 \\ 1 & 0 & 1 \end{bmatrix}$$

be the matrix for a change of basis. Find the matrix representing T corresponding to the new basis.

Let $\mathbf{B}$ be the desired new matrix. Then

$$\begin{aligned} \mathbf{B} &= \mathbf{C}^{-1}\mathbf{AC} \\ &= \begin{bmatrix} 1 & 0 & 0 \\ -1 & 1 & 0 \\ -1 & 0 & 1 \end{bmatrix} \begin{bmatrix} 1 & 0 & 1 \\ 0 & 1 & 1 \\ 0 & 0 & 1 \end{bmatrix} \begin{bmatrix} 1 & 0 & 0 \\ 1 & 1 & 0 \\ 1 & 0 & 1 \end{bmatrix} \\ &= \begin{bmatrix} 2 & 0 & 1 \\ 0 & 1 & 0 \\ -1 & 0 & 0 \end{bmatrix}. \end{aligned}$$

Exercises 6.2

1. Let

$$\mathbf{A} = \begin{bmatrix} 1 & 2 & 3 \\ -1 & -1 & 2 \\ 2 & 2 & 2 \end{bmatrix}$$

be the matrix of a transformation on V_3, relative to the basis {[1 0 0]′, [0 1 0]′, [0 0 1]′}. Find the matrix of the transformation relative to the basis {[3 1 3]′, [2 0 0]′, [1 −1 0]′}.

2. By attempting to find a matrix **C** such that $\mathbf{B} = \mathbf{C}^{-1}\mathbf{AC}$, show that

$$\mathbf{A} = \begin{bmatrix} 2 & 1 \\ 1 & 3 \end{bmatrix} \quad \text{and} \quad \mathbf{B} = \begin{bmatrix} 1 & 0 \\ 2 & 1 \end{bmatrix}$$

are not similar. Show however that

$$\mathbf{A}_1 = \begin{bmatrix} 5 & 1 \\ -5 & 0 \end{bmatrix}$$

is similar to **A** and

$$\mathbf{B}_1 = \begin{bmatrix} -7 & -32 \\ 2 & 9 \end{bmatrix}$$

is similar to **B**. Is a matrix similar to **A** unique?

3. If

$$\mathbf{A} = \begin{bmatrix} 1 & 2 & 3 \\ 2 & 1 & 2 \\ 3 & 2 & 1 \end{bmatrix} \quad \text{and} \quad \mathbf{C} = \begin{bmatrix} 2 & 3 & 0 \\ 1 & 1 & 2 \\ 2 & 2 & 2 \end{bmatrix},$$

find the images of the elementary basis vectors, and of the second set of basis vectors in exercise 1, under the transformation **A** and also under the transformation $\mathbf{C}^{-1}\mathbf{AC}$.

6.3. *Characteristic Values and Characteristic Vectors*

For the linear homogeneous transformations of vectors discussed in the preceding section, certain vectors exist that are *fixed* or *invariant* under a given transformation **A**. That is, given a matrix **A** of order n with elements from a field $\mathscr{F}$, the problem is to determine simultaneously a non-zero vector **x** with elements in $\mathscr{F}$ and a scalar λ such that the equation

$$\mathbf{Ax} = \lambda\mathbf{x} \tag{6.3.1}$$

is satisfied. Vectors satisfying Eq. (6.3.1) for certain values of λ are *fixed* or *invariant* vectors under the transformation **A**. The problem presented by

Eq. (6.3.1) is the *characteristic value problem*; it arises frequently in the study of matrices and in the applications of matrices, and is discussed more fully in the next few sections.

Geometrically speaking; if $\mathscr{F}$ is a field of real numbers, if $\mathbf{A}$ is a matrix of order two or three, and if $\mathbf{x}$ is a geometric vector that satisfies Eq. (6.3.1) for some λ, then the vector $\mathbf{x}$ under the transformation $\mathbf{A}$ has the same direction or the opposite direction to that of $\mathbf{x}$, and the transformed vector has a length $|\lambda|$ times that of $\mathbf{x}$. (See Sections 1.8, 4.1, and 6.2.)

Equation (6.3.1) may be rewritten as

$$\begin{aligned} a_{11}x_1 + a_{12}x_2 + \cdots + a_{1n}x_n &= \lambda x_1 \\ a_{21}x_1 + a_{22}x_2 + \cdots + a_{2n}x_n &= \lambda x_2 \\ \cdots \\ a_{n1}x_1 + a_{n2}x_2 + \cdots + a_{nn}x_n &= \lambda x_n \end{aligned} \tag{6.3.2}$$

or

$$\begin{aligned} (a_{11} - \lambda)x_1 + a_{12}x_2 \quad &+ \cdots + a_{1n}x_n &= 0 \\ a_{21}x_1 \quad + (a_{22} - \lambda)x_2 &+ \cdots + a_{2n}x_n &= 0 \\ \cdots \\ a_{n1}x_1 \quad + a_{n2}x_2 \quad &+ \cdots + (a_{nn} - \lambda)x_n &= 0; \end{aligned} \tag{6.3.3}$$

this, in turn, may be written as

$$(\mathbf{A} - \lambda\mathbf{I})\mathbf{x} = \mathbf{0}. \tag{6.3.4}$$

Since the zero vector $\mathbf{0}$ always satisfies Eq. (6.3.4), it is an invariant vector. By Theorem 5.5.3, the necessary and sufficient condition for Eq. (6.3.4) to have non-trivial solutions is that the determinant of the coefficient matrix be equal to zero. That is, for non-trivial solutions,

$$f(\lambda) = \det(\mathbf{A} - \lambda\mathbf{I}) = 0. \tag{6.3.5}$$

Writing $\det(\mathbf{A} - \lambda\mathbf{I})$ in Eq. (6.3.5) out explicitly,

$$f(\lambda) = \begin{vmatrix} a_{11} - \lambda & a_{12} & \cdots & a_{1n} \\ a_{21} & a_{22} - \lambda & \cdots & a_{2n} \\ \cdots \\ a_{n1} & a_{n2} & \cdots & a_{nn} - \lambda \end{vmatrix}. \tag{6.3.6}$$

The expanded form of $f(\lambda)$ is a polynomial of degree n in λ with leading coefficient $(-1)^n$ and constant term $|\mathbf{A}|$. That is,

$$f(\lambda) = (-1)^n\lambda^n + \cdots + |\mathbf{A}|\,; \tag{6.3.7}$$

the remaining coefficients of $f(\lambda)$ are elements of $\mathscr{F}$. The polynomial $f(\lambda)$ is the *characteristic polynomial of* $\mathbf{A}$.

The equation

$$f(\lambda) = 0 \tag{6.3.8}$$

is the *characteristic equation of* $\mathbf{A}$. It has n roots, the *characteristic roots* or *characteristic values* of **A**. (Some authors prefer the terms *eigenvalues* or *latent roots.*)

For any characteristic value λ satisfying Eq. (6.3.8), a non-trivial vector **x** exists satisfying Eq. (6.3.4). Such vectors are *characteristic vectors* (or *eigenvectors* or *latent vectors*) of **A**. That is, the characteristic vectors are the invariant vectors under the transformation **A**.

Theorem 6.3.1. *The necessary and sufficient condition that*

$$\mathbf{A}\mathbf{x} = \lambda\mathbf{x} \tag{6.3.9}$$

have non-trivial solutions **x** *is that* λ *be a characteristic root of* **A**.

Example 6.3.1. Determine the eigenvalues and eigenvectors for the matrix **A** if

$$\mathbf{A} = \begin{bmatrix} 2 & 3 \\ 2 & 1 \end{bmatrix}.$$

For the matrix **A** the characteristic polynomial is

$$f(\lambda) = \begin{vmatrix} 2-\lambda & 3 \\ 2 & 1-\lambda \end{vmatrix} = \lambda^2 - 3\lambda - 4 = (\lambda - 4)(\lambda + 1).$$

The eigenvalues of **A** are thus $\lambda = 4$ and $\lambda = -1$. Each of these values of λ yields one independent equation. That is, for $\lambda = 4$,

$$\begin{bmatrix} 2-4 & 3 \\ 2 & 1-4 \end{bmatrix}\begin{bmatrix} x_1 \\ x_2 \end{bmatrix} = \begin{bmatrix} -2x_1 + 3x_2 \\ 2x_1 - 3x_2 \end{bmatrix} = \begin{bmatrix} 0 \\ 0 \end{bmatrix},$$

or $2x_1 - 3x_2 = 0$. For $\lambda = -1$,

$$\begin{bmatrix} 2+1 & 3 \\ 2 & 1+1 \end{bmatrix}\begin{bmatrix} x_1 \\ x_2 \end{bmatrix} = \begin{bmatrix} 3x_1 + 3x_2 \\ 2x_1 + 2x_2 \end{bmatrix} = \begin{bmatrix} 0 \\ 0 \end{bmatrix},$$

or $x_1 + x_2 = 0$. Thus the eigenvalue $\lambda = 4$ has the one-dimensional linear vector space of eigenvectors

$$\begin{bmatrix} x_1 \\ x_2 \end{bmatrix} = k_1\begin{bmatrix} 3 \\ 2 \end{bmatrix}$$

associated with it, since all vectors **x** satisfying $(\mathbf{A} - 4\mathbf{I})\mathbf{x} = \mathbf{0}$ are multiples of the vector $[3 \;\; 2]'$. Similarly the eigenvalue $\lambda = -1$ has all vectors that are multiples of $[1 \;\; -1]'$ as eigenvectors, since

$$\begin{bmatrix} x_1 \\ x_2 \end{bmatrix} = k_2\begin{bmatrix} 1 \\ -1 \end{bmatrix}.$$

This equation is equivalent to the two equations

$$x_1 = k_2 \qquad \text{and} \qquad x_2 = -k_2.$$

Eliminating the parameter k_2 yields $x_1 + x_2 = 0$, the one independent equation obtained for $\lambda = -1$. (A similar observation applies for $\lambda = 4$.)

To recapitulate, for the eigenvalue $\lambda = 4$ and for any value of k_1 (say $k_1 = 3$):

$$3\begin{bmatrix}3\\2\end{bmatrix} = \begin{bmatrix}9\\6\end{bmatrix},$$

which is an *invariant* vector under the transformation **A**. More simply,

$$\begin{bmatrix}9\\6\end{bmatrix}$$

is an eigenvector corresponding to the eigenvalue $\lambda = 4$. That is,

$$\begin{bmatrix}2 & 3\\2 & 1\end{bmatrix}\begin{bmatrix}9\\6\end{bmatrix} = \begin{bmatrix}2\cdot 9 + 3\cdot 6\\2\cdot 9 + \phantom{3\cdot{}} 6\end{bmatrix} = \begin{bmatrix}36\\24\end{bmatrix} = 4\begin{bmatrix}9\\6\end{bmatrix}.$$

(A similar result is obtained using $\lambda = -1$.)

Example 6.3.2. Determine the characteristic roots and the corresponding characteristic vectors for the matrix **B** if

$$\mathbf{B} = \begin{bmatrix}2 & 2 & -7\\2 & 1 & 2\\0 & 1 & -3\end{bmatrix}.$$

The characteristic polynomial in this case is

$$f(\lambda) = -\lambda^3 + 13\lambda - 12,$$

and $f(\lambda) = 0$ for $\lambda = 1, 3, -4$. For $\lambda = 1$,

$$\begin{bmatrix}2-1 & 2 & -7\\2 & 1-1 & 2\\0 & 1 & -3-1\end{bmatrix}\begin{bmatrix}x_1\\x_2\\x_3\end{bmatrix} = \begin{bmatrix}0\\0\\0\end{bmatrix},$$

or, as a system of homogeneous equations,

$$x_1 + 2x_2 - 7x_3 = 0$$

$$2x_1 \qquad + 2x_3 = 0.$$

$$x_2 - 4x_3 = 0.$$

These equations are not linearly independent, since their coefficient matrix must be singular. (In fact, 2 times the first minus the second is 4 times the third equation.) From the last two equations, $x_1 = -x_3$ and $x_2 = 4x_3$, so any vector satisfying these equations generates the one-dimensional linear vector space of vectors satisfying $\mathbf{Bx} = \lambda\mathbf{x}$ for $\lambda = 1$. In particular

$$\begin{bmatrix} x_1 \\ x_2 \\ x_3 \end{bmatrix} = k_1 \begin{bmatrix} -1 \\ 4 \\ 1 \end{bmatrix}$$

for k_1 an arbitrary parameter from $\mathscr{F}$, the field from which the elements of $\mathbf{B}$ are chosen.

In a similar manner, for $\lambda = 3$,

$$\begin{bmatrix} -1 & 2 & -7 \\ 2 & -2 & 2 \\ 0 & 1 & -6 \end{bmatrix} \begin{bmatrix} x_1 \\ x_2 \\ x_3 \end{bmatrix} = \begin{bmatrix} 0 \\ 0 \\ 0 \end{bmatrix},$$

or

$$\begin{aligned} -x_1 + 2x_2 - 7x_3 &= 0 \\ 2x_1 - 2x_2 + 2x_3 &= 0 \\ x_2 - 6x_3 &= 0, \end{aligned}$$

from which $x_1 = 5x_3$ and $x_2 = 6x_3$. Then

$$\begin{bmatrix} x_1 \\ x_2 \\ x_3 \end{bmatrix} = k_2 \begin{bmatrix} 5 \\ 6 \\ 1 \end{bmatrix}.$$

Finally $\lambda = -4$ yields

$$\begin{bmatrix} 6 & 2 & -7 \\ 2 & 5 & 2 \\ 0 & 1 & 1 \end{bmatrix} \begin{bmatrix} x_1 \\ x_2 \\ x_3 \end{bmatrix} = \mathbf{0},$$

or

$$\begin{aligned} 6x_1 + 2x_2 - 7x_3 &= 0 \\ 2x_1 + 5x_2 + 2x_3 &= 0 \\ x_2 + x_3 &= 0, \end{aligned}$$

from which $x_1 = (-3/2)x_2$ and $x_3 = -x_2$. Then

$$\begin{bmatrix} x_1 \\ x_2 \\ x_3 \end{bmatrix} = k_3 \begin{bmatrix} -3 \\ 2 \\ -2 \end{bmatrix}.$$

From Example 6.3.2, the three distinct characteristic values of $\mathbf{B}$ are 1, 3, -4, and the three corresponding characteristic vectors are

$$\begin{bmatrix} -1 \\ 4 \\ 1 \end{bmatrix}, \quad \begin{bmatrix} 5 \\ 6 \\ 1 \end{bmatrix}, \quad \text{and} \quad \begin{bmatrix} -3 \\ 2 \\ -2 \end{bmatrix}.$$

These three vectors are linearly independent, since the only set of c_i's that satisfy the equation

$$c_1\begin{bmatrix}-1\\4\\1\end{bmatrix}+c_2\begin{bmatrix}5\\6\\1\end{bmatrix}+c_3\begin{bmatrix}-3\\2\\-2\end{bmatrix}=\begin{bmatrix}0\\0\\0\end{bmatrix}$$

is $c_1 = c_2 = c_3 = 0$. The following theorem states this result in general for distinct characteristic values:

Theorem 6.3.2. *If for the matrix* $\mathbf{A}$ *the vectors* $\{\mathbf{x}_i\}$, $i = 1, 2, \cdots, n$, *are the characteristic vectors corresponding to the distinct characteristic values* $\{\lambda_i\}$, $i = 1, 2, \cdots, n$, *then the vectors* $\{\mathbf{x}_i\}$ *are linearly independent.*

Before proving Theorem 6.3.2, we state a similar theorem, in which the vectors form a real orthogonal set. This occurs, for example, if $\mathbf{A}$ is a real symmetric matrix. (See Theorem 6.6.4.)

Theorem 6.3.3. *If the characteristic vectors* $\{\mathbf{x}_i\}$, $i = 1, 2, \cdots, n$, *of the matrix* $\mathbf{A}$ *form a real othogonal set, then the vectors are linearly independent.*

Proof: If the set $\{\mathbf{x}_i\}$ is an orthogonal set (as in number 10 of Exercise 1.9), then $\mathbf{x}_i'\mathbf{x}_j = d_j\delta_{ij}$, $d_j > 0$, where $j = 1, 2, \cdots, n$, (since the vectors are real), and δ_{ij} is the Kronecker delta.

We assume that the vectors are linearly dependent and encounter a contradiction. Thus,

$$c_1\mathbf{x}_1 + c_2\mathbf{x}_2 + \cdots + c_n\mathbf{x}_n = \mathbf{0}, \tag{6.3.10}$$

with not all $c_i = 0$. If we multiply each side by $\mathbf{x}_i'$,

$$c_1\mathbf{x}_i'\mathbf{x}_1 + \cdots + c_i\mathbf{x}_i'\mathbf{x}_i + \cdots + c_n\mathbf{x}_i'\mathbf{x}_n = 0. \tag{6.3.11}$$

Since the vectors are orthogonal, each $\mathbf{x}_i'\mathbf{x}_j = 0$ if $i \neq j$. Furthermore, since the $\mathbf{x}_i$ are real, then $\mathbf{x}_i'\mathbf{x}_i > 0$. These results imply that $c_i = 0$; similarly, all c's are zero. Thus, the vectors in a real orthogonal set are linearly independent.

Return now to the proof of Theorem 6.3.2. If the vectors are not necessarily orthogonal, the standard technique is to multiply both sides of Eq. (6.3.10) by $\mathbf{A}$ and then use the fact that $\mathbf{A}\mathbf{x}_i = \lambda_i\mathbf{x}_i$ for each characteristic value λ_i and for each characteristic vector $\mathbf{x}_i$. Thus,

(6.3.12)

$$c_1\mathbf{A}\mathbf{x}_1 + c_2\mathbf{A}\mathbf{x}_2 + \cdots + c_n\mathbf{A}\mathbf{x}_n = c_1\lambda_1\mathbf{x}_1 + c_2\lambda_2\mathbf{x}_2 + \cdots + c_n\lambda_n\mathbf{x}_n = \mathbf{0}.$$

Multiplying the right equation in Eq. (6.3.12) by $\mathbf{A}$, and replacing $\mathbf{A}\mathbf{x}_i$ by $\lambda_i\mathbf{x}_i$ again,

$$c_1\lambda_1^2\mathbf{x}_1 + c_2\lambda_2^2\mathbf{x}_2 + \cdots + c_n\lambda_n^2\mathbf{x}_n = \mathbf{0}. \tag{6.3.13}$$

Continuing this process eventually yields

$$c_1\lambda_1^{n-1}\mathbf{x}_1 + c_2\lambda_2^{n-1}\mathbf{x}_2 + \cdots + c_n\lambda_n^{n-1}\mathbf{x}_n = \mathbf{0}. \tag{6.3.14}$$

After taking the transpose of each equation, the resulting n equations may be written as

$$\begin{bmatrix} 1 & 1 & & 1 \\ \lambda_1 & \lambda_2 & \cdots & \lambda_n \\ \cdots & & & \\ \lambda_1^{n-1} & \lambda_2^{n-1} & \cdots & \lambda_n^{n-1} \end{bmatrix} \begin{bmatrix} c_1\mathbf{x}_1' \\ c_2\mathbf{x}_2' \\ \cdots \\ c_n\mathbf{x}_n' \end{bmatrix} = \mathbf{0}. \tag{6.3.15}$$

Since the first matrix in the product is the Vandermonde matrix (of number 11 of Exercises 2.6), and since such a matrix is singular if and only if two of the λ_i are equal, it is nonsingular by the assumption that the λ_i are distinct. Thus

$$\begin{bmatrix} c_1\mathbf{x}_1' \\ c_2\mathbf{x}_2' \\ \cdots \\ c_n\mathbf{x}_n' \end{bmatrix} = \mathbf{0}, \tag{6.3.16}$$

which implies the each $c_i = 0$ and the theorem is proved.

Since the vectors in Theorem 6.3.2 are linearly independent, the vectors in any subset of these vectors are also linearly independent. (See section 5.1.)

Exercises 6.3

1. For each of the following matrices, find the characteristic values and the corresponding characteristic vectors.

(a) $\begin{bmatrix} -1 & -2 & -1 \\ -2 & 1 & 1 \\ -3 & 8 & 3 \end{bmatrix}$ (b) $\begin{bmatrix} 7 & 4 & -1 \\ 4 & 7 & -1 \\ -4 & -4 & 4 \end{bmatrix}$ (c) $\begin{bmatrix} 1 & 2 & 4 \\ 0 & 1 & 0 \\ 0 & 2 & 1 \end{bmatrix}$

2. Prove or disprove that the characteristic vectors of

$$\begin{bmatrix} 2 & 1 & 1 \\ -2 & -1 & -1 \\ 0 & 0 & 2 \end{bmatrix}$$

are orthogonal. (See number 4 of Exercises 2.3.)

3. Show that if **A** and **B** are similar they have the same characteristic equation.

4. Show that the characteristic values of $\mathbf{A}^{-1}$ are the reciprocals of the characteristic values of **A**.

5. Show that if **x** is a characteristic vector of $\mathbf{Ax} = \lambda\mathbf{x}$, then $\mathbf{Bx}$ is also a characteristic vector associated with λ if **B** commutes with **A** under multiplication.

6. Multiply both sides of $\mathbf{Ax} = \lambda\mathbf{x}$ by $\mathbf{x}'$ and show how to determine λ if $\mathbf{x}$ is known.
7. In the plane, sketch the geometric vectors that are left invariant under the transformation

$$\begin{bmatrix} 3 & 3 \\ 5 & 1 \end{bmatrix}.$$

On the same sketch show both

$$\begin{bmatrix} 1 \\ 0 \end{bmatrix} \text{ and } \begin{bmatrix} 1 \\ -1 \end{bmatrix}$$

and their images under this transformation. Do any of the vectors have the same magnitude as their corresponding image?

8. Work exercise 7 using

$$\text{(a)}\quad \mathbf{I} = \begin{bmatrix} 1 & 0 \\ 0 & 1 \end{bmatrix}, \qquad \text{(b)}\quad \mathbf{B} = \begin{bmatrix} 1 & 2 \\ 0 & 1 \end{bmatrix}, \qquad \text{(c)}\quad \mathbf{C} = \begin{bmatrix} 0 & 1 \\ 1 & 0 \end{bmatrix}.$$

9. Show that if $\mathbf{x}$ is a characteristic vector of $\mathbf{Ax} = \lambda\mathbf{x}$ and $\mathbf{y}$ is a characteristic vector of $\mathbf{A}'\mathbf{y} = \mu\mathbf{y}$, and if $\lambda \neq \mu$, then $\mathbf{x}$ and $\mathbf{y}$ are orthogonal. (See number 4 of Exercises 2.3.)

6.4. *The Characteristic Polynomial*

The expansion of $\det(\mathbf{A} - \lambda\mathbf{I})$ yields the characteristic polynomial $f(\lambda)$ of Eq. (6.3.7):

(6.4.1) $$f(\lambda) = (-1)^n\lambda^n + \cdots + |\mathbf{A}|.$$

Several properties of the polynomial $f(\lambda)$ can be verified easily:

(a) The characteristic polynomial $f(\lambda)$ is a polynomial of degree n in λ.
(b) The leading coefficient of $f(\lambda)$ is $(-1)^n$ and the constant term is $|\mathbf{A}|$.
(c) The remaining coefficients of $f(\lambda)$ are elements of $\mathscr{F}$.
(d) If α_1 is a root of $f(\lambda) = 0$, then $|\mathbf{A} - \alpha_1\mathbf{I}| = 0$, and the rank of $(\mathbf{A} - \alpha_1\mathbf{I})$ is r where $r \leqq n - 1$.
(e) Since $(\mathbf{A} - \alpha_1\mathbf{I})$ has rank r there are $n - r$ linearly independent solutions of $(\mathbf{A} - \alpha_1\mathbf{I})\mathbf{x} = \mathbf{0}$. (See Theorem 5.5.1.)

To elaborate on (c) above, and find the other coefficients in the characteristic polynomial, consider the situation when $n = 3$. Section 2.12 stated that a determinant of order n may be written as the sum of two determinants of order n. In the following expansion, the characteristic equation is first written as a sum of two determinants; each of these is then written as a sum of two determinants (in order); next each of these four determinants is written as a sum of two determinants (in order); and finally the determinants are each (partially) expanded, using Laplace's expansion, to give the characteristic equation in an expanded form. That is,

(6.4.2)

$$f(\lambda) = \begin{vmatrix} a_{11}-\lambda & a_{12} & a_{13} \\ a_{21} & a_{22}-\lambda & a_{23} \\ a_{31} & a_{32} & a_{33}-\lambda \end{vmatrix}$$

$$= \begin{vmatrix} a_{11} & a_{12} & a_{13} \\ a_{21} & a_{22}-\lambda & a_{23} \\ a_{31} & a_{32} & a_{33}-\lambda \end{vmatrix} + \begin{vmatrix} -\lambda & a_{12} & a_{13} \\ 0 & a_{22}-\lambda & a_{23} \\ 0 & a_{32} & a_{33}-\lambda \end{vmatrix}$$

$$= \begin{vmatrix} a_{11} & a_{12} & a_{13} \\ a_{21} & a_{22} & a_{23} \\ a_{31} & a_{32} & a_{33}-\lambda \end{vmatrix} + \begin{vmatrix} a_{11} & 0 & a_{13} \\ a_{21} & -\lambda & a_{23} \\ a_{31} & 0 & a_{33}-\lambda \end{vmatrix}$$

$$+ \begin{vmatrix} -\lambda & a_{12} & a_{13} \\ 0 & a_{22} & a_{23} \\ 0 & a_{32} & a_{33}-\lambda \end{vmatrix} + \begin{vmatrix} -\lambda & 0 & a_{13} \\ 0 & -\lambda & a_{23} \\ 0 & 0 & a_{33}-\lambda \end{vmatrix}$$

$$= \begin{vmatrix} a_{11} & a_{12} & a_{13} \\ a_{21} & a_{22} & a_{23} \\ a_{31} & a_{32} & a_{33} \end{vmatrix} + \begin{vmatrix} a_{11} & a_{12} & 0 \\ a_{21} & a_{22} & 0 \\ a_{31} & a_{32} & -\lambda \end{vmatrix} + \begin{vmatrix} a_{11} & 0 & a_{13} \\ a_{21} & -\lambda & a_{23} \\ a_{31} & 0 & a_{33} \end{vmatrix}$$

$$+ \begin{vmatrix} a_{11} & 0 & 0 \\ a_{21} & -\lambda & 0 \\ a_{31} & 0 & -\lambda \end{vmatrix} + \begin{vmatrix} -\lambda & a_{12} & a_{13} \\ 0 & a_{22} & a_{23} \\ 0 & a_{32} & a_{33} \end{vmatrix} + \begin{vmatrix} -\lambda & a_{12} & 0 \\ 0 & a_{22} & 0 \\ 0 & a_{32} & -\lambda \end{vmatrix}$$

$$+ \begin{vmatrix} -\lambda & 0 & a_{13} \\ 0 & -\lambda & a_{23} \\ 0 & 0 & a_{33} \end{vmatrix} + \begin{vmatrix} -\lambda & 0 & 0 \\ 0 & -\lambda & 0 \\ 0 & 0 & -\lambda \end{vmatrix}$$

$$= (-1)^3\lambda^3 + (-1)^2\lambda^2(a_{11}+a_{22}+a_{33})$$

$$+ (-1)\lambda\left(\begin{vmatrix} a_{22} & a_{23} \\ a_{32} & a_{33} \end{vmatrix} + \begin{vmatrix} a_{11} & a_{13} \\ a_{31} & a_{33} \end{vmatrix} + \begin{vmatrix} a_{11} & a_{12} \\ a_{21} & a_{22} \end{vmatrix}\right) + \det \mathbf{A};$$

the terms in the final expression are not taken in order.

From the final form of Eq. (6.4.2), the result can be generalized to a determinant of order n:

Theorem 6.4.1. *The characteristic polynomial for the square matrix* $\mathbf{A}$ *is*

(6.4.3) $$f(\lambda) = (-1)^n\lambda^n + (-1)^{n-1}\lambda^{n-1}(\text{tr } \mathbf{A})$$

$+ (-1)^{n-2}\lambda^{n-2}$ (*sum of principal minors of order* 2)
$+ \cdots - \lambda$ (*sum of principal minors of order* $n-1$) $+ \det \mathbf{A}$.

Note in the coefficient of λ^{n-1} in Eq. (6.4.3) that the sum of the principal minors of order one is tr **A** (defined in Section 1.4). Also observe in Eq. (6.4.3) that the signs of the terms of $f(\lambda)$ alternate. (No proof is given here for the theorem, since a proof by this method would be extremely tedious.)

Example 6.4.1. Use Theorem 6.4.1 to determine the characteristic polynomial of **A** if

$$\mathbf{A} = \begin{bmatrix} 1 & 0 & -1 \\ 1 & 2 & 1 \\ 2 & 2 & 3 \end{bmatrix}.$$

By Theorem 6.4.1,

$$\begin{aligned} f(\lambda) &= \begin{vmatrix} 1 & 0 & -1 \\ 1 & 2 & 1 \\ 2 & 2 & 3 \end{vmatrix} - \left(\begin{vmatrix} 2 & 1 \\ 2 & 3 \end{vmatrix} + \begin{vmatrix} 1 & -1 \\ 2 & 3 \end{vmatrix} + \begin{vmatrix} 1 & 0 \\ 1 & 2 \end{vmatrix} \right) \lambda \\ &\quad + (1 + 2 + 3)\lambda^2 - \lambda^3 \\ &= 6 - 11\lambda + 6\lambda^2 - \lambda^3, \end{aligned}$$

which is the same result as that obtained by direct expansion of $\det(\mathbf{A} - \lambda\mathbf{I})$.

Exercises 6.4

1. Find the characteristic polynomial of the following matrices **A**, first from the definition and then by Theorem 6.4.1.

(a) $\begin{bmatrix} 1 & 2 \\ 3 & 4 \end{bmatrix}$ (b) $\begin{bmatrix} 1 & 0 & 1 \\ -1 & -1 & 0 \\ 1 & 1 & 1 \end{bmatrix}$ (c) $\begin{bmatrix} 1 & 0 & 0 & 0 \\ 1 & 2 & 0 & 0 \\ 1 & 2 & 1 & 0 \\ 4 & 5 & 6 & -1 \end{bmatrix}$

2. Find $f'(\lambda)$, $f''(\lambda)$, $f'''(\lambda)$, using Section 2.13, and also by evaluating $f(\lambda)$ and differentiating, if $f(\lambda)$ is the characteristic polynomial of

(a) $\begin{bmatrix} 1 & 1 \\ 2 & 5 \end{bmatrix}$, (b) $\begin{bmatrix} 1 & 0 & 0 \\ -1 & 2 & 3 \\ -2 & 1 & 1 \end{bmatrix}$.

3. If $\mathbf{Ax} = \lambda\mathbf{x}$ and **A** is nonsingular, show that $\mathbf{A}^{-1}\mathbf{x} = \lambda^{-1}\mathbf{x}$.

4. For each matrix **A** in exercise 1 find the rank of $\mathbf{A} - \lambda_i\mathbf{I}$ for each λ_i. Then verify property (e) following Eq. (6.4.1) for each.

5. Find the characteristic polynomial associated with **A** if **A** is (a) a scalar matrix, (b) a diagonal matrix, (c) a triangular matrix.

6. Find the characteristic polynomial for a skew symmetric matrix of order 3. Then prove that if the matrix is real it has no positive or negative characteristic values.

7. Show that

$$f^{(k)}(\lambda) = \begin{cases} (-1)^k k! \text{ (sum of the principal minors of} \\ \mathbf{A} - \lambda\mathbf{I} \text{ of order } n-k) \text{ for } k < n, \\ (-1)^n n!, \text{ for } k = n, \text{ and} \\ 0, \text{ for } k > n. \end{cases}$$

Hint: Use Section 2.13 and

$$f(\lambda) = \begin{vmatrix} a_{11} - \lambda & \cdots & a_{1n} \\ \cdots & & \\ a_{n1} & \cdots & a_{nn} - \lambda \end{vmatrix}.$$

6.5. *The Characteristic Value Problem Continued*

The characteristic value problem is a most important topic in a number of areas of mathematics. Actually, only a few of the basic ideas can be presented in this book; a great number of interesting and powerful theorems may be found in more advanced discussions in the literature.

In the preceding sections of this chapter, the examples and exercises were concerned only with real distinct characteristic values of a matrix. This section considers some instances in which the characteristic equation has repeated roots or has complex roots, as well as certain other important ideas regarding the characteristic equation.

If **A** is a singular matrix, then **A** has at least one characteristic value that is zero. In the characteristic polynomial $f(\lambda)$ of Eq. (6.4.1), the constant term is det **A**, and the remaining terms of the polynomial have λ as a common factor. That is, $\lambda = 0$ is a characteristic value. This result is stated as a theorem:

Theorem 6.5.1. *Any singular matrix* **A** *has a zero characteristic value.*

Although in most of our examples and exercises the characteristic values are real numbers (generally integers), there are important cases (such as in solving systems of differential equations) where the characteristic values are complex numbers. If **A** is a matrix with real elements, the characteristic polynomial is a polynomial of degree n with real coefficients, Then, from elementary algebra we know that the characteristic equation has n roots. Furthermore, if one root is complex, then the complex conjugate is also a root.

Example 6.5.1. Find the characteristic values for

$$\begin{bmatrix} 1 & -2 & 1 \\ 1 & -1 & 0 \\ 0 & -1 & 1 \end{bmatrix}.$$

The characteristic polynomial is $-\lambda^3 + \lambda^2 - \lambda$, and thus the characteristic values are 0, $(1 \pm \sqrt{3})/2$. Note that the matrix is singular.

From property (d) of the preceding section, $\mathbf{A} - \lambda_i \mathbf{I}$ is singular if λ_i is a root of the characteristic equation, whether λ_i is a repeated root or not. That is, if r is the rank of $\mathbf{A} - \lambda_i \mathbf{I}$, then $r \leqq n - 1$. If λ_i is a k-fold root of the characteristic equation, what further can be said about the rank of $\mathbf{A} - \lambda_i \mathbf{I}$? What can be said about the number of independent vectors required to span the vector space associated with the characteristic root λ_i of $\mathbf{A}$?

The following example shows that if λ_i is a k-fold root of the characteristic equation of $\mathbf{A}_n$, then the rank of $\mathbf{A} - \lambda_i \mathbf{I}$ may be $n - 1, n - 2, \cdots, n - k$, and the dimension of the associated invariant vector space may be $1, 2, \cdots, k$.

Example 6.5.2. Find the characteristic values of $\mathbf{A}$, the rank of $\mathbf{A} - \lambda_i \mathbf{I}$, and a basis of characteristic vectors for the matrix $\mathbf{A} - \lambda_i \mathbf{I}$ if $\mathbf{A}$ is

(a) $\begin{bmatrix} 0 & 1 & 0 \\ 0 & 0 & 1 \\ 6 & -11 & 6 \end{bmatrix}$, (b) $\begin{bmatrix} 0 & 1 & 0 \\ 0 & 0 & 1 \\ -2 & -5 & -4 \end{bmatrix}$,

(c) $\begin{bmatrix} 0 & 1 & 0 \\ 0 & 0 & 1 \\ -1 & -3 & -3 \end{bmatrix}$, (d) $\begin{bmatrix} 1 & 0 & 1 \\ 0 & 1 & 0 \\ 0 & 0 & 1 \end{bmatrix}$, (e) $\mathbf{I}_3$.

The details of this example are left as an exercise; the results are given here.

In (a) the characteristic values are 1, 2, 3, the corresponding ranks of $\mathbf{A} - \lambda_i \mathbf{I}$ are 2, 2, 2, and possible corresponding characteristic vectors are $[1 \ 1 \ 1]'$, $[1 \ 2 \ 4]'$, and $[1 \ 3 \ 9]'$.

The corresponding results for (b) are $-1, -1, -2$ as characteristic values, the rank is 2 in each case, and corresponding characteristic vectors are $[1 \ -1 \ 1]'$, for -1 and $[1 \ -2 \ 4]'$ for -2. Note that only one vector is required to span the vector space associated with the characteristic value -1.

For (c) the characteristic values are $-1, -1, -1$, the rank is 2, and there is one linearly independent vector $[1 \ -1 \ 1]'$ required to span the vector space associated with this characteristic value.

In case (d), however, the characteristic values are 1, 1, 1, the rank is 1, and possible independent vectors are $[1 \ 2 \ 0]'$ and $[0 \ 1 \ 0]'$.

For (e) the characteristic values are again 1, 1, 1, the rank is zero, and possible independent vectors are $[1\ \ 0\ \ 0]'$, $[0\ \ 1\ \ 0]'$, and $[0\ \ 0\ \ 1]'$.

Observe that all of the invariant vectors associated with each matrix are linearly independent as required by Theorem 6.3.2.

The preceding example gives special cases of the following theorem.

Theorem 6.5.2. *If the matrix* $\mathbf{A}$ *is of order* n *and if* λ_i *is a* k*-fold root of the characteristic equation* $\det(\mathbf{A} - \lambda \mathbf{I}) = 0$, *then the rank* r *of* $\mathbf{A} - \lambda_i \mathbf{I}$ *is* $n - k \leqq r \leqq n - 1$; *and the nullity* j *for* $\mathbf{A} - \lambda_i \mathbf{I}$, *the dimension of the invariant vector space of* $\mathbf{A}$ *associated with* λ_i, *is* $1 \leqq j \leqq k$.

Proof: If λ_i is a k-fold root of $f(\lambda) = 0$, then we can write $f(\lambda) = (\lambda - \lambda_i)^k g(\lambda)$, where $g(\lambda)$ is a polynomial in λ of degree $n - k$ not containing the factor $\lambda - \lambda_i$. Then, by Taylor's expansion of $f(\lambda)$, we have that $f^{(j)}(\lambda_i) = 0$, $j = 0, 1, \cdots, k - 1$, while $f^{(k)}(\lambda_i) \neq 0$. By number 7 of Exercises 6.4, since $f^{(k)}(\lambda_i) \neq 0$, not all principal minors of order $n - k$ can be zero. Hence the rank r of $\mathbf{A} - \lambda_i \mathbf{I}$ is at least $n - k$. The rank is no greater than $n - 1$, since $\mathbf{A} - \lambda_i \mathbf{I}$ must be singular. Thus we have that $n - k \leqq r \leqq n - 1$.

By Section 5.5, if the matrix $\mathbf{A} - \lambda_i \mathbf{I}$ has rank r, then the nullity is $j = n - r$. Thus, substituting $r = n - j$ in $n - k \leqq r \leqq n - 1$ yields $1 \leqq j \leqq k$. That is, the number j of invariant vectors associated with λ_i is at least one and is no greater than k.

This section concludes with one more result dealing with the characteristic values of a matrix $\mathbf{A}$. This result, known as Gerschgorin's Theorem,* is concerned with a rough approximation of the characteristic values of $\mathbf{A}$ in terms of the elements of $\mathbf{A}$.†

If the elements of $\mathbf{A}$ are assumed to be from $\mathscr{F}_r$ or $\mathscr{F}_c$, then the characteristic values of $\mathbf{A}$ are from $\mathscr{F}_c$ (although they may be real). If $\mathbf{x}$ is a characteristic vector of $\mathbf{A}$ corresponding to the characteristic value λ, then $\mathbf{A}\mathbf{x} = \lambda \mathbf{x}$, or

$$\lambda x_i = \sum_j a_{ij} x_j, \qquad i = 1, 2, \cdots, n. \tag{6.5.1}$$

This equation may also be written as

$$(\lambda - a_{ii}) x_i = \sum_j{}' a_{ij} x_j, \qquad i = 1, 2, \cdots, n, \tag{6.5.2}$$

where $\sum_j{}'$ indicates that the summation is for $j = 1, 2, \cdots, n$ excluding $j = i$. If

$$K_i = \sum_j{}' |a_{ij}|$$

*Named after the Russian mathematician S. Gerschgorin who published an article in Russian with some of these results in 1931.

†See "A Recurring Theorem on Determinants" by Olga Taussky in the *American Mathematical Monthly*, Vol. 56 (1949), pp. 672–676, for an interesting discussion and an excellent list of references over topics in this area.

and $m = \max\{|x_1|, \cdots, |x_n|\}$, then

(6.5.3) $$|\lambda - a_{ii}|\,|x_i| \leqq \sum_j{}' |a_{ij}|\,|x_j| \leqq m \sum_j{}' |a_{ij}| = K_i m.$$

If k is the integer such that $|x_k| = m > 0$, then

(6.5.4) $$|\lambda - a_{kk}| \leqq K_k,$$

after dividing through by $|x_k|$. This leads us to *Gerschgorin's Theorem:**

Theorem 6.5.3. *The characteristic values of* **A** *lie in the union of the sets of all points* Λ *such that*

(6.5.5) $$|\Lambda - a_{ii}| \leqq K_i, \qquad i = 1, 2, \cdots, n.$$

By this theorem if one constructs circles in the complex plane for $i = 1, 2, \cdots, n$ with the elements a_{ii} as centers and the sum of the absolute values of the remaining elements in the ith row as the corresponding radii, then each characteristic value for **A** must lie in or on one of the circles, the *Gerschgorin discs.*

Since the characteristic values for **A** are the same as for **A**′, a corresponding result holds for columns of **A** as for rows. Since the set of discs is generally not the same in the two cases, the characteristic values all lie in the intersection of the two sets of discs, and thus are determined more precisely.

Example 6.5.3. Sketch the Gerschgorin discs and verify that the characteristic values found for **A** in Example 6.5.1 satisfy Theorem 6.5.3.

The points common to the discs with centers at 1, -1, and 1 and corresponding radii 3, 1, and 1 all lie in or on the first circle. Furthermore the characteristic values 0, $(1 \pm \sqrt{3})/2$ all lie within this circle.

Exercises 6.5

1. Find the characteristic values and characteristic vectors for the matrix **C** if **C** is

$$\text{(a)} \begin{bmatrix} 0 & 1 & 1 \\ 1 & 0 & 1 \\ 2 & 1 & 3 \end{bmatrix}, \quad \text{(b)} \begin{bmatrix} 0 & 1 & 0 \\ 0 & 0 & 1 \\ -8 & 4 & -2 \end{bmatrix}, \quad \text{(c)} \begin{bmatrix} 0 & 0 & 1 \\ 0 & 1 & 0 \\ 1 & 0 & 0 \end{bmatrix}.$$

2. Determine the ranks of $\mathbf{C} - \lambda_i \mathbf{I}$ in each case in exercise 1. Find the number of invariant vectors associated with each eigenvalue in exercise 1.

3. Verify that the results of Example 6.5.2 are correct.

4. (a) Find the characteristic values for

$$\mathbf{A} = \begin{bmatrix} 1 & -1 & 0 & 0 \\ 1 & 3 & 0 & 0 \\ 0 & 0 & 3 & 1 \\ 0 & 0 & 1 & 3 \end{bmatrix}.$$

   (b) Find the bounds for the rank and nullity of $\mathbf{A} - \lambda_i \mathbf{I}$ for each characteristic value, using Theorem 6.5.2.

   (c) Actually determine the rank of $\mathbf{A} - \lambda_i \mathbf{I}$ and find a basis of characteristic vectors for each characteristic value found in (a).

5. Prove that $\mu\lambda_i$, $i = 1, 2, \cdots, n$, are the characteristic values of $\mu\mathbf{A}$, if λ_i, $i = 1, 2, \cdots, n$, are the characteristic values of $\mathbf{A}$, and μ is a scalar.

6. Prove that $\lambda_i - \mu$, $i = 1, 2, \cdots, n$, are the characteristic values of $\mathbf{A} - \mu\mathbf{I}$, if λ_i, $i = 1, 2, \cdots, n$, are the characteristic values of $\mathbf{A}$, and μ is a scalar.

7. Verify that Gerschgorin's Theorem is satisfied for

(a) $\begin{bmatrix} 2 & 1 & 1 \\ -2 & -1 & 1 \\ 0 & 0 & 2 \end{bmatrix}$, (b) $\begin{bmatrix} 1 & 0 & -1 \\ 1 & 2 & 1 \\ 2 & 2 & 3 \end{bmatrix}$, (c) $\begin{bmatrix} 1 & 0 & 1 \\ -1 & -1 & 0 \\ 1 & 1 & 1 \end{bmatrix}$,

(d) $\begin{bmatrix} 2i & 1-i \\ 2 & -i-1 \end{bmatrix}$, (e) $\begin{bmatrix} 1+i & 1 \\ 1 & -1-i \end{bmatrix}$.

6.6. *Symmetric Matrices*

A matrix $\mathbf{A}$ is *symmetric* if it is equal to its transpose: $\mathbf{A} = \mathbf{A}'$. (See Section 1.10.) This section examines some of the properties associated with the characteristic value problem when $\mathbf{A}$ is symmetric.

If $\mathbf{A}$ is a symmetric matrix, then the characteristic values and characteristic vectors of $\mathbf{A}$ are the same as for $\mathbf{A}'$, since $\mathbf{A} = \mathbf{A}'$. More important, even if $\mathbf{B}$ is not symmetric, $\mathbf{B}$ and $\mathbf{B}'$ have the same characteristic values:

Theorem 6.6.1. *Any square matrix* $\mathbf{B}$ *and its transpose* $\mathbf{B}'$ *have the same characteristic values.*

Proof: By Theorem 6.4.1, the coefficients of λ^k in the characteristic polynomial $f(\lambda)$ are $(-1)^k$ times the sum of principal minors of $\mathbf{B}$ of order $n - k$. Since the principal minors of $\mathbf{B}$ are the same as those of $\mathbf{B}'$, the coefficients in $f(\lambda)$ are the same for $\mathbf{B}$ and $\mathbf{B}'$. Hence, $\mathbf{B}$ and $\mathbf{B}'$ have the same characteristic values.

Another theorem that holds for any square matrix is the following. (If the matrix is real, this theorem becomes the same as Theorem 6.6.1.)

Theorem 6.6.2. *The characteristic values of a square matrix* **B** *are the conjugates of the characteristic values of* **B***.

Proof: By Theorem 6.4.1, since the principal minors of $\overline{\mathbf{B}}$ are the conjugates of the principal minors of **B**, then the roots of the characteristic equation of $\overline{\mathbf{B}}$ are the conjugates of the roots of the characteristic equation of **B**. Note by Theorem 6.6.1 that this proof need not use $\overline{\mathbf{B}}'(= \mathbf{B}^*)$.

Theorem 6.6.3. *If* **A** *is a real symmetric matrix, then the characteristic values and characteristic vectors of* **A** *are all real.*

Proof: For the first part of this theorem we assume the contrary case: if **x** is a characteristic vector corresponding to λ, then $\overline{\mathbf{x}}$ is a characteristic vector corresponding to $\overline{\lambda}$. Thus

$$\mathbf{Ax} = \lambda\mathbf{x} \quad \text{and} \quad \mathbf{A}\overline{\mathbf{x}} = \overline{\lambda}\overline{\mathbf{x}}.$$

Multiplying both sides of the first equation by $\overline{\mathbf{x}}'$ and the second by $\mathbf{x}'$,

$$\overline{\mathbf{x}}'\mathbf{Ax} = \lambda\overline{\mathbf{x}}'\mathbf{x} \quad \text{and} \quad \mathbf{x}'\mathbf{A}\overline{\mathbf{x}} = \overline{\lambda}\mathbf{x}'\overline{\mathbf{x}}.$$

Then, taking the transpose in the second equation,

$$\overline{\mathbf{x}}'\mathbf{Ax} = \lambda\overline{\mathbf{x}}'\mathbf{x} \quad \text{and} \quad \overline{\mathbf{x}}'\mathbf{Ax} = \overline{\lambda}\overline{\mathbf{x}}'\mathbf{x},$$

since **A** is symmetric. From these two equations,

$$0 = (\lambda - \lambda)\overline{\mathbf{x}}'\mathbf{x}.$$

This implies that $\lambda = \overline{\lambda}$, so that λ is real, since **x** is a characteristic vector and thus is not the zero vector. The proof of the second part of the theorem is left as an exercise.

Theorem 6.6.4. *If* **x** *and* **y** *are distinct characteristic vectors associated with distinct characteristic values* λ *and* μ *of a real symmetric matrix* **A**, *then* **x** *and* **y** *are orthogonal.*

Proof: By assumption,

$$\mathbf{Ax} = \lambda\mathbf{x} \quad \text{and} \quad \mathbf{Ay} = \mu\mathbf{y} \quad \text{where} \quad \lambda \neq \mu.$$

Then, as in the preceding proof,

$$\mathbf{y}'\mathbf{Ax} = \lambda\mathbf{y}'\mathbf{x} \quad \text{and} \quad \mathbf{x}'\mathbf{Ay} = \mu\mathbf{x}'\mathbf{y},$$

or

$$\mathbf{x}'\mathbf{Ay} = \lambda\mathbf{x}'\mathbf{y} \quad \text{and} \quad \mathbf{x}'\mathbf{Ay} = \mu\mathbf{x}'\mathbf{y},$$

since **A** is symmetric. Thus

$$0 = (\lambda - \mu)\mathbf{x}'\mathbf{y}.$$

Since $\lambda \neq \mu$, $\mathbf{x}'\mathbf{y} = 0$, proving that **x** and **y** are orthogonal.

Exercises 6.6

1. Give examples of matrices of order 2 and of order 3 to show that even though **B** and **B′** have the same characteristic values (by Theorem 6.6.1), they need not have the same characteristic vectors. Give an example of a matrix of order 3 that has the same characteristic values and characteristic vectors as its transpose.

2. Prove that if **A** is a real skew symmetric matrix then all of the characteristic values are pure imaginary.

3. Verify Theorem 6.6.2 for

$$\begin{bmatrix} 0 & 0 & 1-i \\ 0 & i & 0 \\ -1+i & 0 & 0 \end{bmatrix}.$$

4. Verify Theorem 6.6.3 for

(a) $\begin{bmatrix} 2 & 2 & -2 \\ 2 & 3 & 0 \\ -2 & 0 & 1 \end{bmatrix}$, (b) $\begin{bmatrix} -1 & -2 & 1 \\ -2 & 0 & -2 \\ 1 & -2 & 1 \end{bmatrix}$, (c) $\begin{bmatrix} 0 & 1 & 1 \\ 1 & 1 & -1 \\ 1 & -1 & 0 \end{bmatrix}$.

5. Find the characteristic values for each matrix in exercise 4 and verify that they are mutually orthogonal if the characteristic vectors are distinct.

6. Prove the theorem: *If* **A** *is an Hermitian matrix, then the characteristic values of* **A** *are all real.*

7. Prove Theorem 6.6.4 for Hermitian matrices instead of real symmetric matrices.

8. Prove that the characteristic vectors of a real symmetric matrix are all real.

6.7. *Similar Matrices*

A matrix **B** is *similar* to a matrix **A** if there exists a nonsingular matrix **C** such that

$$\mathbf{B} = \mathbf{C}^{-1}\mathbf{A}\mathbf{C}. \tag{6.7.1}$$

(See Section 6.2.) The transformation from **A** to **B** is a *similarity transformation*, and $\mathbf{C}^{-1}\mathbf{A}\mathbf{C}$ is the *transform* of **A** by **C**.

The study of characteristic value problems has generated a great number of theorems dealing with similar matrices. This section presents a few of the more useful ones.

Theorem 6.7.1. *Similar matrices have equal determinants, the same characteristic equations, and the same characteristic values.*

Note that this theorem does *not* say that similar matrices have the same characteristic vectors; in general, they do not.

Proof: By Theorem 2.10.1, the determinant of the product of matrices is equal to the product of the determinants of the matrices. If $\mathbf{B} = \mathbf{C}^{-1}\mathbf{A}\mathbf{C}$, then

$$|\mathbf{B}| = |\mathbf{C}^{-1}\mathbf{A}\mathbf{C}| = |\mathbf{C}^{-1}|\,|\mathbf{A}|\,|\mathbf{C}| = |\mathbf{A}|, \tag{6.7.2}$$

since $|\mathbf{C}^{-1}| = 1/|\mathbf{C}|$.

The second part of the theorem requires that $|\mathbf{C}^{-1}\mathbf{A}\mathbf{C} - \lambda\mathbf{I}| = |\mathbf{A} - \lambda\mathbf{I}|$. Now,

$$|\mathbf{C}^{-1}\mathbf{A}\mathbf{C} - \lambda\mathbf{I}| = |\mathbf{C}^{-1}\mathbf{A}\mathbf{C} - \lambda\mathbf{C}^{-1}\mathbf{C}| = |\mathbf{C}^{-1}(\mathbf{A} - \lambda\mathbf{I})\mathbf{C}|$$
$$= |\mathbf{C}^{-1}|\,|\mathbf{A} - \lambda\mathbf{I}|\,|\mathbf{C}| = |\mathbf{A} - \lambda\mathbf{I}|,$$

again using the fact that $|\mathbf{C}^{-1}| = 1/|\mathbf{C}|$. Hence $\mathbf{A}$ and $\mathbf{C}^{-1}\mathbf{A}\mathbf{C}$ have the same characteristic equations

$$f(\lambda) = |\mathbf{A} - \lambda\mathbf{I}| = |\mathbf{C}^{-1}\mathbf{A}\mathbf{C} - \lambda\mathbf{I}| = 0, \tag{6.7.3}$$

and thus have the same characteristic values.

Although Theorem 6.7.1 does not say that similar matrices have the same characteristic vectors, the following theorem shows how these vectors may be obtained from the characteristic vectors of a similar matrix.

Theorem 6.7.2. *If* $\mathbf{y}_i$ *is a characteristic vector of* $\mathbf{B} = \mathbf{C}^{-1}\mathbf{A}\mathbf{C}$ *corresponding to the characteristic value* λ_i, *then* $\mathbf{x}_i = \mathbf{C}\mathbf{y}_i$ *is the characteristic vector of* $\mathbf{A}$ *corresponding to the same characteristic value* λ_i *of* $\mathbf{B}$.

Proof: Matrices $\mathbf{B}$ and $\mathbf{A}$ have the same characteristic values by Theorem 6.7.1. Now $\mathbf{B}\mathbf{y}_i = \lambda_i\mathbf{y}_i$ and $\mathbf{C}\mathbf{B} = \mathbf{A}\mathbf{C}$ (from $\mathbf{B} = \mathbf{C}^{-1}\mathbf{A}\mathbf{C}$) are given, and the proof requires that if $\mathbf{x}_i = \mathbf{C}\mathbf{y}_i$, then $\mathbf{A}\mathbf{x}_i = \lambda_i\mathbf{x}_i$. Thus,

$$\mathbf{A}\mathbf{x}_i = \mathbf{A}\mathbf{C}\mathbf{y}_i = \mathbf{C}\mathbf{B}\mathbf{y}_i = \mathbf{C}\lambda_i\mathbf{y}_i = \lambda_i\mathbf{C}\mathbf{y}_i = \lambda_i\mathbf{x}_i,$$

and the theorem is proved.

Theorem 6.7.2 gives us another method for finding the characteristic vectors of a matrix (in addition to those methods given in earlier sections). If a matrix similar to $\mathbf{A}$ can be found that is in a form simpler than $\mathbf{A}$ (say in diagonal or triangular form), then the characteristic values and characteristic vectors are more easily obtained. From these characteristic vectors the characteristic vectors of the original matrix $\mathbf{A}$ can be determined, by Theorem 6.7.2, while the characteristic values are the same for each matrix by Theorem 6.7.1.

Example 6.7.1. Obtain the characteristic values and the characteristic vectors for the matrix $\mathbf{A}$ by using the preceding theorems if

$$\mathbf{A} = \begin{bmatrix} 2 & 2 & 1 \\ 1 & 3 & 1 \\ 1 & 2 & 2 \end{bmatrix}.$$

If **C** is chosen to be

$$\mathbf{C} = \begin{bmatrix} 1 & 2 & 1 \\ 1 & -1 & 0 \\ 1 & 0 & -1 \end{bmatrix}, \qquad \text{then} \quad \mathbf{C}^{-1} = 1/4 \begin{bmatrix} 1 & 2 & 1 \\ 1 & -2 & 1 \\ 1 & 2 & -3 \end{bmatrix} \quad \text{and}$$

$$\mathbf{B} = \mathbf{C}^{-1}\mathbf{AC} = \begin{bmatrix} 5 & 0 & 0 \\ 0 & 1 & 0 \\ 0 & 0 & 1 \end{bmatrix}.$$

The characteristic values for **B** are thus $\lambda_1 = 5$, $\lambda_2 = 1$, and $\lambda_3 = 1$. The characteristic vector $\mathbf{y}_1$ corresponding to $\lambda_1 = 5$ is obtained from

$$(\mathbf{B} - \lambda_1 \mathbf{I})\mathbf{y}_1 = \begin{bmatrix} 0 & 0 & 0 \\ 0 & -4 & 0 \\ 0 & 0 & -4 \end{bmatrix} \begin{bmatrix} y_1 \\ y_2 \\ y_3 \end{bmatrix} = \begin{bmatrix} 0 \\ 0 \\ 0 \end{bmatrix}.$$

Thus y_1 is arbitrary, $y_2 = 0$, and $y_3 = 0$, so $\mathbf{y}_1 = [1 \ \ 0 \ \ 0]'$. Any nonzero multiple of $\mathbf{y}_1$ can serve as the characteristic vector associated with $\lambda_1 = 5$. Similarly, for $\lambda_2 = \lambda_3 = 1$,

$$(\mathbf{B} - \lambda_2 \mathbf{I})\mathbf{y}_2 = \begin{bmatrix} 4 & 0 & 0 \\ 0 & 0 & 0 \\ 0 & 0 & 0 \end{bmatrix} \begin{bmatrix} y_1 \\ y_2 \\ y_3 \end{bmatrix} = \begin{bmatrix} 0 \\ 0 \\ 0 \end{bmatrix},$$

so that $y_1 = 0$, and y_2 and y_3 are each arbitrary. Thus we have *two* linearly independent characteristic vectors $\mathbf{y}_2 = [0 \ \ 1 \ \ 0]'$ and $\mathbf{y}_3 = [0 \ \ 0 \ \ 1]'$. That is, any two linearly independent vectors of the form $\mathbf{y} = h\mathbf{y}_2 + k\mathbf{y}_3$ will satisfy the equation

$$\mathbf{By} = \lambda_2 \mathbf{y}.$$

The vectors $\mathbf{y}_1$, $\mathbf{y}_2$, and $\mathbf{y}_3$ yield the characteristic vectors of **A** by $\mathbf{x}_i = \mathbf{Cy}_i$, $i = 1, 2, 3$, or

$$\begin{bmatrix} x_1 \\ x_2 \\ x_3 \end{bmatrix} = \begin{bmatrix} 1 & 2 & 1 \\ 1 & -1 & 0 \\ 1 & 0 & -1 \end{bmatrix} \begin{bmatrix} y_1 \\ y_2 \\ y_3 \end{bmatrix}$$

in each case. For $\lambda_1 = 5$ we get $\mathbf{x}_1 = [1 \ \ 1 \ \ 1]'$; for $\lambda_2 = 1$ we get $\mathbf{x}_2 = [2 \ \ -1 \ \ 0]'$; and for $\lambda_3 = 1$ we get $\mathbf{x}_3 = [1 \ \ 0 \ \ -1]'$. These are three linearly independent vectors that are, incidentally, the columns of the matrix **C**; other choices for $\mathbf{y}_1$, $\mathbf{y}_2$, and $\mathbf{y}_3$ would lead to vectors different from the columns of **C**.

The reader may inquire whether or not a simple method exists by which the similarity transformation matrix **C** may be obtained that will transform a matrix **A** into a diagonal matrix **D**. A little reflection will lead to the conclusion that there is no simple method; if there were, the characteristic values of **A** could be obtained quite readily, since the diagonal elements of

D are the characteristic values of **D** as well as of **A** by Theorem 6.7.1. In fact a search for the matrix **C** and the diagonal elements of **D** such that $\mathbf{C}^{-1}\mathbf{AC} = \mathbf{D}$ leads essentially to a search for the characteristic values of **A**.

In spite of this difficulty, the study of similar matrices gives us much information about the characteristic values of **A**. The following theorem gives a relationship between the powers of **A** and the characteristic values of **A** that is useful in finding the approximate characteristic values.

Theorem 6.7.3. *If λ is a characteristic value of* **A**, *then λ^k is a characteristic value of* $\mathbf{A}^k$, *k a positive integer. Also if* **x** *is the characteristic vector of* **A** *corresponding to λ, then* **x** *is also the characteristic vector of* $\mathbf{A}^k$ *corresponding to λ^k.*

Proof: Since λ is a characteristic value of **A**,

$$\mathbf{Ax} = \lambda\mathbf{x}, \tag{6.7.4}$$

where **x** is the associated characteristic vector. Multiplying both sides of this equation by **A**,

$$\mathbf{A}^2\mathbf{x} = \lambda\mathbf{Ax} = \lambda^2\mathbf{x}, \tag{6.7.5}$$

by Eq. (6.7.4). By mathematical induction,

$$\mathbf{A}^k\mathbf{x} = \lambda^k\mathbf{x},$$

which completes the proof of both parts of the theorem.

Exercises 6.7

1. If **A** and **B** are similar,
   (a) Show that the squares, cubes, $\cdots$, of **A** and **B** are also similar.
   (b) Show that $\mathbf{A}'$ and $\mathbf{B}'$ are similar.
   (c) Show that $\mathbf{A}^{-1}$ and $\mathbf{B}^{-1}$ are similar if **A** is nonsingular.

2. Complete the mathematical induction proof of Theorem 6.7.3.

3. If

$$\mathbf{A} = \begin{bmatrix} 2 & 1 \\ 0 & 1 \end{bmatrix}, \quad \mathbf{C} = \begin{bmatrix} -2 & -1 \\ 2 & 1 \end{bmatrix},$$

   and the diagonal matrix $\mathbf{D} = \mathbf{I}$, then $\mathbf{AC} = \mathbf{CD}$. Explain why **A** is not similar to **D** in spite of this. Is **A** similar to

$$\begin{bmatrix} 1 & 0 \\ 0 & 2 \end{bmatrix}? \quad \text{to} \quad \begin{bmatrix} 2 & 0 \\ 0 & 1 \end{bmatrix}?$$

4. (a) Find the characteristic values of

$$\mathbf{E} = \begin{bmatrix} 2 & 1 & 1 \\ -2 & -1 & -1 \\ 0 & 0 & 2 \end{bmatrix},$$

(b) Find $\mathbf{E}^3$ and compare the characteristic values of $\mathbf{E}^3$ with those of $\mathbf{E}$.
(c) Find the characteristic vectors for $\mathbf{E}$ and $\mathbf{E}^3$.

5. Prove that similar matrices have the same rank.

6. If

$$\mathbf{A} = 1/3 \begin{bmatrix} -8 & -3 & 7 \\ 8 & 9 & -4 \\ -10 & -6 & 11 \end{bmatrix} \quad \text{and} \quad \mathbf{C} = \begin{bmatrix} 1 & 2 & -1 \\ 0 & -1 & 1 \\ 2 & 1 & -2 \end{bmatrix},$$

(a) Find the characteristic polynomial for $\mathbf{A}$.
(b) Use $\mathbf{C}$ to get a diagonal matrix similar to $\mathbf{A}$ and compare the characteristic values of $\mathbf{D}$ and $\mathbf{A}$.
(c) Use Theorem 6.7.2 to find the characteristic vectors of $\mathbf{A}$.

7. If $\mathbf{A}$ is nonsingular, verify that Theorem 6.7.3 is also true for $k = 0$, where $\mathbf{A}^0 = \mathbf{I}$, and for $k = -1$, where $\mathbf{A}^{-1}$ is the inverse of $\mathbf{A}$. (See Section 7.4 for possible extensions.)

8. Prove the theorem: *If* $\mathbf{A}$ *and* $\mathbf{B}$ *are similar matrices, then* $tr\ \mathbf{A} = tr\ \mathbf{B}$. (Hint: Find the coefficient of λ^{n-1} in the characteristic polynomial of Section 6.4.)

6.8. *Diagonal Matrices*

We now examine the conditions under which a matrix may be reduced to one in diagonal form. If a matrix $\mathbf{A}$ is similar to a diagonal matrix, it is said to be *diagonable.*

Theorem 6.8.1. *If a matrix* $\mathbf{A}$ *is similar to a diagonal matrix* $\mathbf{D}$, *then*

$$\mathbf{D} = \begin{bmatrix} k_1 & 0 & \cdots & 0 \\ 0 & k_2 & \cdots & 0 \\ \cdots \\ 0 & 0 & \cdots & k_n \end{bmatrix}, \tag{6.8.1}$$

where $k_1, k_2, \cdots, k_n$ *are the characteristic roots of the matrix* $\mathbf{A}$.

Proof: By Theorem 6.7.1, the characteristic roots of $\mathbf{A}$ and $\mathbf{D}$ must be the same. Hence, if $\mathbf{D}$ is a diagonal matrix, $|\mathbf{D} - \lambda\mathbf{I}| = 0$ must be written as

$$\begin{bmatrix} k_1 - \lambda & 0 & \cdots & 0 \\ 0 & k_2 - \lambda & \cdots & 0 \\ \cdots \\ 0 & 0 & \cdots & k_n - \lambda \end{bmatrix} = 0,$$

where $k_1, k_2, \cdots, k_n$ are the characteristic roots of $\mathbf{A}$.

The characteristic values for a diagonal matrix Eq. (6.8.1) are simply the diagonal elements. The characteristic vectors of a diagonal matrix are n

linearly independent vectors, the elementary vectors $\mathbf{u}_1 = [1\ 0\ \cdots\ 0]'$, $\mathbf{u}_2 = [0\ 1\ \cdots\ 0]'$, $\cdots$, $\mathbf{u}_n = [0\ 0\ \cdots\ 1]'$. (See Section 6.1.) These vectors satisfy $(\mathbf{D} - \lambda_i \mathbf{I})\mathbf{x} = \mathbf{0}$, where $\mathbf{D}$ is given in Eq. (6.8.1), even though some of the characteristic values are identical.

Example 6.8.1. Show that the elementary vectors $\mathbf{u}_1$, $\mathbf{u}_2$, $\mathbf{u}_3$ are characteristic vectors of a diagonal matrix $\mathbf{D}$ whose characteristic values are $\lambda_1 = 1$, $\lambda_2 = 2$, $\lambda_3 = 2$.

The matrix $\mathbf{D}$ is

$$\mathbf{D} = \begin{bmatrix} 1 & 0 & 0 \\ 0 & 2 & 0 \\ 0 & 0 & 2 \end{bmatrix}.$$

Then

$$(\mathbf{D} - \lambda_1 \mathbf{I})\mathbf{u}_1 = \begin{bmatrix} 0 & 0 & 0 \\ 0 & 1 & 0 \\ 0 & 0 & 1 \end{bmatrix}\begin{bmatrix} 1 \\ 0 \\ 0 \end{bmatrix} = \begin{bmatrix} 0 \\ 0 \\ 0 \end{bmatrix},$$

$$(\mathbf{D} - \lambda_2 \mathbf{I})\mathbf{u}_2 = \begin{bmatrix} -1 & 0 & 0 \\ 0 & 0 & 0 \\ 0 & 0 & 0 \end{bmatrix}\begin{bmatrix} 0 \\ 1 \\ 0 \end{bmatrix} = \begin{bmatrix} 0 \\ 0 \\ 0 \end{bmatrix},$$

$$(\mathbf{D} - \lambda_3 \mathbf{I})\mathbf{u}_3 = \begin{bmatrix} -1 & 0 & 0 \\ 0 & 0 & 0 \\ 0 & 0 & 0 \end{bmatrix}\begin{bmatrix} 0 \\ 0 \\ 1 \end{bmatrix} = \begin{bmatrix} 0 \\ 0 \\ 0 \end{bmatrix}.$$

Theorem 6.8.2. *A matrix* $\mathbf{A}$ *of order n with elements from* $\mathscr{F}$ *is similar to a diagonal matrix* $\mathbf{D}$ *if and only if* $\mathbf{A}$ *has n linearly independent characteristic vectors in* $\mathbf{V}_n(\mathscr{F})$.

Proof: Assume that $\mathbf{A}$ has the n characteristic values $\lambda_1, \lambda_2, \cdots, \lambda_n$ with corresponding linearly independent characteristic vectors $\mathbf{x}_1, \mathbf{x}_2, \cdots, \mathbf{x}_n$ such that $\mathbf{A}\mathbf{x}_i = \lambda_i \mathbf{x}_i$. Let $\mathbf{C}$ be a matrix of the column vectors $\mathbf{C} = [\mathbf{x}_1\ \mathbf{x}_2\ \cdots\ \mathbf{x}_n]$. Then

$$\begin{aligned} \mathbf{AC} &= [\mathbf{Ax}_1\quad \mathbf{Ax}_2\quad \cdots\quad \mathbf{Ax}_n] = [\lambda_1 \mathbf{x}_1\quad \lambda_2 \mathbf{x}_2\quad \cdots\quad \lambda_n \mathbf{x}_n] \\ &= [\mathbf{x}_1\quad \mathbf{x}_2\quad \cdots\quad \mathbf{x}_n]\begin{bmatrix} \lambda_1 & 0 & \cdots & 0 \\ 0 & \lambda_2 & \cdots & 0 \\ \cdots & & & \\ 0 & 0 & \cdots & \lambda_n \end{bmatrix} = \mathbf{CD}. \end{aligned}$$

Hence $\mathbf{C}^{-1}\mathbf{AC} = \mathbf{D}$ under the assumption that $\mathbf{A}$ has n linearly independent characteristic vectors, and thus the first part of the theorem is proved.

Now if $\mathbf{A}$ is similar to a diagonal matrix $\mathbf{D}$, then there exists a nonsingular matrix $\mathbf{C}$ such that $\mathbf{C}^{-1}\mathbf{AC} = \mathbf{D}$. By the above remark $\mathbf{u}_1, \mathbf{u}_2, \cdots, \mathbf{u}_n$ are linearly independent characteristic vectors of $\mathbf{D}$, so, by Theorem 6.7.2, the vectors $\mathbf{x}_i = \mathbf{C}\mathbf{u}_i$ are characteristic vectors of **A**. Since **C** is nonsingular, its column vectors are linearly independent and thus give the n linearly independent characteristic vectors of **A**. This concludes the second part of the proof.

Theorem 6.8.3. *If the characteristic values of a matrix* **A** *are distinct, then the characteristic vectors are distinct, and also* **A** *is similar to a diagonal matrix.*

Proof: First we show that if the characteristic values of **A** are distinct, then the characteristic vectors also are distinct. So assume that $\mathbf{A}\mathbf{x}_i = \lambda_i \mathbf{x}_i$ and also $\mathbf{A}\mathbf{x}_i = \lambda_j \mathbf{x}_i$, with $\lambda_i \neq \lambda_j$. By subtraction

$$\lambda_i \mathbf{x}_i - \lambda_j \mathbf{x}_i = (\lambda_i - \lambda_j)\mathbf{x}_i = 0,$$

which is the required contradiction, since $\lambda_i \neq \lambda_j$ and $\mathbf{x}_i \neq \mathbf{0}$. (This result also follows from Theorem 6.3.2.)

If the characteristic values are distinct, then, by Theorems 6.3.2 and 6.8.2, **A** is diagonable.

Not every matrix of order n is similar to a diagonal matrix. The following example shows that if the characteristic vectors are not linearly independent, then the matrix is not similar to a diagonal matrix.

Example 6.8.2. Find the characteristic values and characteristic vectors for the matrix **A** where

$$\mathbf{A} = \begin{bmatrix} 2 & 1 & 1 \\ 0 & 1 & 1 \\ 0 & 0 & 1 \end{bmatrix}.$$

Clearly, $|\mathbf{A} - \lambda\mathbf{I}| = 0$ has roots $\lambda_1 = 2$, $\lambda_2 = 1$, $\lambda_3 = 1$. The corresponding characteristic vector for λ_1 is $\mathbf{x}_1 = [1 \;\; 0 \;\; 0]'$. For $\lambda_2 = 1$,

$$(\mathbf{A} - \lambda_2 \mathbf{I})\mathbf{x}_2 = \begin{bmatrix} 1 & 1 & 1 \\ 0 & 0 & 1 \\ 0 & 0 & 0 \end{bmatrix} \begin{bmatrix} x_1 \\ x_2 \\ x_3 \end{bmatrix} = \begin{bmatrix} x_1 + x_2 + x_3 \\ x_3 \\ 0 \end{bmatrix} = \begin{bmatrix} 0 \\ 0 \\ 0 \end{bmatrix}$$

so that $x_3 = 0$ and $x_1 + x_2 = 0$. Thus $\mathbf{x}_2 = [1 \;\; -1 \;\; 0]'$. But for $\mathbf{x}_3$ we get a multiple of $\mathbf{x}_2$. Hence the vectors are not linearly independent vectors; by Theorem 6.8.2, **A** is not similar to a diagonal matrix. That is, there is no matrix **C** such that $\mathbf{C}^{-1}\mathbf{A}\mathbf{C} = \mathbf{D}$.

If λ_i is a characteristic root of $|\mathbf{A} - \lambda\mathbf{I}| = 0$ only once, it is a *simple root* of the characteristic equation; if it is a root k times, it is a *root of multiplicity k*. Both Examples 6.8.1 and 6.8.2 include double roots or roots of multiplicity 2, so there must be some other reason why one matrix is diagonable and the other is not.

The reason for the final result in Example 6.8.2 is that the rank of $(\mathbf{A} - \lambda_i \mathbf{I})$ is *not* $n - k$ for each λ_k, where k is the multiplicity of the root for each λ_i.

Note that $\lambda = 2$ is a simple root of $|\mathbf{A} - \lambda\mathbf{I}| = 0$, and the rank of $(\mathbf{A} - 2\mathbf{I})$ is 2, showing that there is $3 - 2 = 1$ independent vector. However, $\lambda = 1$ is a double root of $|\mathbf{A} - \lambda\mathbf{I}| = 0$, but $(\mathbf{A} - 1\mathbf{I})$ has rank 2 also, showing that for this value of λ there is also $3 - 2 = 1$ independent vector, see Theorem 5.5.1.

The following theorem gives in the general case the necessary and sufficient conditions for a matrix to be similar to a diagonal matrix where the characteristic values are not distinct.

Theorem 6.8.4. *A matrix* $\mathbf{A}$ *of order* n *is similar to a diagonal matrix if and only if, for each characteristic value* λ_i, *the multiplicity of* λ_i *is equal to* $k = n - r$, *where* r *is the rank of* $(\mathbf{A} - \lambda_i\mathbf{I})$.

Proof: Assume first that $\mathbf{C}^{-1}\mathbf{AC} = \mathbf{D}$ and that k of the diagonal elements of $\mathbf{D}$ are each equal to λ_i. Then $(\mathbf{D} - \lambda_i\mathbf{I})$ has exactly k zeros on the principal diagonal, and hence has rank $n - k$; thus $n - (n - k) = k$ linearly independent vectors are associated with λ_i. But $\mathbf{A} - \lambda_i\mathbf{I} = \mathbf{C}(\mathbf{D} - \lambda_i\mathbf{I})\mathbf{C}^{-1}$, and thus $\mathbf{A} - \lambda_i\mathbf{I}$ has rank $n - k$ and has k linearly independent vectors, the same as $\mathbf{D} - \lambda_i\mathbf{I}$. (See Section 5.5.)

Now, assume that $\mathbf{A}$ has distinct characteristic values $\lambda_1, \lambda_2, \cdots, \lambda_s$ with λ_i having multiplicity k_i; note that $\sum_{i=1}^{s} k_i = n$, the order of $\mathbf{A}$. That is, λ_1 appears k_1 times, λ_2 appears k_2 times, $\cdots$, and λ_s appears k_s times. For λ_1 there is at least one and no more than k_1 linearly independent characteristic vectors. (See Theorem 6.5.2.) A similar statement can be made regarding $\lambda_2, \cdots, \lambda_s$.

The conclusion of the theorem is easy to see if $\mathbf{A}$ is a diagonal block matrix (as in number 5 of Exercises 1.11) with submatrices $\mathbf{A}_1, \mathbf{A}_2, \cdots, \mathbf{A}_s$ down the principal diagonal such that λ_i is a k_i-fold characteristic value of $\mathbf{A}_i$. Then, by Theorem 6.8.2, each block would have to have k_i linearly independent characteristic vectors for it to be similar to a diagonal matrix. That is, the multiplicity of λ_i in each case would have to be $k_i = n - r_i$, where r_i is the rank of $(\mathbf{A} - \lambda_i\mathbf{I})$.

If $\mathbf{A}$ is not a diagonal block matrix, we proceed in a different manner. By Theorem 6.8.2, unless there are k_i linearly independent vectors associated with λ_i, $\mathbf{A}$ is *not* similar to a diagonal matrix. So assume that $\mathbf{x}_{i1}, \mathbf{x}_{i2}, \cdots, \mathbf{x}_{ik_i}$ are linearly independent vectors associated with λ_i. Then the only way

$$(6.8.2)\qquad \begin{aligned}&(a_{11}\mathbf{x}_{11} + a_{12}\mathbf{x}_{12} + \cdots + a_{1k_1}\mathbf{x}_{1k_1})\\ &+ (a_{21}\mathbf{x}_{21} + a_{22}\mathbf{x}_{22} + \cdots + a_{2k_2}\mathbf{x}_{2k_2})\\ &+ \cdots + (a_{s1}\mathbf{x}_{s1} + a_{s2}\mathbf{x}_{s2} + \cdots + a_{sk_s}\mathbf{x}_{sk_s}) = \mathbf{0},\end{aligned}$$

is for all constants a_{ij} to be zero. By Theorem 6.3.2, the characteristic vectors associated with distinct characteristic values are linearly independent; the vector in the first parenthesis is a vector associated with λ_1, etc., and thus the quantities in each parenthesis must all be identically zero. Hence, all of the $\mathbf{x}$'s are linearly independent; by Theorem 6.8.2, $\mathbf{A}$ is similar to a diagonal matrix.

By the results of Section 3.6 a matrix $\mathbf{A}$ is equivalent to a triangular matrix $\mathbf{T}$ by a proper choice of a nonsingular matrix $\mathbf{Q}$ such that $\mathbf{QA} = \mathbf{T}$. However, for a similarity transformation we need to multiply the product $\mathbf{QA}$ by $\mathbf{Q}^{-1}$ also, so if $\mathbf{QA} = \mathbf{T}$, there is no assurance that the product $\mathbf{R}$ in $\mathbf{QAQ}^{-1} = \mathbf{TQ}^{-1} = \mathbf{R}$ is in triangular form. The proof of the following theorem shows how $\mathbf{Q}$ (called $\mathbf{P}^{-1}$) can be chosen so that $\mathbf{R}$ will be triangular.

Theorem 6.8.5. *Every square matrix* $\mathbf{A}$ *is similar to a triangular matrix* $\mathbf{T}$ *with the characteristic values of* $\mathbf{A}$ *as the diagonal elements of* $\mathbf{T}$.

Proof: If $\lambda_1, \lambda_2, \cdots, \lambda_n$ are the characteristic values of $\mathbf{A}$ and if $\mathbf{x}_1$ is the characteristic vector corresponding to λ_1, form a matrix $\mathbf{P}_1$ with $\mathbf{x}_1$ as the first column, the other columns being arbitrary except that $\mathbf{P}_1$ is nonsingular. Thus in $\mathbf{AP}_1$ the first column is $\mathbf{Ax}_1 = \lambda_1\mathbf{x}_1$, and the first column of $\mathbf{P}_1^{-1}\mathbf{AP}_1$ is $\mathbf{P}_1^{-1}\lambda_1\mathbf{x}_1$. That is, form $\mathbf{P}_1 = [\mathbf{x}_1 \quad \mathbf{B}_1]$, where $\mathbf{B}_1$ is an $n \times (n-1)$ matrix. Thus,

$$\mathbf{AP}_1 = \mathbf{A}[\mathbf{x}_1 \quad \mathbf{B}_1] = [\mathbf{Ax}_1 \quad \mathbf{AB}_1] = [\lambda_1\mathbf{x}_1 \quad \mathbf{AB}_1], \tag{6.8.3}$$

and

$$\mathbf{P}_1^{-1}\mathbf{AP}_1 = [\mathbf{P}_1^{-1}\lambda_1\mathbf{x}_1 \quad \mathbf{P}_1^{-1}\mathbf{AB}_1] = \begin{bmatrix} \lambda_1\mathbf{I}_1 & \mathbf{C}_1 \\ \mathbf{0} & \mathbf{A}_1 \end{bmatrix}, \tag{6.8.4}$$

where $\mathbf{I}_1$ is the identity matrix of order one; the subscripts on the other matrices refer to the step in the iteration process.

Since $\mathbf{P}_1^{-1}\mathbf{AP}_1$ and $\mathbf{A}$ have the same characteristic values, by Theorem 6.7.1, the characteristic values of $\mathbf{A}_1$ are $\lambda_2, \cdots, \lambda_n$. Note that $\mathbf{A}_1$ is of order $n-1$.

In a similar manner we construct a matrix $\mathbf{P}_2$, using the vector $\mathbf{x}_2$ that corresponds to λ_2 in $\mathbf{A}_1$, to obtain

$$\mathbf{P}_2^{-1}\mathbf{A}_1\mathbf{P}_2 = \begin{bmatrix} \lambda_2\mathbf{I}_1 & \mathbf{C}_2 \\ \mathbf{0} & \mathbf{A}_2 \end{bmatrix}. \tag{6.8.5}$$

After $n-1$ steps we obtain a nonsingular matrix $\mathbf{P}$ such that

$$\mathbf{P} = \mathbf{P}_1 \begin{bmatrix} \mathbf{I}_1 & \mathbf{0} \\ \mathbf{0} & \mathbf{P}_2 \end{bmatrix} \begin{bmatrix} \mathbf{I}_2 & \mathbf{0} \\ \mathbf{0} & \mathbf{P}_3 \end{bmatrix} \cdots \begin{bmatrix} \mathbf{I}_{n-2} & \mathbf{0} \\ \mathbf{0} & \mathbf{P}_{n-1} \end{bmatrix}. \tag{6.8.6}$$

Note that the matrix $\mathbf{P}_{n-1}$ obtained at step $n-1$ is of order 2, so that when $\mathbf{P}_{n-1}$ (and $\mathbf{P}_{n-1}^{-1}$) are applied to $\mathbf{A}_{n-2}$, a triangular matrix with λ_n in the lower right-hand corner is obtained. Of course it may happen that a triangular matrix is obtained at some earlier step: if so, the construction is complete. Since each $\mathbf{P}_i$ matrix is nonsingular, the product $\mathbf{P}$ in Eq. (6.8.6) is nonsingular; furthermore the product $\mathbf{P}^{-1}\mathbf{AP}$ is a triangular matrix by construction. That is, the product is

(6.8.7) $$\mathbf{P}^{-1}\mathbf{AP} = \mathbf{T},$$

a triangular matrix with the characteristic values of $\mathbf{A}$ as the diagonal elements.

Note that $\mathbf{A}$ can have repeated characteristic values, $\mathbf{A}$ need not be real, and $\mathbf{A}$ can even be singular. However, the characteristic vectors of $\mathbf{A}$ are not zero, and also the matrix $\mathbf{P}$ as constructed is nonsingular.

Consider the case in which $\mathbf{A}$ is symmetric. By Section 4.4, a real symmetric matrix $\mathbf{A}$ can be transformed into a diagonal matrix by a congruent transformation; if $\mathbf{A}$ is real and symmetric, there exists a matrix $\mathbf{P}$ such that $\mathbf{P}'\mathbf{AP} = \mathbf{D}$. Sometimes $\mathbf{P}' = \mathbf{P}^{-1}$, in which case the congruent transformation is also a similarity transformation. Furthermore, in that case, the diagonal elements of $\mathbf{D}$ are the characteristic values of $\mathbf{A}$, since similar matrices have the same characteristic values.

Theorem 6.8.6. *Every real symmetric matrix is similar to a diagonal matrix.*

Proof: To prove this theorem we use essentially the same construction as that used in the proof of Theorem 6.8.5. Again if $\lambda_1, \lambda_2, \cdots, \lambda_n$ are the characteristic values of $\mathbf{A}$ and if $\mathbf{x}_1$ is the characteristic vector corresponding to λ_1, we form the matrix $\mathbf{P}_1$ with $\mathbf{x}_1$ as the first column. In this proof, however, we divide $\mathbf{x}_1$ by $\sqrt{\mathbf{x}_1'\mathbf{x}_1}$ to make the vector a *unit vector*, $\mathbf{v}_1$. Thus in $\mathbf{P}_1$ we have $\mathbf{v}_1$ in the first column.

Since the remaining columns of $\mathbf{P}_1$ are arbitrary, subject to the condition that $\mathbf{P}_1$ be nonsingular, we let the first row of $\mathbf{P}_1$ be $\mathbf{v}_1'$. Let the second column of $\mathbf{P}_1$ then be chosen as a unit vector orthogonal to $\mathbf{v}_1$—call it $\mathbf{v}_2$. Theorem 6.10.1, discussed later, shows how a vector can be constructed orthogonal to $\mathbf{v}_1$; for matrices of small order a little ingenuity will enable the reader to construct the necessary vector $\mathbf{v}_2$ without recourse to this theorem.

After $\mathbf{v}_2$ is constructed we use $\mathbf{v}_2'$ as the second row of $\mathbf{P}_1$. By proceeding in a similar manner the remaining columns and rows of $\mathbf{P}_1$ are constructed so that the columns or rows form sets of mutually orthogonal unit vectors. That is, we have

(6.8.8) $$\mathbf{v}_i'\mathbf{v}_j = \delta_{ij},$$

where δ_{ij} is the Kronecker delta. Such a matrix is called an *orthogonal matrix*. Clearly,

(6.8.9) $$\mathbf{P}_1' = \mathbf{P}_1^{-1},$$

or

(6.8.10) $$\mathbf{P}_1'\mathbf{P}_1 = [\mathbf{v}_1\mathbf{v}_2\cdots\mathbf{v}_n]'[\mathbf{v}_1\mathbf{v}_2\cdots\mathbf{v}_n] = \mathbf{I},$$

a necessary and sufficient condition for an orthogonal matrix, and thus

$$\mathbf{P}_1'\mathbf{A}\mathbf{P}_1 = \begin{bmatrix} \lambda_1\mathbf{I}_1 & \mathbf{0} \\ \mathbf{0} & \mathbf{A}_1 \end{bmatrix}. \tag{6.8.11}$$

That is, the $1 \times (n-1)$ vector $\mathbf{C}_1$ of Eq. (6.8.4) is now a zero vector. Also since $\mathbf{A}$ is symmetric, $\mathbf{A}_1$ is likewise symmetric; furthermore it has eigenvalues $\lambda_2, \cdots, \lambda_n$.

We next proceed to construct $\mathbf{P}_2$ (corresponding to $\mathbf{P}_2$ in Eq. (6.8.5)) whose columns (and rows) are unit vectors that are mutually orthogonal. Then $\mathbf{P}_3, \cdots, \mathbf{P}_{n-1}$ are constructed similarly. Finally the matrix corresponding to $\mathbf{P}$ in Eq. (6.8.6) is an orthogonal matrix, since each $\mathbf{P}_i$ is, and thus

$$\mathbf{P}'\mathbf{P} = \mathbf{P}^{-1}\mathbf{P} = \mathbf{I}.$$

Since the vectors in the upper right-hand corner at each step, $\mathbf{C}_1, \mathbf{C}_2, \cdots$, are now all zero vectors, the triangular matrix of Theorem 6.8.5 is thus a diagonal matrix with the characteristic values of $\mathbf{A}$ on the diagonal, and the theorem is proved.

The following theorem gives another important result regarding symmetric matrices.

Theorem 6.8.7. *A real symmetric matrix has n linearly independent characteristic vectors.*

Proof: The characteristic vectors of the symmetric matrix $\mathbf{A}$ are linearly independent by Theorems 6.7.1, 6.7.2, and 6.8.4, since $\mathbf{P}^{-1}\mathbf{A}\mathbf{P} = \mathbf{D}$. From the remarks after the proof of Theorem 6.8.1, a diagonal matrix has n linearly independent characteristic vectors. By Theorem 6.7.1, $\mathbf{A}$ and $\mathbf{D}$ have the same characteristic values. Thus, by Theorem 6.7.2, if $\mathbf{D}\mathbf{y}_i = \lambda_i\mathbf{y}_i$, then $\mathbf{x}_i = \mathbf{P}\mathbf{y}_i$ are the characteristic vectors of $\mathbf{A}$. Finally since the $\mathbf{y}_i$ are linearly independent, so are the $\mathbf{x}_i$, and the theorem is proved.

By Theorem 6.5.2, there are bounds for the rank and nullity of a matrix $\mathbf{A}$ for a characteristic value in case the characteristic equation for $\mathbf{A}$ has repeated roots. If, however, $\mathbf{A}$ is symmetric, then these numbers are fixed exactly and are not merely within an interval.

Theorem 6.8.8. *If* $\mathbf{A}_n$ *is a real symmetric matrix and* λ_i *is a k-fold root of* $|\mathbf{A} - \lambda\mathbf{I}| = 0$, *then the rank of* $(\mathbf{A} - \lambda_i\mathbf{I})$ *is* $n - k$, *and the nullity of* $(\mathbf{A} - \lambda_i\mathbf{I})$ *is k.*

Proof: The proof is a direct consequence of Theorem 6.8.6. Since $\mathbf{A}$ is symmetric, it is similar to a diagonal matrix $\mathbf{D}$. Then $\mathbf{P}^{-1}\mathbf{A}\mathbf{P} = \mathbf{D}$, and $\mathbf{A}$ and $\mathbf{D}$ have the same characteristic values. If λ_i is a k-fold root of $|\mathbf{D} - \lambda\mathbf{I}| = 0$, then λ_i appears exactly k times on the principal diagonal of $\mathbf{D}$. For instance, if λ_i is in the first k rows of $\mathbf{D}$, then

$$(6.8.12)\quad \mathbf{D} - \lambda\mathbf{I} = \begin{bmatrix} \lambda_i - \lambda & 0 & \cdots & 0 & 0 & \cdots & 0 \\ 0 & \lambda_i - \lambda & \cdots & 0 & 0 & \cdots & 0 \\ \cdots & & & & & & \\ 0 & 0 & \cdots & \lambda_i - \lambda & 0 & \cdots & 0 \\ 0 & 0 & \cdots & 0 & \lambda_j - \lambda & \cdots & 0 \\ \cdots & & & & & & \\ 0 & 0 & \cdots & 0 & 0 & \cdots & \lambda_m - \lambda \end{bmatrix},$$

and $(\mathbf{D} - \lambda_i\mathbf{I})$ has rank $n - k$. The number of invariant vectors associated with λ_i (the nullity of $\mathbf{D} - \lambda_i\mathbf{I}$) is k. For example, the k elementary vectors $[1\ 0\ \cdots\ 0]'$, $\cdots$ $[0\ 0\ \cdots\ 1\ \cdots\ 0]'$ are k linearly independent vectors corresponding to $(\mathbf{D} - \lambda_i\mathbf{I})$ of Eq. (6.8.12).

Exercises 6.8

1. Determine which of the following matrices are similar to a diagonal matrix $\mathbf{D}$. Write $\mathbf{D}$ where possible.

$$\text{(a)}\ \begin{bmatrix} 3 & -2 & 4 \\ -2 & -2 & 6 \\ 4 & 6 & -1 \end{bmatrix}, \quad \text{(b)}\ \begin{bmatrix} 2 & 1 & 0 \\ 0 & 2 & 1 \\ 0 & 0 & 2 \end{bmatrix}, \quad \text{(c)}\ \begin{bmatrix} 2 & 0 & 1 \\ 0 & 3 & 0 \\ 1 & 0 & 2 \end{bmatrix}.$$

2. (a) Find a matrix $\mathbf{P}$ such that $\mathbf{P}^{-1}\mathbf{C}\mathbf{P} = \mathbf{T}$, a triangular matrix, if

$$\mathbf{C} = \begin{bmatrix} 3 & 3 & 1 \\ 0 & 2 & 0 \\ -2 & -3 & 0 \end{bmatrix}.$$

(b) Verify that $\operatorname{tr} \mathbf{C} = \operatorname{tr} \mathbf{T}$.

(c) Is $\mathbf{C}$ similar to a diagonal matrix? Why?

3. Prove that a sum of characteristic vectors of $\mathbf{A}$ corresponding to the characteristic value λ_i is a characteristic vector of $\mathbf{A}$.

4. If $\mathbf{A}$ is a real symmetric matrix and $\mathbf{P}$ is an orthogonal matrix, prove that the matrix obtained under the similarity transformation by $\mathbf{P}$ is symmetric.

5. Prove the theorem: *If* $\mathbf{A}$ *is similar to a diagonal matrix* $\mathbf{D}$, *then the sum of the elements of* $\mathbf{D}$ *is the same as the trace of* $\mathbf{A}$. (Hint: Find the coefficient of λ^{n-1} in the characteristic polynomial of Section 6.4.)

6.9. Orthogonal Matrices and Orthogonal Transformations

In Section 6.8 an *orthogonal matrix* was introduced as a matrix $\mathbf{A}$ whose transpose is its inverse. The matrix $\mathbf{A}$ is orthogonal if and only if

$$(6.9.1)\qquad \mathbf{A}'\mathbf{A} = \mathbf{I};\ \text{i.e.,}\ \ \mathbf{A}'\mathbf{A} = \mathbf{A}^{-1}\mathbf{A} = \mathbf{I},\ \ \text{or}\ \ \mathbf{A}' = \mathbf{A}^{-1}.$$

This section presents a few of the important theorems and observations concerning orthogonal matrices.

An orthogonal matrix **A** must be square and nonsingular, since $\mathbf{A}^{-1}$ exists. In fact, det **A** can only have one of two values:

Theorem 6.9.1. *If* **A** *is an orthogonal matrix, then*

$$\det \mathbf{A} = \pm 1. \tag{6.9.2}$$

Proof: From Eq. (6.9.1), $\mathbf{A}'\mathbf{A} = \mathbf{I}$ if **A** is orthogonal. Thus,

$$\det \mathbf{A}'\mathbf{A} = \det \mathbf{A}' \det \mathbf{A} = \det \mathbf{I} = 1.$$

Since det A′ = det **A**,

$$(\det \mathbf{A})^2 = 1 \quad \text{or} \quad \det \mathbf{A} = \pm 1.$$

We next observe a relationship existing between the various rows (columns) of **A**.

Theorem 6.9.2. *The rows (columns) of an orthogonal matrix* **A** *are each unit vectors, and the rows (columns) of* **A** *are mutually orthogonal.*

Proof: Since **A** is orthogonal, $\mathbf{A}'\mathbf{A} = \mathbf{I}$:

$$\begin{bmatrix} a_{11} & a_{21} & \cdots & a_{n1} \\ a_{12} & a_{22} & \cdots & a_{n2} \\ \cdots \\ a_{1n} & a_{2n} & \cdots & a_{nn} \end{bmatrix} \begin{bmatrix} a_{11} & a_{12} & \cdots & a_{1n} \\ a_{21} & a_{22} & \cdots & a_{2n} \\ \cdots \\ a_{n1} & a_{n2} & \cdots & a_{nn} \end{bmatrix} = \begin{bmatrix} 1 & 0 & \cdots & 0 \\ 0 & 1 & \cdots & 0 \\ \cdots \\ 0 & 0 & \cdots & 1 \end{bmatrix}. \tag{6.9.3}$$

That is, if $\mathbf{a}_i = [a_{1i} \; a_{2i} \; \cdots \; a_{ni}]'$, then

$$[\mathbf{a}_1 \;\; \mathbf{a}_2 \;\; \cdots \;\; \mathbf{a}_n]'[\mathbf{a}_1 \;\; \mathbf{a}_2 \;\; \cdots \;\; \mathbf{a}_n] = \mathbf{I}, \quad \text{or} \tag{6.9.4}$$

$$\mathbf{a}_i'\mathbf{a}_j = a_{1i}a_{ij} + a_{2i}a_{2j} + \cdots + a_{ni}a_{nj} = 0, \quad i \neq j, \quad \text{and} \tag{6.9.5}$$

$$\mathbf{a}_i'\mathbf{a}_i = a_{1i}^2 + a_{2i}^2 + \cdots + a_{ni}^2 = 1, \; i = 1, 2, \ldots, n. \tag{6.9.6}$$

Equations (6.9.5) and (6.9.6) may be written compactly as

$$\mathbf{a}_i'\mathbf{a}_j = \delta_{ij}. \tag{6.9.7}$$

If the vector $\mathbf{x} = [x_1 \; x_2 \; \cdots \; x_n]'$ is considered as a point in n-space relative to a set of orthogonal axes, then the scalar product

$$\mathbf{x}'\mathbf{x} = x_1^2 + x_2^2 + \cdots + x_n^2 \tag{6.9.8}$$

is the square of the distance from the origin $\mathbf{0} = [0 \; 0 \; \cdots \; 0]'$ to the point **x**. (See Section 2.3.) Now if the axes are rotated about the origin, while remaining orthogonal, the rotation may be expressed by a transformation matrix **A** which produces a new description of the point $\mathbf{Ax}$. The square of the distance from the origin is now $\mathbf{x'A'Ax}$. Since the square of the distance in the transformed system is the same as in the original system,

$$\mathbf{x'A'Ax} = \mathbf{x'x}, \quad \text{or}$$

$$\mathbf{x'(A'A - I)x} = 0, \quad \text{and thus}$$

$$\mathbf{A'A - I} = \mathbf{0} \quad \text{or} \quad \mathbf{A'A} = \mathbf{I}.$$

These results may be stated as a theorem.

Theorem 6.9.3. *If the vectors* $\mathbf{x}$ *in n-space relative to a set of orthogonal axes are transformed by a rotation of axes about a fixed origin* $\mathbf{0}$ *by a matrix* $\mathbf{A}$ *so that the axes remain orthogonal, then* $\mathbf{A}$ *is an orthogonal matrix.*

A transformation of the type $\mathbf{y} = \mathbf{Ax}$, where $\mathbf{A}$ is an orthogonal matrix, is an *orthogonal transformation.*

The distance, or the square of the distance, from the origin to a point in n-space is an *invariant* associated with a vector under an orthogonal transformation. Other examples of invariants are tr $\mathbf{A}$ for the matrix $\mathbf{A}$ under a similarity transformation and det $\mathbf{A}$ under a similarity transformation.

Although Theorem 6.8.6 is true as stated, what was actually proved was the following theorem.

Theorem 6.9.4. *Every real symmetric matrix is orthogonally similar to a diagonal matrix.*

That is, if $\mathbf{A}$ is a symmetric matrix, there exists an orthogonal matrix $\mathbf{B}$ such that

$$\mathbf{B'AB} = \mathbf{B}^{-1}\mathbf{AB} = \mathbf{D}, \quad \text{a diagonal matrix.} \tag{6.9.9}$$

If $\mathbf{A}$ has complex elements then the generalization of the idea of orthogonality leads to the definition of a *unitary matrix*. A matrix $\mathbf{A}$ is a unitary matrix if

$$\mathbf{A^*A} = \mathbf{I}; \quad \text{i.e.,} \quad \mathbf{A^*A} = \mathbf{A}^{-1}\mathbf{A} = \mathbf{I}, \quad \text{so} \quad \mathbf{A^*} = \mathbf{A}^{-1}. \tag{6.9.10}$$

The proof of the following theorem is left as an exercise.

Theorem 6.9.5. *If* $\mathbf{A}$ *and* $\mathbf{B}$ *are unitary matrices, then their product is also a unitary matrix.*

A real unitary matrix is an orthogonal matrix since $\mathbf{A^*} = \mathbf{A'}$ if $\mathbf{A}$ is real, so the results for a unitary matrix can be applied to an orthogonal matrix immediately.

Theorem 6.9.6. *The absolute value of each characteristic value of a unitary matrix is one.*

Proof: If $\mathbf{A}$ is a unitary matrix with λ_i as a characteristic value and $\mathbf{x}_i$ as the corresponding characteristic vector, then $\mathbf{A}\mathbf{x}_i = \lambda_i \mathbf{x}_i$, and $\overline{\mathbf{A}}\overline{\mathbf{x}}_i = \overline{\lambda}_i \overline{\mathbf{x}}_i$. Thus,

$$\overline{\lambda}_i \lambda_i \overline{\mathbf{x}}_i' \mathbf{x}_i = (\overline{\mathbf{A}}\overline{\mathbf{x}}_i)'(\mathbf{A}\mathbf{x}_i) = \overline{\mathbf{x}}_i' \overline{\mathbf{A}}' \mathbf{A}\mathbf{x}_i = \overline{\mathbf{x}}_i' \mathbf{x}_i, \tag{6.9.11}$$

since $\mathbf{A}$ is a unitary matrix. Since $\mathbf{x}_i$ is a characteristic vector, and thus is not the zero vector ($\overline{\mathbf{x}}_i' \mathbf{x}_i$ is the square of the length of $\mathbf{x}_i$),

$$\overline{\lambda}_i \lambda_i = 1. \tag{6.9.12}$$

That is, the absolute value of a characteristic value is 1.

Since $\mathbf{A} = \overline{\mathbf{A}}$ if $\mathbf{A}$ is a real matrix, it follows that the absolute value of each characteristic value of an orthogonal matrix $\mathbf{A}$ is 1. Even if the elements of a matrix (in particular, of an orthogonal matrix) are real, some or all of the characteristic values of $\mathbf{A}$ may be complex. The matrix

$$\begin{bmatrix} 0 & -1 \\ 1 & 0 \end{bmatrix}$$

is an orthogonal matrix with real elements, but its characteristic values are $\pm i$. However, note that the absolute values of the characteristic values are still each 1, as required by Theorem 6.9.6.

Orthogonal matrices may be constructed readily according to the following theorem:

Theorem 6.9.7. *For any real skew symmetric matrix* $\mathbf{S}$ *then*

$$\mathbf{A} = (\mathbf{S} + \mathbf{I})(\mathbf{S} - \mathbf{I})^{-1} \tag{6.9.13}$$

is an orthogonal matrix.

Proof: We need to show first that $(\mathbf{S} - \mathbf{I})$ is a nonsingular matrix and hence possesses an inverse. If $(\mathbf{S} - \mathbf{I})$ were singular, then

$$\det(\mathbf{S} - \mathbf{I}) = 0, \tag{6.9.14}$$

and 1 would be a characteristic value of $\mathbf{S}$. But the characteristic values of a real skew symmetric matrix are all pure imaginary, as shown below. (See number 2 of Exercises 6.6.)

If $\mathbf{x}_j$ is the characteristic vector of the real skew symmetric matrix $\mathbf{S}$ corresponding to the characteristic value λ_j, then

$$\mathbf{S}\mathbf{x}_j = \lambda_j \mathbf{x}_j. \tag{6.9.15}$$

Taking the conjugate and the transpose of both sides of Eq. (6.9.15), and noting that $\overline{\mathbf{S}} = \mathbf{S}$, since $\mathbf{S}$ is real,

$$\mathbf{S}\overline{\mathbf{x}}_j = \overline{\lambda}_j \overline{\mathbf{x}}_j \qquad \text{or} \qquad \overline{\mathbf{x}}_j' \mathbf{S}' = \overline{\lambda}_j \mathbf{x}_j'. \tag{6.9.16}$$

But since $\mathbf{S} = -\mathbf{S}'$ for a skew symmetric matrix,

(6.9.17) $$\bar{\mathbf{x}}_j'\mathbf{S} = -\bar{\lambda}_j\bar{\mathbf{x}}_j'.$$

Then, multiplying Eq. (6.9.15) through by $\bar{\mathbf{x}}_j'$ and Eq. (6.9.17) by $\mathbf{x}_j$ and subtracting,

(6.9.18) $$0 = (\lambda_j + \bar{\lambda}_j)\bar{\mathbf{x}}_j'\mathbf{x}_j.$$

This implies that

(6.9.19) $$\lambda_j + \bar{\lambda}_j = 0, \quad \text{or } \bar{\lambda}_j = \alpha_j + i\beta_j = -\alpha_j + i\beta_j = -\bar{\lambda}_j.$$

That is, λ_j is a pure imaginary number as was to be shown. Hence $(\mathbf{S} - \mathbf{I})$ is a nonsingular matrix, and thus possesses an inverse. It is left as an exercise to show that $(\mathbf{S} + \mathbf{I})$ is also nonsingular.

To prove the theorem, show that the product

$$\mathbf{A} = (\mathbf{S} + \mathbf{I})(\mathbf{S} - \mathbf{I})^{-1}$$

is an orthogonal matrix, by showing that $\mathbf{A}'\mathbf{A} = \mathbf{I}$ and hence $\mathbf{A}' = \mathbf{A}^{-1}$.

(6.9.20) $$\begin{aligned}\mathbf{A}'\mathbf{A} &= [(\mathbf{S} + \mathbf{I})(\mathbf{S} - \mathbf{I})^{-1}]'[(\mathbf{S} + \mathbf{I})(\mathbf{S} - \mathbf{I})^{-1}]\\ &= [(\mathbf{S}' - \mathbf{I}')^{-1}(\mathbf{S}' + \mathbf{I}')][(\mathbf{S} + \mathbf{I})(\mathbf{S} - \mathbf{I})^{-1}]\\ &= (\mathbf{S} + \mathbf{I})^{-1}(\mathbf{S} - \mathbf{I})(\mathbf{S} + \mathbf{I})(\mathbf{S} - \mathbf{I})^{-1}\\ &= (\mathbf{S} + \mathbf{I})^{-1}(\mathbf{SS} + \mathbf{S} - \mathbf{S} - \mathbf{I})(\mathbf{S} - \mathbf{I})^{-1}\\ &= (\mathbf{S} + \mathbf{I})^{-1}(\mathbf{S} + \mathbf{I})(\mathbf{S} - \mathbf{I})(\mathbf{S} - \mathbf{I})^{-1} = \mathbf{I},\end{aligned}$$

so $\mathbf{A}$ is orthogonal. In Eq. (6.9.20) the fact was used that $\mathbf{S} = -\mathbf{S}'$, since $\mathbf{S}$ is a skew symmetric matrix.

There are a number of interesting results connected with positive definite or semi-definite matrices and orthogonal matrices. (See Section 4.5.) One of these is the following:

Theorem 6.9.8. *The characteristic roots of a real symmetric positive definite (semi-definite) matrix are all positive (non-negative).*

Proof: By Theorem 6.9.4, every real symmetric matrix $\mathbf{A}$ is orthogonally similar to a diagonal matrix $\mathbf{D}$ with the characteristic values of $\mathbf{A}$ on the diagonal. That is, there exists an orthogonal matrix $\mathbf{P}$ such that $\mathbf{P}'\mathbf{A}\mathbf{P} = \mathbf{D}$. Thus,

(6.9.21) $$\mathbf{x}'\mathbf{P}'\mathbf{A}\mathbf{P}\mathbf{x} = \mathbf{x}'\mathbf{D}\mathbf{x} = \lambda_1 x_1^2 + \cdots + \lambda_n x_n^2,$$

for any real vector $\mathbf{x}$. Since $\mathbf{A}$ is positive definite, the right side of Eq. (6.9.21) must be positive for all $\mathbf{x}$. Thus each $\lambda_i > 0$.

If $\mathbf{A}$ is semi-definite, then there exists an orthogonal matrix $\mathbf{P}$ such that the last $n - r$ rows of $\mathbf{D}$ are zero, or $n - r$ of the λ_i of $\mathbf{A}$ are zero. Thus, the second part of the theorem follows.

Another result concerns the simultaneous diagonalization of two symmetric matrices if at least one of them is positive definite. That is, if **A** and **B** are symmetric matrices and **A**, say, is positive definite, does there exist a single matrix **P** such that

$$\mathbf{P'AP} = \mathbf{D}_1 \quad \text{and} \quad \mathbf{P'BP} = \mathbf{D}_2, \tag{6.9.22}$$

where $\mathbf{D}_1$ and $\mathbf{D}_2$ are diagonal matrices?

By Theorem 6.9.4, there exists an orthogonal matrix **Q** such that $\mathbf{Q'AQ} = \mathbf{D}$, a diagonal matrix with the characteristic values of **A** on the diagonal. However, it would be too much to expect in Eq. (6.9.22) that the diagonal elements of $\mathbf{D}_1$ and $\mathbf{D}_2$ were the characteristic values of **A** and **B** respectively.

To accomplish the results of Eq. (6.9.22), consider the quadratic form $\mathbf{x'Ax}$, which is positive definite by assumption. That is, there exists an orthogonal matrix **Q** such that

$$\mathbf{x'Ax} = \mathbf{y'Q'AQy} = \lambda_1 \mathbf{y}_1^2 + \cdots + \lambda_n \mathbf{y}_n^2. \tag{6.9.23}$$

By Theorem 6.9.8, all of the λ's in Eq. (6.9.23) are positive, so we make an additional transformation $\mathbf{y} = \mathbf{Ru}$, where

$$\mathbf{R} = \begin{bmatrix} 1/\sqrt{\lambda_1} & \cdots & 0 \\ \cdots & & \\ 0 & \cdots & 1/\sqrt{\lambda_n} \end{bmatrix}. \tag{6.9.24}$$

Thus,

$$\mathbf{x'Ax} = \mathbf{u'R'Q'AQRu} = u_1^2 + \cdots + u_n^2, \tag{6.9.25}$$

or

$$\mathbf{R'Q'AQR} = \mathbf{I} = \mathbf{D}_1. \tag{6.9.26}$$

The matrix $\mathbf{R'Q'BQR}$ is symmetric because **B** is symmetric. Thus, there exists an orthogonal matrix **S** that will reduce this matrix to diagonal form:

$$\mathbf{S'R'Q'BQRS} = \mathbf{D}_2. \tag{6.9.27}$$

If we define the matrix **P** to be $\mathbf{P} = \mathbf{QRS}$, then

$$\mathbf{P'AP} = \mathbf{S'R'Q'AQRS} = \mathbf{S'IS} = \mathbf{I}. \tag{6.9.28}$$

We can state the results of Eqs. (6.9.27) and (6.9.28) as the following theorem.

Theorem 6.9.9. *If* **A** *and* **B** *are symmetric matrices and* **A** *is positive definite, then there exists an orthogonal matrix* **P** *such that*

$$\mathbf{P'AP} = \mathbf{D}_1 \quad \text{and} \quad \mathbf{P'BP} = \mathbf{D}_2, \tag{6.9.29}$$

where $\mathbf{D}_1$ *and* $\mathbf{D}_2$ *are diagonal matrices.*

As mentioned above, the diagonal elements of $\mathbf{D}_1$ and $\mathbf{D}_2$ are not necessarily the characteristic values of $\mathbf{A}$ and $\mathbf{B}$. What are they? By forming the equation

$$\mathbf{P}'(\mathbf{B} - \lambda\mathbf{A})\mathbf{P} = \mathbf{P}'\mathbf{B}\mathbf{P} - \lambda\mathbf{P}'\mathbf{A}\mathbf{P} = \mathbf{D}_2 - \lambda\mathbf{I}, \tag{6.9.30}$$

we see that the characteristic values of $\mathbf{D}_2$ are the roots of $|\mathbf{B} - \lambda\mathbf{A}| = 0$.

Corollary 6.9.1. *If* $\mathbf{A}$ *and* $\mathbf{B}$ *are symmetric matrices and* $\mathbf{A}$ *is positive definite, then the diagonal elements of* $\mathbf{D}_2$ *in Eq.* (6.9.29) *are the roots of* $|\mathbf{B} - \lambda\mathbf{A}| = 0$.

Exercises 6.9

1. Prove that the product of unitary matrices is a unitary matrix.

2. (a) In two dimensions, give as a vector equation the equations of transformation for rotating the x- and y-axis (in a rectangular system) about the origin through an angle θ.
   (b) Verify that the transformation matrix is an orthogonal matrix.

3. Verify that one rotation about the origin of the axes in the plane followed by a second rotation has the effect of a single rotation. (See exercises 1 and 2.)

4. For the matrix

$$\mathbf{u} = \begin{bmatrix} 1/\sqrt{3} & (1-i)/\sqrt{3} \\ (1+i)/\sqrt{3} & -1/\sqrt{3} \end{bmatrix} = [\mathbf{x}_1 \quad \mathbf{x}_2] = \begin{bmatrix} \mathbf{y}_1 \\ \mathbf{y}_2 \end{bmatrix},$$

   (a) Verify that $\mathbf{x}_1^*\mathbf{x}_1 = 1$, $\mathbf{x}_2^*\mathbf{x}_2 = 1$, $\mathbf{x}_1^*\mathbf{x}_2 = 0$,
   $\mathbf{y}_1\mathbf{y}_1^* = 1$, $\mathbf{y}_2\mathbf{y}_2^* = 1$, $\mathbf{y}_1\mathbf{y}_2^* = 0$.
   (b) Verify that $\mathbf{u}^*\mathbf{u} = \mathbf{I}$.
   (c) Find $\mathbf{u}^{-1}$.

5. Prove that orthogonal matrices of order n form a group under multiplication.

6. Show that the cofactor of an element of an orthogonal matrix $\mathbf{A}$ is equal to the element or to the negative of the element: $a_{ij} = \pm A_{ij}$.

7. Show that $\mathbf{S} + \mathbf{I}$ is nonsingular when $\mathbf{S}$ is a skew symmetric matrix. (Hint: See Theorem 6.9.7.)

8. (a) If $\mathbf{A}$ is orthogonal, start with $\mathbf{A} = (\mathbf{S} + \mathbf{I})(\mathbf{S} - \mathbf{I})^{-1}$ and solve for $\mathbf{S}$.
   (b) Show that $\mathbf{S}$ must be skew symmetric (in general).

9. (a) If

$$\mathbf{S} = \begin{bmatrix} 0 & k \\ -k & 0 \end{bmatrix},$$

   construct an orthogonal matrix according to Theorem 6.9.7.
   (b) Make the substitution $k = \tan \theta/2$ and simplify the result.

10. (a) Verify that

$$\mathbf{B} = \begin{bmatrix} -2/3 & 2/3 & 1/3 \\ 2/3 & 1/3 & 2/3 \\ 1/3 & 2/3 & -2/3 \end{bmatrix}$$

is an orthogonal matrix by finding $\mathbf{B}'\mathbf{B}$.
(b) Verify that the rows of **B** are mutually orthogonal.
(c) Verify that the columns of **B** are mutually orthogonal.
(d) Verify that the rows of **B** are unit vectors.
(e) Verify that the columns of **B** are unit vectors.

11. Verify that Theorem 6.9.1 holds or does not hold for unitary matrices; for Hermitian matrices.

12. Verify that Theorem 6.9.2 holds or does not hold for unitary matrices after necessary modifications.

13. (a) Include additional matrices in the set of Pauli spin matrices so that the set forms a group under multiplication. (See number 4 of Exercises 1.4.)
(b) Verify that the enlarged set is a set of unitary matrices.
(c) Find the inverse and transposed conjugate of each matrix in the set.

6.10.† The Gram-Schmidt Process of Orthogonalization*

Earlier (in number 4 of Exercises 2.3), two vectors **x** and **y** were defined to be *orthogonal* if $\mathbf{x}'\mathbf{y} = 0$ (or $\mathbf{x}\mathbf{y}' = 0$). In Section 6.9, the orthogonality of vectors was used in discussing orthogonal matrices.

Any column (row) of an orthogonal matrix has length one. If **A** is an orthogonal matrix with columns $\mathbf{a}_1, \mathbf{a}_2, \cdots, \mathbf{a}_n$, then $\mathbf{a}_i'\mathbf{a}_i = 1$ for $i = 1, 2, \cdots, n$. The columns of **A** are then *normalized.* The set of columns (rows) of an orthogonal matrix forms a normalized orthogonal, or *orthonormal*, set of vectors.

For any nonzero column vector **x**,

(6.10.1)
$$\frac{\mathbf{x}'}{\sqrt{\mathbf{x}'\mathbf{x}}}$$

is a normalized vector, since

(6.10.2)
$$\frac{\mathbf{x}'}{\sqrt{\mathbf{x}'\mathbf{x}}}\,\frac{\mathbf{x}}{\sqrt{\mathbf{x}'\mathbf{x}}} = \frac{\mathbf{x}'\mathbf{x}}{\mathbf{x}'\mathbf{x}} = 1.$$

That is, the vector in Eq. (6.10.1) is a *unit vector.*

*Named after J. P. Gram, who wrote in German and French toward the end of the 19th century and Erhard Schmidt (1876–1959), a German mathematician.

Theorem 6.10.1. *A set of orthonormal vectors can be formed from any set of m vectors of dimension n.*

The procedure for constructing orthogonal vectors is known as the *Gram-Schmidt process* for orthogonalizing vectors.* Once the orthogonal vectors are obtained, the nonzero vectors can be normalized by Eq. (6.10.1). We assume that the vectors are column vectors and consider all possibilities for $m \gtreqless n$.

Let $\{\mathbf{x}_1, \mathbf{x}_2, \cdots, \mathbf{x}_m\}$ be a set of nonzero column vectors of dimension n. (If one or more of the vectors is the zero vector, then it is orthogonal to all of the others already, and need not be considered in the following construction.) To form a set of orthogonal vectors $\{\mathbf{y}_1, \mathbf{y}_2, \cdots, \mathbf{y}_m\}$ from these, let

(6.10.3)
$$\mathbf{y}_1 = \mathbf{x}_1, \quad \text{and} \quad \mathbf{y}_2 = \mathbf{x}_2 - \frac{\mathbf{y}_1'\mathbf{x}_2}{\mathbf{y}_1'\mathbf{y}_1}\mathbf{y}_1.$$

Clearly, $\mathbf{y}_1'\mathbf{y}_2 = 0$. Similarly,

(6.10.4)
$$\mathbf{y}_3 = \mathbf{x}_3 - \frac{\mathbf{y}_1'\mathbf{x}_3}{\mathbf{y}_1'\mathbf{y}_1}\mathbf{y}_1 - \frac{\mathbf{y}_2'\mathbf{x}_3}{\mathbf{y}_2'\mathbf{y}_2}\mathbf{y}_2,$$

is orthogonal to both $\mathbf{y}_1$ and $\mathbf{y}_2$. We assume that $\mathbf{y}_2 \neq \mathbf{0}$; however, if $\mathbf{y}_2 = \mathbf{0}$, then $\mathbf{y}_3$ is still orthogonal to both $\mathbf{y}_1$ and $\mathbf{y}_2$, when the final term in Eq. (6.10.4) is omitted.

Other vectors $\mathbf{y}_4, \cdots, \mathbf{y}_m$ are constructed similarly:

(6.10.5)
$$\mathbf{y}_m = \mathbf{x}_m - \frac{\mathbf{y}_1'\mathbf{x}_m}{\mathbf{y}_1'\mathbf{y}_1}\mathbf{y}_1 - \frac{\mathbf{y}_2'\mathbf{x}_m}{\mathbf{y}_2'\mathbf{y}_2}\mathbf{y}_2 - \cdots - \frac{\mathbf{y}_{m-1}'\mathbf{x}_m}{\mathbf{y}_{m-1}'\mathbf{y}_{m-1}}\mathbf{y}_{m-1}.$$

The term involving any $\mathbf{y}_i$ that is the zero vector is omitted in the construction of succeeding vectors. It is left as an exercise for the reader to show that the various vectors as constructed are actually mutually orthogonal.

Once the set of vectors $\{\mathbf{y}_1, \mathbf{y}_2, \cdots, \mathbf{y}_m\}$ has been constructed, any nonzero vector $\mathbf{y}_i$ in the set can be normalized by

(6.10.6)
$$\mathbf{z}_i = \frac{\mathbf{y}_i}{\sqrt{\mathbf{y}_i'\mathbf{y}_i}}.$$

These normalized vectors form an *orthonormal set* of vectors.

If $m \geqq n$, then no more than n of the vectors are required to form a basis of the vector space spanned by the m vectors of dimension n. A total of m mutually orthogonal vectors can be obtained by the Gram-Schmidt process from the m given vectors. However, only r *nonzero* mutually orthogonal

*The process for orthogonalizing a set of linearly independent functions is analogous to the process described here for vectors.

vectors can be obtained, where r is the rank of the matrix of the given vectors. In other words, if the given set of vectors contains r linearly independent vectors, then the Gram-Schmidt process gives m mutually orthogonal vectors; all but r of them are the zero vector, which is orthogonal to any other vector including itself.

Note that whether $m > n$, $m = n$, or $m < n$ there can be no more than r mutually orthogonal nonzero vectors, $r \leqq n$; and if $m < n$ then $r \leqq m$. For instance, the set of vectors $\{[1\ 0\ 0]', [2\ 0\ 0]', [0\ 1\ 0]', [0\ 2\ 0]', [0\ 3\ 0]'\}$ has $m = 5$ and $n = 3$, but $r = 2$. The vectors $[1\ 0\ 0]'$ and $[0\ 1\ 0]'$ are mutually orthogonal (and also normalized), while the other vectors are dependent on them.

We thus direct our attention to a set of basis vectors $\{\mathbf{x}_1, \mathbf{x}_2, \cdots, \mathbf{x}_m\}$ which span the linear vector space V, and $m \leqq n$. A set of m orthogonal vectors that span V can then be constructed from these using the Gram-Schmidt process.

Theorem 6.10.2. *If* $\{\mathbf{x}_1, \mathbf{x}_2, \cdots, \mathbf{x}_m\}$ *is a basis set of vectors of dimension* n *with* $m \leqq n$, *then none of the orthogonal vectors as constructed by the Gram-Schmidt process is the zero vector.*

Proof: The set of m vectors as given spans the vector space V. If any of the constructed vectors were the zero vector, then V could be spanned by fewer than m vectors. This would mean that some of the m basis vectors were dependent, contrary to Theorem 5.2.5. Therefore, the m mutually orthogonal vectors as constructed will all be nonzero, and will form a basis for V.

Theorem 6.10.3. *If* $\{\mathbf{x}_1, \mathbf{x}_2, \cdots, \mathbf{x}_m\}$ *is a basis set of orthogonal unit vectors of dimension* n *with* $m \leqq n$, *then there exist* $n - m$ *unit vectors such that the entire set of* n *vectors forms an orthonormal basis for all vectors of dimension* n.

If the vectors of the basis set are not unit vectors, we make them unit vectors by Eq. (6.10.1). To complete the set we adjoin any $n - m$ vectors so that the entire set of n vectors is a linearly independent one. From the adjoined vectors we construct orthogonal vectors using the Gram-Schmidt process and then normalize them to complete the set of n mutually orthogonal unit vectors.

Example 6.10.1. (a) Form an orthonormal set of basis vectors for the vector space V that is spanned by the vectors $[3, 4, 0]'$ and $[1\ 1\ 1]'$. (b) Adjoin a unit vector to the vectors found in (a) to complete the set of orthonormal vectors required to span the space of three-dimensional vectors. (c) Form an orthogonal matrix $\mathbf{A}$ from the vectors in (b) and verify that the rows of $\mathbf{A}$ are a basis of orthonormal vectors for row vectors of dimension three.

(a) Let

$$\mathbf{y}_1 = \begin{bmatrix} 3 \\ 4 \\ 0 \end{bmatrix}$$

$$\mathbf{y}_2 = \begin{bmatrix} 1 \\ 1 \\ 1 \end{bmatrix} - \frac{[3 \quad 4 \quad 0]\begin{bmatrix} 1 \\ 1 \\ 1 \end{bmatrix}}{25}\begin{bmatrix} 3 \\ 4 \\ 0 \end{bmatrix} = \begin{bmatrix} 4/25 \\ -3/25 \\ 1 \end{bmatrix}.$$

The orthogonal basis vectors are thus

$$\mathbf{u}_1 = \begin{bmatrix} 3/5 \\ 4/5 \\ 0 \end{bmatrix} \quad \text{and} \quad \mathbf{u}_2 = \begin{bmatrix} 4/(5\sqrt{26}) \\ -3/(5\sqrt{26}) \\ 25/(5\sqrt{26}) \end{bmatrix}.$$

(b) For the third vector we choose any vector $[a \ b \ c]'$ so that

$$\begin{vmatrix} 3 & 4/25 & a \\ 4 & -3/25 & b \\ 1 & 1 & c \end{vmatrix} \neq 0;$$

the three vectors will be linearly independent. The vector $[0 \ 0 \ 1]'$ will serve adequately for the third vector. Thus to get a vector orthogonal to $\mathbf{y}_1$ and $\mathbf{y}_2$ we form

$$\mathbf{y}_3 = \begin{bmatrix} 0 \\ 0 \\ 1 \end{bmatrix} - \frac{[3 \quad 4 \quad 0]\begin{bmatrix} 0 \\ 0 \\ 1 \end{bmatrix}}{25}\begin{bmatrix} 3 \\ 4 \\ 0 \end{bmatrix} - \frac{[4/25 \quad -3/25 \quad 1]\begin{bmatrix} 0 \\ 0 \\ 1 \end{bmatrix}}{650/625}\begin{bmatrix} 4/25 \\ -3/25 \\ 1 \end{bmatrix}$$

$$= \begin{bmatrix} 0 \\ 0 \\ 1 \end{bmatrix} - \begin{bmatrix} 0 \\ 0 \\ 0 \end{bmatrix} - \begin{bmatrix} 4/26 \\ -3/26 \\ 25/26 \end{bmatrix} = \begin{bmatrix} -4/26 \\ 3/26 \\ 1/26 \end{bmatrix}.$$

Then

$$\mathbf{u}_3 = \begin{bmatrix} -4/\sqrt{26} \\ 3/\sqrt{26} \\ 1/\sqrt{26} \end{bmatrix},$$

and $\mathbf{u}_1$, $\mathbf{u}_2$, and $\mathbf{u}_3$ are a basis set of unit vectors for the vector space of three-dimensional vectors.

(c) From $\mathbf{u}_1$, $\mathbf{u}_2$, and $\mathbf{u}_3$ we form

$$\mathbf{A} = [\mathbf{u}_1 \quad \mathbf{u}_2 \quad \mathbf{u}_3] = \begin{bmatrix} 3/5 & 4/(5\sqrt{26}) & -4/\sqrt{26} \\ 4/5 & -3/(5\sqrt{26}) & 3/\sqrt{26} \\ 0 & 25/(5\sqrt{26}) & 1/\sqrt{26} \end{bmatrix}.$$

Since det $\mathbf{A} = -1 \neq 0$, the rows as well as the columns of $\mathbf{A}$ are linearly independent. Hence, the rows of $\mathbf{A}$ form a basis for three-dimensional row vectors. Since the rows of $\mathbf{A}$ are unit vectors and are also orthonormal, the basis is an orthonormal basis.

Exercises 6.10

1. In Eqs. (6.10.3), (6.10.4), and (6.10.5), show that $\mathbf{y}_1$ is orthogonal to $\mathbf{y}_2$, $\mathbf{y}_3$, and $\mathbf{y}_m$, that $\mathbf{y}_2$ is orthogonal to $\mathbf{y}_3$ and $\mathbf{y}_m$, and that $\mathbf{y}_3$ and $\mathbf{y}_m$ are orthogonal.
2. (a) Construct an orthogonal matrix $\mathbf{A}$ with unit vectors obtained from $[1 \ \ 1 \ \ 1]'$ and $[1 \ \ -2 \ \ 1]'$ as its first two columns.
   (b) Verify that the rows of $\mathbf{A}$ are orthonormal vectors.
3. Work exercise 2 for vectors $[1 \ \ 2 \ \ 2]'$ and $[2 \ \ -2 \ \ 1]'$.
4. Form a set of orthogonal vectors from the vectors $[1 \ \ 1 \ \ 0]$, $[0 \ \ 1 \ \ 1]$, $[1 \ \ 0 \ \ 1]$, and $[1 \ \ 1 \ \ 1]$.
5. Form a set of orthogonal vectors from the vectors $[2 \ \ 1 \ \ 0 \ \ 2]$, $[1 \ \ 0 \ \ 2 \ \ 1]$, and $[-1 \ \ 1 \ \ 1 \ \ 0]$.
6. Work Example 6.10.1 starting with vectors $[7 \ \ 0 \ \ 12]$ and $[1 \ \ 0 \ \ 1]$.
7. The vectors $[1 \ \ 3 \ \ 2]'$, $[-1 \ \ 2 \ \ -1]'$, and $[1 \ \ 4 \ \ 2]'$ are linearly independent, and thus span the linear vector space V of vectors of dimension three. Find an orthogonal basis for V.

6.11.† Minimum Polynomial of a Matrix

When we consider powers of a matrix $\mathbf{A}$, we assume that $\mathbf{A}$ is square. When we consider sums of such powers, we are led immediately to the analogy between the *scalar polynomial* in the variable x

$$f(x) = \sum_{j=0}^{m} a_j x^j, \tag{6.11.1}$$

and the sum

$$\sum_{j=0}^{m} a_j \mathbf{A}^j, \tag{6.11.2}$$

with the matrix $\mathbf{A}$ as the variable. (It is understood that $\mathbf{A}^0 = \mathbf{I}$; see Section 7.4 for a more complete discussion of the powers of matrices.) Since the analogy between Eqs. (6.11.1) and (6.11.2) holds to a certain extent, we refer to polynomials in Eq. (6.11.2) as *polynomial functions of matrices.**

*We reserve the term *matrix polynomials* for expressions such as $\mathbf{A}x^3 + \mathbf{B}x^2 + \mathbf{C}x + \mathbf{D}$ in which the coefficients of the variable are matrices. Such polynomials can be expressed merely as a matrix with polynomial elements.

If we consider a square matrix of order n as a vector with n^2 elements, then any n^2+1 such matrices are linearly dependent. (See Theorem 5.1.6.) Thus, in particular, the matrices $\mathbf{I}, \mathbf{A}, \mathbf{A}^2, \cdots, \mathbf{A}^m$, where $m \leqq n^2$, are linearly dependent. That is, there exist constants $c_0, c_1, \cdots, c_m$, not all zero, such that

$$c_m\mathbf{A}^m + c_{m-1}\mathbf{A}^{m-1} + \cdots + c_1\mathbf{A} + c_0\mathbf{I} = \mathbf{0}. \tag{6.11.3}$$

We state this result as a theorem.

Theorem 6.11.1. *There exists a positive integer k, where $k \leqq n^2$, such that any square matrix* $\mathbf{A}$ *of order n satisfies a polynomial function of matrices equation of the form*

$$\mathbf{A}^k + a_{k-1}\mathbf{A}^{k-1} + \cdots + a_1\mathbf{A} + a_0\mathbf{I} = \mathbf{0}. \tag{6.11.4}$$

Proof: By the preceding discussion, at least one of the c's $\neq 0$ in Eq. (6.11.3), so assume that c_k is the coefficient of the greatest power of $\mathbf{A}$ that is different from zero. By dividing through by c_k, Eq. (6.11.4) results.

Another way to express the result of Theorem 6.11.1 is to say that there exists a polynomial

$$f(x) = x^k + a_{k-1}x^{k-1} + \cdots + a_1x + a_0 \tag{6.11.5}$$

such that $f(x) = 0$ has $\mathbf{A}$ as a "root". That is,

$$f(\mathbf{A}) = \mathbf{0}. \tag{6.11.6}$$

A scalar polynomial such as $f(x)$ in Eq. (6.11.5) with leading coefficient one is a *monic polynomial.*

A matrix $\mathbf{A}$ may satisfy a monic polynomial equation of degree less than n^2. For instance, $\mathbf{A} = \mathbf{I}$ satisfies the monic polynomial equation $f(x) = x - 1 = 0$, since $f(\mathbf{A}) = \mathbf{I} - \mathbf{I} = \mathbf{0}$ for $\mathbf{A}$ of any order. A matrix may also satisfy several monic polynomials; it satisfies one, at least, of degree $k \leqq n^2$ by Theorem 6.11.1.

The monic polynomial of *least degree* satisfied by a given matrix $\mathbf{A}$ is the *minimum polynomial* of the matrix $\mathbf{A}$.

Example 6.11.1. Find the minimum polynomial for

$$\mathbf{A} = \begin{bmatrix} 1 & 2 \\ 2 & 1 \end{bmatrix}.$$

The minimum polynomial for $\mathbf{A}$ is of degree 4 or less, since there are 4 elements of $\mathbf{A}$. Also $\mathbf{A}$ does not satisfy a polynomial equation of degree one, say $f_1(x) = x + a_0 = 0$, because

$$\mathbf{A} + a_0\mathbf{I} = \mathbf{0} \qquad \text{or} \qquad \begin{bmatrix} 1 & 2 \\ 2 & 1 \end{bmatrix} + \begin{bmatrix} a_0 & 0 \\ 0 & a_0 \end{bmatrix} = \begin{bmatrix} 0 & 0 \\ 0 & 0 \end{bmatrix}$$

would require that $\mathbf{A}$ be a scalar matrix. Therefore, we try $f(x) = x^2 + a_1x + a_0 = 0$, or

$$\begin{bmatrix} 5 & 4 \\ 4 & 5 \end{bmatrix} + a_1\begin{bmatrix} 1 & 2 \\ 2 & 1 \end{bmatrix} + a_0\begin{bmatrix} 1 & 0 \\ 0 & 1 \end{bmatrix} = \begin{bmatrix} 0 & 0 \\ 0 & 0 \end{bmatrix}.$$

The equations

$$5 + a_1 + a_0 = 0 \quad \text{and} \quad 4 + 2a_1 = 0,$$

with two other scalar equations the same as these, must be satisfied. They are satisfied for $a_1 = -2$ and $a_0 = -3$, and so $\mathbf{A}$ has the minimum polynomial

$$f(x) = x^2 - 2x - 3.$$

This example illustrates an elementary approach to determining the minimum polynomial of a matrix (the only approach used in this book).

By Theorem 6.11.1, any matrix $\mathbf{A}$ satisfies a polynomial function of matrices equation, and hence it satisfies a monic polynomial equation of least degree, say k. We now determine whether $\mathbf{A}$ can satisfy two or more monic polynomial equations of degree k. Assume that

(6.11.7) $$f(x) = x^k + a_{k-1}x^{k-1} + \cdots + a_1x + a_0 = 0 \quad \text{and}$$

(6.11.8) $$g(x) = x^k + c_{k-1}x^{k-1} + \cdots + c_1x + c_0 = 0$$

both have $\mathbf{A}$ as a root, so that $f(\mathbf{A}) = g(\mathbf{A}) = \mathbf{0}$, and

(6.11.9)

$$f(\mathbf{A}) - g(\mathbf{A}) = (a_{k-1} - c_{k-1})\mathbf{A}^{k-1} + \cdots + (a_1 - c_1)\mathbf{A} + (a_0 - c_0)\mathbf{I} = \mathbf{0}.$$

Either all of the coefficients on the right are zero and $f(x) = g(x)$, or $a_j - c_j$ (with $j \leqq k - 1$) is the first nonzero coefficient. Dividing through by this coefficient yields a monic polynomial equation satisfied by $\mathbf{A}$. But the degree of this polynomial is less than k, contrary to the assumption that the minimum polynomial is of degree k. Thus all of the coefficients in Eq. (6.11.9) must be zero. This result is stated as a theorem.

Theorem 6.11.2. *The minimum polynomial for a square matrix* $\mathbf{A}$ *is unique.*

We can go one step further and say:

Theorem 6.11.3. *If* $\mathbf{A}$ *has* $f(x)$ *as its minimum polynomial and* $g(x)$ *is any polynomial such that* $g(\mathbf{A}) = \mathbf{0}$, *then* $g(x)$ *is divisible by* $f(x)$.

Proof: If $f(x)$ is of degree k, then by Theorem 6.11.2 $g(x)$ is of degree greater than or equal to k. Dividing $g(x)$ by $f(x)$,

$$g(x) = q(x)f(x) + r(x), \tag{6.11.10}$$

where $q(x)$ and $r(x)$ are polynomials and $r(x) \equiv 0$ or $r(x)$ is of degree less than k. But

$$g(\mathbf{A}) = q(\mathbf{A})f(\mathbf{A}) + r(\mathbf{A}), \tag{6.11.11}$$

so $r(x) \equiv 0$, since $g(\mathbf{A}) = \mathbf{0}$ and $f(\mathbf{A}) = \mathbf{0}$. Thus there are no polynomials of degree less than k such that $r(\mathbf{A}) = \mathbf{0}$; that is, $g(x)$ is divisible by $f(x)$.

Note that in Example 6.11.1 the minimum polynomial $f(x)$ may be factored:

$$f(x) = x^2 - 2x - 3 = (x - 3)(x + 1).$$

Thus

$$f(\mathbf{A}) = (\mathbf{A} - 3\mathbf{I})(\mathbf{A} + \mathbf{I}) = \mathbf{0}.$$

We cannot say that $\mathbf{A} - 3\mathbf{I} = \mathbf{0}$ or $\mathbf{A} + \mathbf{I} = \mathbf{0}$, because then the minimum polynomial would be of degree one. We *can* say that both of the factors are singular. (See Theorem 3.6.8.)

Theorem 6.11.4. *If* $\mathbf{A}$ *has the minimum polynomial* $f(x)$ *given in Eq.* (6.11.5), *then the necessary and sufficient condition that* $\mathbf{A}$ *have an inverse is that* $a_0 \neq 0$.

Proof: If $f(x)$ is the minimum polynomial for $\mathbf{A}$, then

$$f(\mathbf{A}) = \mathbf{A}^k + a_{k-1}\mathbf{A}^{k-1} + \cdots + a_1\mathbf{A} + a_0\mathbf{I} = \mathbf{0} \quad \text{or} \tag{6.11.12}$$

$$\mathbf{A}^k + a_{k-1}\mathbf{A}^{k-1} + \cdots + a_1\mathbf{A} = -a_0\mathbf{I}. \tag{6.11.13}$$

If $a_0 \neq 0$, we can divide both sides of Eq. (6.11.13) by $-a_0$:

$$b_k\mathbf{A}^k + \cdots + b_1\mathbf{A} = \mathbf{I}, \tag{6.11.14}$$

where $b_k = -1/a_0, \cdots, b_1 = -a_1/a_0$. Equation (6.11.14) can also be written as

$$\mathbf{A}(b_k\mathbf{A}^{k-1} + \cdots + b_1\mathbf{I}) = (b_k\mathbf{A}^{k-1} + \cdots + b_1\mathbf{I})\mathbf{A} = \mathbf{I}; \tag{6.11.15}$$

the quantity in parenthesis is the inverse of $\mathbf{A}$.

To prove the necessary condition, we assume that $\mathbf{A}$ has an inverse, and that $a_0 = 0$. We write Eq. (6.11.12) as

$$\mathbf{A}^k + a_{k-1}\mathbf{A}^{k-1} + \cdots + a_1\mathbf{A} = \mathbf{0} \tag{6.11.16}$$

and multiply through by $\mathbf{A}^{-1}$:

$$\mathbf{A}^{-1}(\mathbf{A}^k + \cdots + a_1\mathbf{A}) = \mathbf{A}^{-1}\mathbf{A}(\mathbf{A}^{k-1} + \cdots + a_1\mathbf{I}) = \mathbf{0}, \quad \text{or}$$

$$\mathbf{A}^{k-1} + \cdots + a_1\mathbf{I} = \mathbf{0}. \tag{6.11.17}$$

Since this contradicts the fact that the degree of the minimum polynomial is k, $a_0 \neq 0$ if $\mathbf{A}$ has an inverse.

Equation (6.11.15) can be used to construct the inverse of a matrix, especially if a computer is used.

Exercises 6.11

1. Find the minimum polynomial of the matrix

$$\text{(a)}\ \begin{bmatrix} 0 & 1 \\ 1 & 0 \end{bmatrix}, \quad \text{(b)}\ \begin{bmatrix} 1 & 2 \\ 3 & 4 \end{bmatrix}, \quad \text{(c)}\ \begin{bmatrix} 2 & 0 \\ 0 & 2 \end{bmatrix},$$

$$\text{(d)}\ \begin{bmatrix} 0 & 2 & 1 \\ 2 & 0 & -1 \\ 1 & -1 & 0 \end{bmatrix}, \quad \text{(e)}\ \begin{bmatrix} 3 & 0 & 1 \\ 0 & 3 & 0 \\ 0 & 0 & 3 \end{bmatrix}, \quad \text{(f)}\ \begin{bmatrix} 2 & -1 & 3 \\ 1 & 0 & 2 \\ -3 & 2 & 1 \end{bmatrix}.$$

2. Use the minimum polynomial of $\mathbf{A}$ to calculate $\mathbf{A}^{-1}$ if $\mathbf{A}$ is

$$\text{(a)}\ \begin{bmatrix} 1 & 2 \\ 3 & 4 \end{bmatrix}, \quad \text{(b)}\ \begin{bmatrix} 2 & 1 & -1 \\ 1 & 0 & 2 \\ -1 & 2 & 1 \end{bmatrix}.$$

3. (a) Find the minimum polynomial $f(x)$ for

$$\mathbf{A} = \begin{bmatrix} 0 & 1 & 0 \\ 0 & 0 & 1 \\ 1 & 0 & 0 \end{bmatrix}.$$

   (b) Factor $f(x)$ into two factors with rational coefficients, say $f(x) = q(x)r(x)$, and show that both $q(\mathbf{A})$ and $r(\mathbf{A})$ are singular matrices but are not the zero matrix.

4. Prove that a matrix $\mathbf{A}$ and its transpose $\mathbf{A}'$ have the same minimum polynomial.

5. Prove that

$$\mathbf{A} = \begin{bmatrix} 3 & 0 & 0 \\ 0 & 3 & 0 \\ 0 & 0 & 3 \end{bmatrix}$$

   is a "root" of the equation $f(x) = x^2 - 4x + 3 = 0$ but that $f(x)$ is not the minimum polynomial for $\mathbf{A}$. Explain why.

6. (a) Using the matrices in exercise 2, find the corresponding characteristic polynomial $f(\lambda)$.
   (b) Verify that $f(\mathbf{A}) = \mathbf{0}$ in each case.
   (c) Determine whether or not $f(\lambda)$ is a minimum polynomial in each case. (Compare with the results found in exercise 2.)
   (d) What conclusion might you be tempted to make from (c)?

7. Use Theorem 6.11.4 to determine the inverse of $\mathbf{A}$ in each case in exercise 2. (Use the results found in exercise 2.)

8. Using the results of exercise 1, verify that the constant term in each minimum polynomial is the same as det **A**. Explain why this is true.

9. Prove that if $\Phi(\lambda)$ is a polynomial function of the eigenvalue λ associated with **A**, then $\Phi(\mathbf{A})\mathbf{x} = \Phi(\lambda)\mathbf{x}$. (Hint: Show that $\mathbf{A}^2\mathbf{x} = \lambda^2\mathbf{x}, \cdots, \mathbf{A}^k\mathbf{x} = \lambda^k\mathbf{x}$.)

10. Find the characteristic values of $\mathbf{A}^2$ if

$$\mathbf{A} = \begin{bmatrix} 0 & 0 & 1 \\ 0 & 4 & 0 \\ 4 & 0 & 0 \end{bmatrix}.$$

From these find the characteristic values of **A**. (Hint: Use exercise 9.)

6.12. The Cayley-Hamilton* Theorem

The preceding section showed that every square matrix **A** of order n satisfies a polynomial equation of degree k where $k \leqq n^2$. This section shows (among other results) that $k \leqq n$.

By Theorems 3.6.8 and 5.2.4 we can state the following theorem:

Theorem 6.12.1. *If a set of vectors* $\{\mathbf{x}_1, \mathbf{x}_2, \cdots, \mathbf{x}_n\}$ *span the vector space V of n-dimensional vectors, and if* $\mathbf{B}\mathbf{x}_i = \mathbf{0}$ *for* $i = 1, 2, \cdots, n$, *then* $\mathbf{B} = \mathbf{0}$.

Since the matrix of the vectors **X** has rank n, $\mathbf{BX} = \mathbf{0}$ implies that $\mathbf{B} = \mathbf{0}$. This result is used to prove the following *special case* of the *Cayley-Hamilton Theorem.*

Theorem 6.12.2. *If* $f(\lambda)$ *is the characteristic polynomial for the matrix* **A** *whose characteristic vectors* $\{\mathbf{x}_1, \mathbf{x}_2, \cdots, \mathbf{x}_n\}$ *span the vector space V of n-dimensional vectors, then* $f(\mathbf{A}) = \mathbf{0}$.

Proof: We write the characteristic polynomial $f(\lambda)$ as

(6.12.1) $$f(\lambda) = (-1)^n\lambda^n + c_{n-1}\lambda^{n-1} + \cdots + c_1\lambda + c_0,$$

and then define the matrix **B** by

(6.12.2) $$\mathbf{B} = (-1)^n\mathbf{A}^n + c_{n-1}\mathbf{A}^{n-1} + \cdots + c_1\mathbf{A} + c_0\mathbf{I}.$$

Then if $\mathbf{x}_i$ is the characteristic vector corresponding to the characteristic value λ_i,

(6.12.3) $$\begin{aligned} \mathbf{B}\mathbf{x}_i &= (-1)^n\mathbf{A}^n\mathbf{x}_i + c_{n-1}\mathbf{A}^{n-1}\mathbf{x}_i + \cdots + c_1\mathbf{A}\mathbf{x}_i + c_0\mathbf{I}\mathbf{x}_i \\ &= [(-1)^n\lambda_i^n + c_{n-1}\lambda_i^{n-1} + \cdots + c_1\lambda_i + c_0]\mathbf{x}_i \\ &= 0\mathbf{x}_i = \mathbf{0} \qquad \text{for} \quad i = 1, 2, \cdots, n. \end{aligned}$$

*Named after the British mathematicians A. Cayley (1821–1895) and Sir W. R. Hamilton (1805–1865).

Equation (6.12.3) used the fact that if $\mathbf{A}\mathbf{x}_i = \lambda_i \mathbf{x}_i$, then $\mathbf{A}^k \mathbf{x}_i = \lambda_i^k \mathbf{x}_i$. (See Theorem 6.7.3.) By Theorem 6.12.1, Eq. (6.12.3) implies that $\mathbf{B} = \mathbf{0}$. Therefore, Eq. (6.12.2) can be written as

$$(6.12.4) \qquad f(\mathbf{A}) = (-1)^n \mathbf{A}^n + c_{n-1}\mathbf{A}^{n-1} + \cdots + c_1 \mathbf{A} + c_0 \mathbf{I} = \mathbf{0}.$$

We now state and prove the *Cayley-Hamilton Theorem* for any square matrix.

Theorem 6.12.3. *If $f(\lambda)$ is the characteristic polynomial for the matrix* $\mathbf{A}$, *then* $f(\mathbf{A}) = \mathbf{0}$.

Proof: Speaking loosely, this theorem says that a matrix $\mathbf{A}$ satisfies its own characteristic equation. We start the proof by considering the matrix $\mathbf{A} - \lambda\mathbf{I}$:

$$(6.12.5) \qquad \frac{\operatorname{adj}(\mathbf{A} - \lambda\mathbf{I})}{\det(\mathbf{A} - \lambda\mathbf{I})}(\mathbf{A} - \lambda\mathbf{I}) = \mathbf{I}.$$

Since $\det(\mathbf{A} - \lambda\mathbf{I}) = f(\lambda)$, the characteristic polynomial for $\mathbf{A}$,

$$(6.12.6) \qquad \operatorname{adj}(\mathbf{A} - \lambda\mathbf{I})(\mathbf{A} - \lambda\mathbf{I}) = f(\lambda)\mathbf{I}.$$

The elements of $\operatorname{adj}(\mathbf{A} - \lambda\mathbf{I})$ are determinants of order $n - 1$. When expanded, they give polynomials in λ of degree $n - 1$ (at most) as the elements. Thus $\operatorname{adj}(\mathbf{A} - \lambda\mathbf{I})$ may be written as a *matrix polynomial*; (See Section 6.11.)

$$(6.12.7) \qquad \operatorname{adj}(\mathbf{A} - \lambda\mathbf{I}) = \mathbf{B}_{n-1}\lambda^{n-1} + \mathbf{B}_{n-2}\lambda^{n-2} + \cdots + \mathbf{B}_1\lambda + \mathbf{B}_0;$$

the terms involving like powers of λ^j have been combined into the coefficient matrix $\mathbf{B}_j$.

We now write Eq. (6.12.6) as

$$(6.12.8) \qquad (\mathbf{B}_{n-1}\lambda^{n-1} + \cdots + \mathbf{B}_1\lambda + \mathbf{B}_0)(\mathbf{A} - \lambda\mathbf{I}) = [(-1)^n\lambda^n + c_{n-1}\lambda^{n-1} + \cdots + c_1\lambda + c_0]\mathbf{I};$$

equating the coefficients of λ (since this is an identity in λ) yields the set of equations

$$(6.12.9) \qquad \begin{aligned} -\mathbf{B}_{n-1} &= (-1)^n\mathbf{I}, \\ \mathbf{B}_{n-1}\mathbf{A} - \mathbf{B}_{n-2} &= c_{n-1}\mathbf{I}, \\ \mathbf{B}_{n-2}\mathbf{A} - \mathbf{B}_{n-3} &= c_{n-2}\mathbf{I}, \\ &\cdots \\ \mathbf{B}_1\mathbf{A} - \mathbf{B}_0 &= c_1\mathbf{I}, \\ \mathbf{B}_0\mathbf{A} &= c_0\mathbf{I}. \end{aligned}$$

If we postmultiply the first equation by $\mathbf{A}^n$, the second by $\mathbf{A}^{n-1}$, $\cdots$, and the last by $\mathbf{I}$, and then add, the sum on the left side vanishes because pairs of terms cancel:

$$(6.12.10) \qquad \mathbf{0} = (-1)^n\mathbf{A}^n + c_{n-1}\mathbf{A}^{n-1} + \cdots + c_1\mathbf{A} + c_0\mathbf{I} = f(\mathbf{A}),$$

and the theorem is proved.

A corollary to Theorem 6.12.3 is that the minimum polynomial for a square matrix **A** has degree k where $k \leqq n$. If $k < n$, then **A** is a *derogatory matrix*.*

Example 6.12.1. Show that

$$\mathbf{A} = \begin{bmatrix} 2 & 0 \\ 0 & 2 \end{bmatrix}$$

is a derogatory matrix.

The characteristic polynomial for **A** is

$$f(\lambda) = \det\left(\begin{bmatrix} 2 & 0 \\ 0 & 2 \end{bmatrix} - \lambda\begin{bmatrix} 1 & 0 \\ 0 & 1 \end{bmatrix}\right) = \lambda^2 - 4\lambda + 4,$$

which is of degree 2. (Also, $f(\mathbf{A}) = \mathbf{0}$.) The minimum polynomial for for **A** is

$$g(x) = x - 2,$$

since

$$g(\mathbf{A}) = \begin{bmatrix} 2 & 0 \\ 0 & 2 \end{bmatrix} - 2\begin{bmatrix} 1 & 0 \\ 0 & 1 \end{bmatrix} = \mathbf{0}.$$

Therefore **A** is a derogatory matrix, because the degrees of the two polynomials are not the same.

Exercises 6.12

1. For each of the following matrices, determine the characteristic polynomial $f(\lambda)$ and verify that $f(\mathbf{A}) = \mathbf{0}$.

(a) $\begin{bmatrix} 2 & -1 \\ -2 & 3 \end{bmatrix}$, (b) $\begin{bmatrix} 1 & 2 & -1 \\ 2 & 0 & 3 \\ -1 & 3 & 1 \end{bmatrix}$, (c) $\begin{bmatrix} 2 & 0 & 0 & 0 \\ 0 & 1 & 0 & 0 \\ 0 & 0 & 0 & 0 \\ 0 & 0 & 0 & 3 \end{bmatrix}$.

2. Write $\operatorname{adj}(\mathbf{A} - \lambda\mathbf{I})$ as a matrix polynomial if

$$\mathbf{A} = \begin{bmatrix} 1 & 0 & 2 \\ 0 & 1 & 0 \\ 2 & 0 & -1 \end{bmatrix}.$$

*A brief summary of results connected with problems in this area is to be found in the article "Defective and Derogatory Matrices" by Robert T. Gregory, *SIAM Review*, Vol. 2 (1960), pp. 134–139.

3. Determine which if any of the following matrices are derogatory by determining the minimum polynomial and the characteristic polynomial.

(a) $\begin{bmatrix} 1 & 0 & -1 \\ 1 & 2 & 1 \\ 2 & 2 & 3 \end{bmatrix}$, (b) $\begin{bmatrix} 1 & 0 & 1 \\ 0 & 1 & 0 \\ 0 & 0 & 1 \end{bmatrix}$, (c) $\begin{bmatrix} 0 & 1 & 0 \\ 0 & 0 & 1 \\ -1 & -3 & -3 \end{bmatrix}$,

(d) $\begin{bmatrix} 1 & -2 & 1 \\ 1 & -1 & 0 \\ 0 & -1 & 1 \end{bmatrix}$, (e) $\mathbf{I}_3$.

4. Write

$$\begin{bmatrix} x^2 + x & x^3 - 2x + 1 \\ x^3 - 2 & 2x^2 - x \end{bmatrix}$$

as a matrix polynomial.

5. Using $\mathbf{B} = [b_{ij}]$ and vectors $[1\ 1\ 1]'$, $[1\ 2\ 4]'$, and $[1\ 3\ 9]'$, verify Theorem 6.12.1 by showing that $\mathbf{B} \equiv \mathbf{0}$.

6. Using the Cayley-Hamilton Theorem and the characteristic equations already found, determine $\mathbf{A}^2$ for (a) and $\mathbf{A}^3$ for (b) in exercise 1.

7. Use the Cayley-Hamilton Theorem and the characteristic equations already found in exercise 1 to find $\mathbf{A}^{-1}$ for (a) and (b). Why cannot $\mathbf{A}^{-1}$ be found similarly for (c)?

8. Prove that the minimum polynomial of $\mathbf{A}$ divides the characteristic polynomial of $\mathbf{A}$.

7

The Calculus of Matrices

This chapter considers certain operations for matrices analogous to those considered in scalar calculus. For such operations, the matrices, and hence their elements, must be functions of one or more variables. In the general case, the elements of a matrix are *functions* that assume values from a number field $\mathscr{F}$.

7.1. *Matrices of Functions*

Section 6.11 hinted that a *matrix polynomial*, such as

$$\mathbf{A}x^3 + \mathbf{B}x^2 + \mathbf{C}x + \mathbf{D}, \tag{7.1.1}$$

could be written as a matrix with polynomial elements:

$$\begin{bmatrix} 2 & 1 \\ 1 & 0 \end{bmatrix} x^2 + \begin{bmatrix} 0 & 1 \\ 1 & 0 \end{bmatrix} x + \begin{bmatrix} 1 & 3 \\ 0 & 5 \end{bmatrix} = \begin{bmatrix} 2x^2+1 & x+3 \\ x^2+x & x^2+5 \end{bmatrix} = \mathbf{F}(x). \tag{7.1.2}$$

This is an elementary example of a matrix with elements that are functions of the variable x. Note that a *matrix polynomial* is generally not the same as a *polynomial function of matrices.* (See Section 6.11.)

In Eq. (7.1.2), $\mathbf{F}(x)$ is a matrix of functions. A more general matrix of functions would be

$$\mathbf{G}(x) = \begin{bmatrix} e^x & x^2-1 \\ \sin x & xe^x \end{bmatrix},$$

since the elements are not all polynomials. A *matrix of functions* (or merely a *matrix function*) of the variable x is the $m \times n$ matrix,

$$\mathbf{F}(x) = [f_{ij}(x)]_{m,n}, \tag{7.1.3}$$

in which the scalar functions $f_{ij}(x)$ are defined for x in some interval.

The *norm* of a matrix $\mathbf{A}$, written as $\|\mathbf{A}\|$, is the non-negative number

$$\|\mathbf{A}\| = \sum_{i,j=1}^{m,n} |a_{ij}|, \tag{7.1.4}$$

for any matrix of order $m \times n$. In other words, the norm of $\mathbf{A}$ is the sum of the absolute values of the elements of $\mathbf{A}$. (Although several other definitions have been used for the norm of a matrix, this definition is probably the commonest.) It is left as an exercise for the reader to show that this definition meets the requirements listed in Eq. (2.3.2) for a norm (after the word "vector" is replaced by "matrix").

If the matrix is $m \times 1$ or $1 \times n$ (a column or row vector), then the norm given here (the sum of the absolute values of the elements) is different from that given in Section 2.3. If $\mathbf{A}$ is square, then the norm is another number associated with $\mathbf{A}$ besides det $\mathbf{A}$; in general, $\|\mathbf{A}\|$ is different from det $\mathbf{A}$. For example, det $\mathbf{A}$ may be negative while $\|\mathbf{A}\|$ is never negative.

For the scalar function $f(x)$, we write

$$\lim_{x \to x_0} f(x) = A, \tag{7.1.5}$$

to indicate the limit (if it exists) of $f(x)$ as $x \to x_0$, where A is a scalar constant. This equation does not imply that $f(x_0)$ exists, or that $f(x_0) = A$ even if $f(x_0)$ does exist. Equation (7.1.5) means that for each positive number ε there exists a positive number δ such that

$$|f(x) - A| < \varepsilon \text{ whenever } 0 < |x - x_0| < \delta. \tag{7.1.6}$$

The analogous definition for the matrix $\mathbf{F}(x)$ is that the *limit* of $\mathbf{F}(x)$ as $x \to x_0$ is $\mathbf{A}$, written as

$$\lim_{x \to x_0} \mathbf{F}(x) = \mathbf{A}, \tag{7.1.7}$$

(if it exists), means that for each positive number ε there exists a positive number δ such that

$$\|\mathbf{F}(x) - \mathbf{A}\| < \varepsilon \text{ whenever } 0 < |x - x_0| < \delta \tag{7.1.8}$$

for some constant matrix $\mathbf{A} = [a_{ij}]$.

Since $\mathbf{F}(x) = [f_{ij}(x)]$,

(7.1.9)

$$\begin{aligned} \|\mathbf{F}(x) - \mathbf{A}\| &= \|f_{ij}(x) - a_{ij}\| \\ &= \sum_{i,j=1}^{m,n} |f_{ij}(x) - a_{ij}| < \varepsilon, \qquad \text{whenever} \quad 0 < |x - x_0| < \delta. \end{aligned}$$

This implies that the limit for each element of $\mathbf{F}(x)$ exists as $x \to x_0$. We write the consequence of these observations as a theorem.

Theorem 7.1.1. *If* $\lim_{x \to x_0} f_{ij}(x)$ *exists for each* $i = 1, 2, \cdots, m$ *and* $j = 1, 2, \cdots, n$, *then*

(7.1.10)
$$\lim_{x \to x_0} \mathbf{F}(x) = \left[\lim_{x \to x_0} f_{ij}(x)\right].$$

Similarly, a scalar function $f(x)$ is continuous at a point x_0 if $f(x_0)$ exists and if, for each positive number ε, there exists a positive number δ such that

$$|f(x) - f(x_0)| < \varepsilon \text{ whenever } |x - x_0| < \delta.$$

The analogous definition for matrices is that a matrix function $\mathbf{F}(x)$ is *continuous* at a point x_0 if $\mathbf{F}(x_0)$ exists and if, for each positive number ε, there exists a positive number δ such that

(7.1.11)
$$\|\mathbf{F}(x) - \mathbf{F}(x_0)\| < \varepsilon \text{ whenever } |x - x_0| < \delta.$$

Notice that, for continuity, $\mathbf{F}(x)$ is defined at x_0, and that furthermore $\lim_{x \to x_0} \mathbf{F}(x) = \mathbf{F}(x_0)$.

Since $\mathbf{F}(x) = [f_{ij}(x)]$,

(7.1.12)
$$\begin{aligned}\|\mathbf{F}(x) - \mathbf{F}(x_0)\| &= \|[f_{ij}(x) - f_{ij}(x_0)]\| \\ &= \sum_{i,j=1}^{m,n} |f_{ij}(x) - f_{ij}(x_0)| < \varepsilon, \qquad \text{whenever} \quad |x - x_0| < \delta.\end{aligned}$$

Since Eq. (7.1.6) implies that each element of $\mathbf{F}(x)$ is continuous at x_0, a more usable definition of continuity can be given: A matrix function $\mathbf{F}(x)$ is continuous at a point x_0 if each element of $\mathbf{F}(x)$ is a continuous function at x_0.

Exercises 7.1

1. Prove that the definition of the norm of a matrix given in Eq. (7.1.4) satisfies the conditions for a norm given in Eq. (2.3.2).

2. If
$$\mathbf{F}(x) = \begin{bmatrix} \dfrac{1}{x} & \dfrac{x^2 - 4}{x - 2} \\ \dfrac{\sin x}{x} & \cosh x \end{bmatrix} \quad \text{for all } x, \quad x \neq 0, 2, \quad \text{and}$$
$$\mathbf{F}(2) = \begin{bmatrix} \dfrac{1}{2} & 2 \\ \dfrac{\sin 2}{2} & \cosh 2 \end{bmatrix} \quad \text{and} \quad \mathbf{F}(0) = \begin{bmatrix} 1 & 2 \\ 1 & 1 \end{bmatrix},$$

   (a) Does $\lim_{x \to 2} \mathbf{F}(x)$ exist? Does $\lim_{x \to 0} \mathbf{F}(x)$ exist?
   (b) Is $\mathbf{F}(x)$ continuous at $x = 2$? at $x = 0$?

3. Write

$$\begin{bmatrix} x^3 - 3 & x^2 - 2 \\ x^2 + x + 1 & x + 1 \end{bmatrix}$$

as a matrix polynomial.

4. Write adj$(\mathbf{A} - \lambda\mathbf{I})(\mathbf{A} - \lambda\mathbf{I})$ as a matrix polynomial in λ if

$$\mathbf{A} = \begin{bmatrix} 0 & 0 & 1 \\ 0 & 4 & 0 \\ 4 & 0 & 0 \end{bmatrix}.$$

(Hint: See Eq. (6.12.6).)

5. Find (i) $\|\mathbf{A}\|$ and (ii) $|\mathbf{A}|$, if $\mathbf{A}$ is

(a) $\begin{bmatrix} 2 & 1 & -3 \\ 1 & 0 & 2 \\ -1 & 2 & 1 \end{bmatrix}$, (b) $\begin{bmatrix} 1 & 2 & 0 \\ -2 & -4 & -1 \\ 1 & 2 & 1 \end{bmatrix}$.

6. Find 2×2 nonsingular symmetric matrices $\mathbf{A}$ such that $\|\mathbf{A}\| = |\mathbf{A}|$.

7.2. *The Derivative and Integral of a Matrix*

The definition of the derivative of a matrix analogous to that for scalars is that if $\mathbf{F}(x)$ is such that

(7.2.1) $$\lim_{\Delta x \to 0} \frac{\mathbf{F}(x_0 + \Delta x) - \mathbf{F}(x_0)}{\Delta x} = \frac{d}{dx}\mathbf{F}(x_0) = \mathbf{F}'(x_0)$$

exists, where $\Delta x = x - x_0$, then Eq. (7.2.1) defines the derivative of $\mathbf{F}(x)$ at x_0. But

(7.2.2) $$\lim_{\Delta x \to 0} \frac{\mathbf{F}(x_0 + \Delta x) - \mathbf{F}(x_0)}{\Delta x} = \lim_{\Delta x \to 0} \left[\frac{f_{ij}(x_0 + \Delta x) - f_{ij}(x_0)}{\Delta x}\right];$$

this equation implies that each element of $\mathbf{F}(x)$ must be continuous at x_0, and thus that the derivative of each element of $\mathbf{F}(x)$ must exist at x_0. Therefore, the *derivative* with respect to x of $\mathbf{F}(x)$ at x_0 is

(7.2.3) $$\frac{d}{dx}\mathbf{F}(x_0) = \left[\frac{d}{dx} f_{ij}(x_0)\right],$$

if each element in $\mathbf{F}(x)$ is differentiable at x_0.

Similarly, the *definite integral* of $\mathbf{F}(x)$ over the interval $[a, b]$ is

(7.2.4) $$\int_a^b \mathbf{F}(x)\, dx = \left[\int_a^b f_{ij}(x)\, dx\right].$$

The *indefinite integral* of the matrix $\mathbf{F}(x)$ is

$$\int \mathbf{F}(x)\,dx = \mathbf{G}(x) + \mathbf{C},$$

where $\mathbf{G}(x)$ is any matrix such that $d\mathbf{G}(x)/dx = \mathbf{F}(x)$, and $\mathbf{C}$ is a constant matrix.

Note that the definition for the derivative of a matrix is different from that for the derivative of a determinant. (See Section 2.13.) Here we have the derivative of each element; there we had a sum of determinants in which the derivatives of the elements in a row (column) appeared. Thus, in general,

$$\det \frac{d}{dx}\mathbf{F}(x) \neq \frac{d}{dx}\det \mathbf{F}(x).$$

One immediate result from Eq. (7.2.3) is that if $\mathbf{A}$ is a matrix with constant elements, then

$$\frac{d}{dx}\mathbf{A} = \mathbf{0}. \tag{7.2.5}$$

Other results that follow directly from Eq. (7.2.3) and are easy to verify are the following. If the various derivatives exist, then

$$\frac{d}{dx}(\mathbf{F}(x)\mathbf{G}(x)) = \mathbf{F}(x)\left(\frac{d}{dx}\mathbf{G}(x)\right) + \left(\frac{d}{dx}\mathbf{F}(x)\right)\mathbf{G}(x). \tag{7.2.6}$$

If $\mathbf{F}(x)$ is square and n is a positive integer, then

$$\frac{d}{dx}\mathbf{F}^n(x) = \sum_{i=1}^{n}\left[\mathbf{F}^{n-i}(x)\left(\frac{d}{dx}\mathbf{F}(x)\right)\mathbf{F}^{i-1}(x)\right]. \tag{7.2.7}$$

If $\mathbf{F}(x)$ possesses a differentiable inverse, then

$$\frac{d}{dx}\mathbf{F}^{-1}(x) = -\mathbf{F}^{-1}\left(\frac{d}{dx}\mathbf{F}\right)\mathbf{F}^{-1}. \tag{7.2.8}$$

The proofs of the first two of the above results are left as exercises; the proof of the final one is as follows. Since $\mathbf{F}$ possesses an inverse, then

$$\mathbf{F}^{-1}\mathbf{F} = \mathbf{I} \quad \text{and} \quad \mathbf{F}^{-1}\left(\frac{d}{dx}\mathbf{F}\right) + \left(\frac{d}{dx}\mathbf{F}^{-1}\right)\mathbf{F} = \mathbf{0}$$

from Eqs. (7.2.5) and (7.2.6). The final equation can then be written as

$$\left(\frac{d}{dx}\mathbf{F}^{-1}\right)\mathbf{F} = -\mathbf{F}^{-1}\left(\frac{d}{dx}\mathbf{F}\right) \quad \text{or} \quad \frac{d}{dx}\mathbf{F}^{-1} = -\mathbf{F}^{-1}\left(\frac{d}{dx}\mathbf{F}\right)\mathbf{F}^{-1}.$$

Note, in attempting to simplify expressions such as Eq. (7.2.7) by combining factors, that the various matrices involved do not generally commute with each other. Also note that 1×1 matrices are isomorphic to scalars; since the commutative law holds for scalar multiplication, the usual scalar results are essentially obtained as special cases.

Exercises 7.2

1. (a) State the definition of the Riemann definite integral over $[a, b]$ of the scalar function $f(x)$.
   (b) State the analogous definition to that given in (a) for the matrix function $\mathbf{F}(x)$.
   (c) Verify that the definition given in (b) is equivalent to that given in Eq. (7.2.4).

2. Prove Eq. (7.2.6).

3. Prove Eq. (7.2.7) by mathematical induction.

4. Find the derivative of $\mathbf{A}^3$ and write the result as one matrix, if

$$\mathbf{A}(x) = \begin{bmatrix} e^x & x^2 + x \\ x - 1 & x \end{bmatrix}.$$

5. (a) Find $\mathbf{A}^{-1}$ and (b) find $\dfrac{d}{dx}(\mathbf{A}^{-1})$, if

$$\mathbf{A} = \begin{bmatrix} x^2 - 1 & x + 1 \\ x - 1 & x \end{bmatrix}.$$

   (c) Find the value(s) of x for which the derivative does not exist.

6. (a) Find $\dfrac{d}{dx}(g(x)\, \mathbf{F}(x))$, where $g(x)$ is a differentiable scalar function of x.

   (b) Find $\dfrac{d}{dx}(C\, \mathbf{F}(x))$, where C is a constant.

7. Find $\dfrac{d}{dx}(\mathbf{F}(x)\, \mathbf{u}(x))$, where $\mathbf{u}(x)$ is a differentiable vector function of x.

8. Find $\dfrac{d}{dx}(\mathbf{A}(x) + \mathbf{B}(x))$.

9. Prove that a necessary and sufficient condition that

$$\frac{d}{dx}(\mathbf{F}^n) = n\, \mathbf{F}^{n-1}\left(\frac{d}{dx}\mathbf{F}\right) \quad \text{is that} \quad \mathbf{F}\left(\frac{d}{dx}\mathbf{F}\right) = \left(\frac{d}{dx}\mathbf{F}\right)\mathbf{F}.$$

10. Prove that if $\mathbf{F}$ is a diagonal matrix, then

$$\frac{d}{dx}\mathbf{F}^n = n\, \mathbf{F}^{n-1}\frac{d}{dx}\mathbf{F}.$$

11. If $\mathbf{A}(x)$ is an $m \times n$ matrix defined over $[a, b]$, prove that

$$\left\| \int \mathbf{A}(x)\, dx \right\| \leqq \int \|\mathbf{A}(x)\|\, dx.$$

12. By mathematical induction prove that

$$\|\mathbf{A}^n(x)\| \leqq \|\mathbf{A}(x)\|^n.$$

7.3. Limits of Matrices

This section considers the idea of the *convergence* of a *sequence of matrices.* Let

(7.3.1) $$\{\mathbf{A}^{(k)}\} = \{\mathbf{A}^{(1)}, \mathbf{A}^{(2)}, \cdots\} = \{[a_{ij}^{(k)}]\}$$

denote a sequence of $m \times n$ matrices. (Note that superscripts do not necessarily denote powers of matrices; indeed, $\mathbf{A}^{(k)}$ need not even be a square matrix.) The sequence of matrices converges to a matrix $\mathbf{A}$ if and only if the sequence $\{a_{ij}^{(k)}\}$ converges for all i and j.

Example 7.3.1. Determine whether or not the sequence of matrices $\{\mathbf{A}^{(k)}\}$ converges if

$$\mathbf{A}^{(k)} = \begin{bmatrix} \dfrac{k-1}{k+1} & 5 \\ \dfrac{1}{k} & k \end{bmatrix}.$$

In $\{\mathbf{A}^{(k)}\}$ the sequence $\{k - 1/k + 1\}$ converges to 1, the sequence $\{5\}$ converges to 5, and the sequence $\{1/k\}$ converges to 0. However, since the sequence $\{k\}$ does not converge, the sequence of matrices $\{\mathbf{A}^{(k)}\}$ does not converge.

For an infinite series of matrices,

(7.3.2) $$\sum_{n=0}^{\infty} \mathbf{A}^{(n)} = \sum_{n=0}^{\infty} [a_{ij}^{(n)}],$$

the question arises as to the *convergence* of such *a series of matrices.* Again we generalize the result of scalar calculus, and consider the partial sum

(7.3.3) $$\mathbf{S}_n = \sum_{k=0}^{n} \mathbf{A}^{(k)}.$$

If the sequence of partial sums in Eq. (7.3.3) has a limit as n becomes infinite, then the infinite sum in Eq. (7.3.1) converges to this limit.

Using the norm defined by Eq. (7.1.4), we obtain

$$\|\mathbf{A}^{(k)}\| = \sum_{i,j=1}^{m,n} |a_{ij}^{(k)}| = a_k. \tag{7.3.4}$$

From Eq. (7.3.3),

$$\|\mathbf{S}_n\| \leq \sum_{k=0}^{n} \|\mathbf{A}^{(k)}\| = \sum_{k=0}^{n} a_k. \tag{7.3.5}$$

If the partial sums of scalars of Eq. (7.3.5) converge, then the matrix sums $\mathbf{S}_n$ has a limit.

Example 7.3.2. Find a sufficient condition on **A** for the convergence of

$$\mathbf{I} + \mathbf{A} + \mathbf{A}^2 + \cdots = \sum_{n=0}^{\infty} A^n. \tag{7.3.6}$$

Since $\mathbf{A}^n$ refers here to the nth power of **A**, **A** must be square.

From Eq. (7.3.5),

$$\|\mathbf{S}_n\| \leq \sum_{k=0}^{n} a^k, \qquad \text{where} \quad \|\mathbf{A}^k\| = a^k. \tag{7.3.7}$$

From scalar calculus, the sequence in Eq. (7.3.7) has a limit provided that $a < 1$. Thus a sufficient condition for the convergence of

$$\sum_{n=0}^{\infty} \mathbf{A}^n$$

is that $\|\mathbf{A}\| < 1$. Actually, this is a test for the *absolute convergence* of the series; absolute convergence of course implies convergence.

Since

$$\frac{1}{1-x} = 1 + x + x^2 + \cdots \tag{7.3.8}$$

holds for $|x| < 1$, we are tempted to write

$$(\mathbf{I} - \mathbf{A})^{-1} = \mathbf{I} + \mathbf{A} + \mathbf{A}^2 + \cdots \tag{7.3.9}$$

for a square matrix **A**. If this is true, then

$$\begin{aligned} \mathbf{I} &= (\mathbf{I} - \mathbf{A})(\mathbf{I} - \mathbf{A})^{-1} = (\mathbf{I} - \mathbf{A})(\mathbf{I} + \mathbf{A} + \mathbf{A}^2 + \cdots) \\ &= (\mathbf{I} + \mathbf{A} + \mathbf{A}^2 + \cdots) - (\mathbf{A} + \mathbf{A}^2 + \mathbf{A}^3 + \cdots) = \mathbf{I}, \end{aligned}$$

after combining terms. By Example 7.3.2, the series in Eq. (7.3.9) converges if $\|\mathbf{A}\| < 1$; this provides another method for constructing the inverse of $\mathbf{B} = \mathbf{I} - \mathbf{A}$, for a "small enough" **B**.

Another definition of the *convergence* of an infinite sum of matrices Eq. (7.3.2) requires that each infinite sum

$$\sum_{n=0}^{\infty} a_{ij}^{(n)}$$

converge. This is a weaker definition of convergence than the first. Although every series that converges under the first definition also converges under the second definition, the converse is not true. (See Example 7.3.4.)

Example 7.3.3. Find

$$\sum_{n=0}^{\infty} \mathbf{A}^{(n)}, \quad \text{if}$$

$$\mathbf{A}^{(n)} = \begin{bmatrix} \dfrac{1}{2^n} & \dfrac{1}{(n+1)^2} \\ \dfrac{1}{n!} & \dfrac{1}{(1+n)(2+n)} \end{bmatrix}.$$

Using the second definition of convergence,

$$\sum_{n=0}^{\infty} \mathbf{A}^{(n)} = \begin{bmatrix} 2 & \pi^2/6 \\ e & 1/2 \end{bmatrix}$$

by considering the various series involved.

Example 7.3.4. Show that the infinite series of matrices, for which the general matrix $\mathbf{A}^{(n)}$ is defined by

$$\mathbf{A}^{(n)} = \begin{bmatrix} \dfrac{(-1)^n}{n+1} & \dfrac{(-1)^n}{(2n+1)!} \\ 0 & \dfrac{(-1)^n}{2n+1} \end{bmatrix},$$

converges under the second definition but not under the first.

Under the second definition,

$$\sum_{n=0}^{\infty} \mathbf{A}^{(n)} = \begin{bmatrix} \ln 2 & \sin 1 \\ 0 & \pi/4 \end{bmatrix}.$$

Under the first definition, we would have the convergence of

$$\sum_{n=0}^{\infty} \frac{1}{n+1},$$

since we are dealing with the sum of the absolute value of the elements. Since this is a divergent series, the infinite series of matrices does not converge under the first definition.

Exercises 7.3

1. By using four terms in Eq. (7.3.9), determine an approximation to the inverse of **B** if

$$\mathbf{B} = \begin{bmatrix} 1.06 & .2 \\ .3 & 1 \end{bmatrix}.$$

Compare your result with the inverse found directly.

2. Determine the limit of the convergent sequence of vectors

$$\left\{ \begin{bmatrix} \dfrac{k^2+2k}{2k^2+1} & \dfrac{1}{k^2} & 2+\dfrac{1}{k} \end{bmatrix} \right\}.$$

3. Find the sum of the infinite series of matrices

$$\sum_{k=0}^{\infty} \mathbf{A}^{(k)}, \quad \text{where}$$

$$\mathbf{A}^{(k)} = \begin{bmatrix} (.5)^k & \dfrac{(-1)^k}{(2k)!} \\ \dfrac{1}{k!} & (.1)^k \end{bmatrix}.$$

7.4. *Functions of Matrices*

When we were considering the minimum polynomial of a matrix in Section 6.11, we defined the sum of powers of a matrix in Eq. (6.11.2) as a polynomial function of a matrix. This section considers more general *functions of matrices*. These are usually different from the *matrices of functions* considered in Section 7.1. Since powers of matrices are generally involved, the matrices considered in this section are all square matrices, so that their powers are defined.

By Theorem 6.9.4, if **A** is a real symmetric matrix, then it is orthogonally similar to a diagonal matrix. That is,

$$\mathbf{B}'\mathbf{A}\mathbf{B} = \mathbf{B}^{-1}\mathbf{A}\mathbf{B} = \mathbf{D}, \tag{7.4.1}$$

where **B** is an orthogonal matrix, **A** is a real symmetric matrix, and **D** is a diagonal matrix whose elements on the main diagonal are the characteristic values of **A**. Thus,

$$\mathbf{A} = \mathbf{B}\begin{bmatrix} \lambda_1 & 0 & \cdots & 0 \\ 0 & \lambda_2 & \cdots & 0 \\ \cdot & \cdot & \cdots & \cdot \\ 0 & 0 & \cdots & \lambda_n \end{bmatrix}\mathbf{B}^{-1} = \mathbf{BDB}^{-1}, \tag{7.4.2}$$

where the λ_i are all real numbers, the characteristic values of **A**. (See Theorem 6.6.3.)

From Eq. (7.4.2),

$$\mathbf{A}^2 = (\mathbf{BDB}^{-1})(\mathbf{BDB}^{-1}) = \mathbf{BD}^2\mathbf{B}^{-1}, \cdots,$$

and in general

$$\mathbf{A}^k = \mathbf{BD}^k\mathbf{B}^{-1} = \mathbf{B}\begin{bmatrix} \lambda_1^k & 0 & \cdots & 0 \\ 0 & \lambda_2^k & \cdots & 0 \\ \cdot & \cdot & \cdots & \cdot \\ 0 & 0 & \cdots & \lambda_n^k \end{bmatrix}\mathbf{B}^{-1}. \tag{7.4.3}$$

It is left as an exercise for the reader to prove that Eq. (7.4.3) is true for any positive integer k.

Theorem 7.4.1. *For any analytic function $f(x)$ that is defined for each of the λ's, the characteristic values of the real symmetric matrix* $\mathbf{A}$, *then*

$$f(\mathbf{A}) = \mathbf{B}\begin{bmatrix} f(\lambda_1) & 0 & \cdots & 0 \\ 0 & f(\lambda_2) & \cdots & 0 \\ \cdot & \cdot & \cdots & \cdot \\ 0 & 0 & \cdots & f(\lambda_n) \end{bmatrix}\mathbf{B}^{-1}. \tag{7.4.4}$$

Proof: For $f(x)$, an analytic function of x, it may be expressed as

$$f(x) = a_0 + a_1 x + a_2 x^2 + \cdots, \tag{7.4.5}$$

and we can write

$$\begin{aligned} f(\mathbf{A}) &= a_0\mathbf{I} + a_1\mathbf{A} + a_2\mathbf{A}^2 + \cdots \\ &= a_0\mathbf{BIB}^{-1} + a_1\mathbf{BDB}^{-1} + a_2\mathbf{BD}^2\mathbf{B}^{-1} + \cdots, \end{aligned} \tag{7.4.6}$$

in which $\mathbf{D}$ is a diagonal matrix with the characteristic values of $\mathbf{A}$ on the main diagonal, using Eq. (7.4.3). By distributing $a_0, a_1, a_2, \cdots$, in $\mathbf{I}, \mathbf{D}, \mathbf{D}^2, \cdots$, respectively, then Eq. (7.4.6) may be written as Eq. (7.4.4). Since each $f(\lambda_i)$ in Eq. (7.4.4) is assumed to be defined, the theorem is proved.

From Eq. (7.4.4), in a manner analogous to the scalar definitions,

$$e^{\mathbf{A}} = \mathbf{I} + \frac{\mathbf{A}}{1!} + \frac{\mathbf{A}^2}{2!} + \cdots = \mathbf{B}\begin{bmatrix} e^{\lambda_1} & 0 & \cdots & 0 \\ 0 & e^{\lambda_2} & \cdots & 0 \\ \cdot & \cdot & \cdots & \cdot \\ 0 & 0 & \cdots & e^{\lambda_n} \end{bmatrix}\mathbf{B}^{-1}, \tag{7.4.7}$$

$$\sin\mathbf{A} = \mathbf{A} - \frac{\mathbf{A}^3}{3!} + \frac{\mathbf{A}^5}{5!} - \cdots = \mathbf{B}\begin{bmatrix} \sin\lambda_1 & 0 & \cdots & 0 \\ 0 & \sin\lambda_2 & \cdots & 0 \\ \cdot & \cdot & \cdots & \cdot \\ 0 & 0 & \cdots & \sin\lambda_n \end{bmatrix}\mathbf{B}^{-1}, \tag{7.4.8}$$

$$\cos\mathbf{A} = \mathbf{I} - \frac{\mathbf{A}^2}{2!} + \frac{\mathbf{A}^4}{4!} - \cdots = \mathbf{B}\begin{bmatrix} \cos\lambda_1 & 0 & \cdots & 0 \\ 0 & \cos\lambda_2 & \cdots & 0 \\ \cdot & \cdot & \cdots & \cdot \\ 0 & 0 & \cdots & \cos\lambda_n \end{bmatrix}\mathbf{B}^{-1}, \tag{7.4.9}$$

for $\mathbf{A}$ a real symmetric matrix and $\mathbf{A} = \mathbf{BDB}^{-1}$, $\mathbf{B}$ and $\mathbf{D}$ defined above.

In Eqs. (7.4.7) and (7.4.9), it apparently would be convenient to say that $\mathbf{A}^0 = \mathbf{I}$. To show that this is an acceptable definition, we consider *powers of matrices.*

If h and k are positive integers and $\mathbf{A}$ is a square matrix,

$$\mathbf{A}^h\mathbf{A}^k = \mathbf{A}^{h+k}. \tag{7.4.10}$$

Similarly, if $\mathbf{A}$ is nonsingular,

$$(\mathbf{A}^k)^{-1} = (\mathbf{A}^{-1})^k = \mathbf{A}^{-k}, \tag{7.4.11}$$

where k is a positive integer. Equation (7.4.11) also holds if k is a negative integer, and thus Eq. (7.4.10) holds if h and k are merely non-zero integers with $h \neq -k$. If $h = \pm 1$ and $k = \mp 1$, then the left side of Eq. (7.4.10) is $\mathbf{I}$. Thus, it is natural to define $\mathbf{A}^0 = \mathbf{I}$; Eq. (7.4.10) then holds for h and k any integers.

What is meant by $\mathbf{A}^{1/m}$, m a positive integer? If $\mathbf{B}$ is any square matrix such that $\mathbf{A} = \mathbf{B}^m$, then $\mathbf{B}$ is said to be an mth root of $\mathbf{A}$: $\mathbf{B} = \mathbf{A}^{1/m}$. The preceding statement hints that there may be several (perhaps even more than m) matrices that are mth roots of $\mathbf{A}$. This is true; there may even be an infinite number of such matrices.

Using the preceding definitions, Eq. (7.4.7) can be rewritten as

$$e^{\mathbf{A}} = \exp \mathbf{A} = \sum_{n=0}^{\infty} \frac{\mathbf{A}^n}{n!}. \tag{7.4.12}$$

Other series can similarly be written in summation notation.

Exercises 7.4

1. Prove Eq. (7.4.3) by mathematical induction.

2. Prove that $(\mathbf{A}^2)^{-1} = (\mathbf{A}^{-1})^2$ and in general that $(\mathbf{A}^k)^{-1} = (\mathbf{A}^{-1})^k = \mathbf{A}^{-k}$, k an integer, if $\mathbf{A}^{-1}$ exists.

3. Define $\mathbf{A}^{1/2}$. Find $\mathbf{I}_2^{1/2}$. Find $\mathbf{A}^{1/2}$ if

$$\mathbf{A} = \begin{bmatrix} 3 & 1 \\ -4 & -1 \end{bmatrix}.$$

4. If $\mathbf{A}$ is a real symmetric matrix with characteristic values $\{\lambda_i\}$, show that the analytic function of the matrix $\mathbf{A}$, $f(\mathbf{A})$, has characteristic values $f(\lambda_i)$.

5. Use Eq. (7.4.7) to find $e^{\mathbf{A}}$ if

$$\mathbf{A} = \begin{bmatrix} 2 & 1 \\ 1 & 2 \end{bmatrix}.$$

6. Define sinh $\mathbf{A}$ and cosh $\mathbf{A}$ if $\mathbf{A}$ is a symmetric matrix.

7.5. *Functions of Matrices Continued*

Even if **A** is not a symmetric matrix,

(7.5.1)
$$e^{\mathbf{A}} = \exp \mathbf{A} = \sum_{k=0}^{\infty} \frac{\mathbf{A}^k}{k!},$$

(7.5.2)
$$\sin \mathbf{A} = \sum_{k=0}^{\infty} \frac{(-1)^k \mathbf{A}^{2k+1}}{(2k+1)!}, \quad \text{etc.}$$

Although the convergence of such series can always be considered by the methods of Section 7.3, there are several other approaches found in the literature that may also be used. It is left as an exercise for the reader to prove the convergence of the series for exp **A** by one such suggested method.

Actually evaluating or approximating a function of a matrix such as exp **A** would seem to be very tedious even if **A** is merely a 2×2 matrix, since apparently $\mathbf{A}^2$, $\mathbf{A}^3$, $\cdots$, would all need to be calculated. However, by the Cayley-Hamilton Theorem (Theorem 6.12.3), $\mathbf{A}^n$ is a linear combination of $\mathbf{A}^{n-1}, \cdots, \mathbf{A}, \mathbf{I}$. Therefore, only these powers of **A** need to be determined, instead of all powers of **A**.

Thus for an infinite series of matrices of order n,

(7.5.3)
$$f(\mathbf{A}) = \sum_{k=0}^{\infty} a_k \mathbf{A}^k,$$

we can replace $\mathbf{A}^n$ by a sum containing lower powers of **A**:

(7.5.4)
$$f(\mathbf{A}) = b_0 \mathbf{I} + b_1 \mathbf{A} + \cdots + b_{n-1} \mathbf{A}^{n-1} = \sum_{k=0}^{n-1} b_k \mathbf{A}^k,$$

where each b_k is an infinite series of scalars. If each series of scalars converges, then the series $f(\mathbf{A})$ converges.

Example 7.5.1. Find the first five terms of exp **A**, and thus form an approximation to exp **A**, by direct computation if

$$\mathbf{A} = \begin{bmatrix} 1 & 1 \\ -2 & 1 \end{bmatrix}.$$

Then use the Cayley-Hamilton Theorem to find the first five terms in the expansion of exp **A**.

The sum of the first five terms of exp **A** is

(7.5.5)
$$\mathbf{I} + \mathbf{A} + \frac{\mathbf{A}^2}{2} + \frac{\mathbf{A}^3}{6} + \frac{\mathbf{A}^4}{24}, \quad \text{or}$$

$$\begin{bmatrix} 1 & 0 \\ 0 & 1 \end{bmatrix} + \begin{bmatrix} 1 & 1 \\ -2 & 1 \end{bmatrix} + 1/2\begin{bmatrix} -1 & 2 \\ -4 & -1 \end{bmatrix} + 1/6\begin{bmatrix} -5 & 1 \\ -2 & -5 \end{bmatrix}$$
$$+ 1/24\begin{bmatrix} -7 & -4 \\ 8 & -7 \end{bmatrix} = \begin{bmatrix} 3/8 & 2 \\ -4 & 3/8 \end{bmatrix}.$$

The characteristic polynomial for $\mathbf{A}$ is $f(\lambda) = \lambda^2 - 2\lambda + 3$. By the Cayley-Hamilton Theorem,

$$\begin{aligned} f(\mathbf{A}) &= \mathbf{A}^2 - 2\mathbf{A} + 3\mathbf{I} = \mathbf{0}, \quad \text{or} \\ \mathbf{A}^2 &= 2\mathbf{A} - 3\mathbf{I}, \\ \mathbf{A}^3 &= \mathbf{A}(2\mathbf{A} - 3\mathbf{I}) = \mathbf{A} - 6\mathbf{I}, \quad \text{and} \\ \mathbf{A}^4 &= 4\mathbf{A}^2 - 12\mathbf{A} + 9\mathbf{I} = -4\mathbf{A} - 3\mathbf{I}. \end{aligned}$$

Thus, in Eq. (7.5.5),

$$\exp \mathbf{A} \doteq \mathbf{I} + \mathbf{A} + (2\mathbf{A} - 3\mathbf{I})/2 + (\mathbf{A} - 6\mathbf{I})/6 + (-4\mathbf{A} - 3\mathbf{I})/24$$

$$= -(13/8)\,\mathbf{I} + 2\mathbf{A} = -13/8\begin{bmatrix} 1 & 0 \\ 0 & 1 \end{bmatrix} + 2\begin{bmatrix} 1 & 1 \\ -2 & 1 \end{bmatrix} = \begin{bmatrix} 3/8 & 2 \\ -4 & 3/8 \end{bmatrix}.$$

Notice how much simpler the work would be by the second method if $\mathbf{A}$ were a 4×4 matrix, say, rather than a 2×2 matrix.

Exercises 7.5

1. Work Example 7.5.1 if

$$\mathbf{A} = \begin{bmatrix} 0 & 1 \\ 2 & 1 \end{bmatrix}.$$

2. Work Example 7.5.1 for $\sin \mathbf{A}$ instead of $\exp \mathbf{A}$.
3. Work exercise 2 if

$$\mathbf{A} = \begin{bmatrix} 0 & 1 \\ 2 & 1 \end{bmatrix}.$$

4. If $\mathbf{B}^3 = \mathbf{0}$ but $\mathbf{B}^2 \neq \mathbf{0}$ and $\mathbf{B}$ is of order 3, write all of the terms occurring in the expansion of $\sin \mathbf{B}$.
5. Find five terms in the expansion of $\exp \mathbf{A}$ using the Cayley-Hamilton Theorem, and compare the result with that obtained in number 5, Exercises 7.4, if

$$\mathbf{A} = \begin{bmatrix} 2 & 1 \\ 1 & 2 \end{bmatrix}.$$

6. Prove that $\exp \mathbf{A} = \mathbf{I} + \mathbf{A} + \mathbf{A}^2/2 + \cdots$ converges by considering an upper bound for each element in $\mathbf{A}$ and then finding an upper bound for each element of $\mathbf{A}^k$. (Hint: If M is an upper bound for a_{ij}, the elements of $\mathbf{A}^2$ are bounded by nM, the elements of $\mathbf{A}^3$ are bounded by $n^2M^2, \cdots$.)

7.6. The Matrix Exponential

In Eq. (7.5.1), the matrix exponential was defined in general as

$$e^{\mathbf{A}(x)} = \exp \mathbf{A}(x) = \mathbf{I} + \mathbf{A}(x) + \frac{\mathbf{A}^2(x)}{2!} + \cdots = \sum_{k=0}^{\infty} \frac{\mathbf{A}^k(x)}{k!}, \tag{7.6.1}$$

although it was defined earlier, in Eq. (7.4.5), for $\mathbf{A}$, a real symmetric matrix. Here we explicitly indicate that the elements of $\mathbf{A}$ may be functions of x. In this section we present a few theorems regarding this matrix function analogous to those for the corresponding scalar function, and show that not all such scalar theorems carry over to matrices. For example, it is not always true that $e^{\mathbf{A}}e^{\mathbf{B}} = e^{\mathbf{A}+\mathbf{B}}$.

Example 7.6.1. Find $e^{\mathbf{A}}e^{\mathbf{B}}$ and $e^{\mathbf{A}+\mathbf{B}}$ if

$$\mathbf{A} = \begin{bmatrix} 0 & 1 \\ 0 & 0 \end{bmatrix} \quad \text{and} \quad \mathbf{B} = \begin{bmatrix} 0 & 0 \\ 1 & 0 \end{bmatrix}.$$

Since $\mathbf{A}$ and $\mathbf{B}$ are each nilpotent, then

$$e^{\mathbf{A}}e^{\mathbf{B}} = (\mathbf{I} + \mathbf{A})(\mathbf{I} + \mathbf{B}),$$

and all of the remaining terms in the expansion are $\mathbf{0}$. Thus

$$e^{\mathbf{A}}e^{\mathbf{B}} = \mathbf{I} + \mathbf{A} + \mathbf{B} + \mathbf{AB} = \begin{bmatrix} 2 & 1 \\ 1 & 1 \end{bmatrix}.$$

On the other hand,

$$\mathbf{A} + \mathbf{B} = \begin{bmatrix} 0 & 1 \\ 1 & 0 \end{bmatrix} = \mathbf{C}, \quad \text{and}$$

$$\begin{aligned} e^{\mathbf{C}} &= \begin{bmatrix} 1 & 0 \\ 0 & 1 \end{bmatrix} + \begin{bmatrix} 0 & 1 \\ 1 & 0 \end{bmatrix} + 1/2\begin{bmatrix} 1 & 0 \\ 0 & 1 \end{bmatrix} + 1/6\begin{bmatrix} 0 & 1 \\ 1 & 0 \end{bmatrix} + \cdots \\ &= \mathbf{I}(1 + 1/2! + 1/4! + \cdots) + \mathbf{C}(1 + 1/3! + 1/5! + \cdots) \\ &= \begin{bmatrix} 1 & 0 \\ 0 & 1 \end{bmatrix}\cosh 1 + \begin{bmatrix} 0 & 1 \\ 1 & 0 \end{bmatrix}\sinh 1 = \begin{bmatrix} \cosh 1 & \sinh 1 \\ \sinh 1 & \cosh 1 \end{bmatrix}. \end{aligned}$$

That is, $\exp \mathbf{A} \exp \mathbf{B} \neq \exp(\mathbf{A} + \mathbf{B})$ in this case.

If, however, $\mathbf{A}$ and $\mathbf{B}$ commute under matrix multiplication, then $\exp \mathbf{A} \exp \mathbf{B} = \exp(\mathbf{A} + \mathbf{B})$.

Theorem 7.6.1. *If* $\mathbf{AB} = \mathbf{BA}$, *then* $\exp \mathbf{A} \exp \mathbf{B} = \exp(\mathbf{A} + \mathbf{B})$.

Proof: Using the Cauchy product of the infinite series of matrices along with the assumed commutativity property,

$$\begin{aligned} e^{\mathbf{A}}e^{\mathbf{B}} &= \left(\sum_{k=0}^{\infty} \frac{\mathbf{A}^k}{k!}\right)\left(\sum_{k=0}^{\infty} \frac{\mathbf{B}^k}{k!}\right) = \sum_{k=0}^{\infty} \sum_{h=0}^{k} \frac{\mathbf{A}^{k-h}\mathbf{B}^h}{(k-h)!h!} \\ &= \sum_{k=0}^{\infty} \frac{1}{k!} \sum_{h=0}^{k} \frac{k!\mathbf{A}^{k-h}\mathbf{B}^h}{(k-h)!h!} = \sum_{k=0}^{\infty} \frac{1}{k!} (\mathbf{A} + \mathbf{B})^k = e^{\mathbf{A}+\mathbf{B}}. \end{aligned} \tag{7.6.2}$$

The next to last equality is true because of the two different expressions for the expansion of the binomial $(\mathbf{A}+\mathbf{B})^k$ in which the commutative property is necessary.

The following two corollaries are immediate consequences of Theorem 7.6.1.

Corollary 7.6.1. *If* $\mathbf{A}$ *and* $\mathbf{B}$ *are diagonal matrices, then* $\exp \mathbf{A} \exp \mathbf{B} = \exp(\mathbf{A}+\mathbf{B})$.

Since number 5 of Exercises 1.7 proved that diagonal matrices commute under multiplication, they meet the requirements of Theorem 7.6.1. In particular, if $\mathbf{A}$ and $\mathbf{B}$ are scalar matrices, then the corollary applies.

Corollary 7.6.2. *The inverse of* $e^{\mathbf{A}}$ *always exists and is* $e^{-\mathbf{A}}$.

Since $e^{\mathbf{0}} = \mathbf{I}$ from the definition of $e^{\mathbf{A}}$, then, if $e^{\mathbf{A}}$ has an inverse,

$$e^{\mathbf{A}}(e^{\mathbf{A}})^{-1} = \mathbf{I}.$$

But $e^{\mathbf{A}}e^{-\mathbf{A}} = e^{\mathbf{0}} = \mathbf{I}$, and hence

$$(e^{\mathbf{A}})^{-1} = e^{-\mathbf{A}}, \tag{7.6.3}$$

since the inverse of a matrix is unique. This corollary also shows that $e^{\mathbf{A}}$ is never singular.

In a number of places (particularly in the solution of matrix differential equations or systems of differential equations) the matrix $e^{\mathbf{A}(x)x}$ arises, where $\mathbf{A}(x)$ may or may not be a constant matrix. If $\mathbf{A}$ is a constant matrix, then

$$e^{\mathbf{A}x} = \mathbf{I} + \mathbf{A}x + \frac{\mathbf{A}^2x^2}{2!} + \frac{\mathbf{A}^3x^3}{3!} + \cdots, \quad \text{and} \tag{7.6.4}$$

$$\begin{aligned} \frac{d}{dx}(e^{\mathbf{A}x}) &= \mathbf{A} + \frac{2\mathbf{A}^2x}{2!} + \frac{3\mathbf{A}^3x^2}{3!} + \cdots \\ &= \mathbf{A}\left(\mathbf{I} + \mathbf{A}x + \frac{\mathbf{A}^2x^2}{2!} + \cdots\right) \\ &= \left(\mathbf{I} + \mathbf{A}x + \frac{A^2x^2}{2!} + \cdots\right)\mathbf{A} \\ &= \mathbf{A}e^{\mathbf{A}x} = e^{\mathbf{A}x}\mathbf{A}. \end{aligned} \tag{7.6.5}$$

These results are summarized in the following theorem.

Theorem 7.6.2. *If* $\mathbf{A}$ *is a constant square matrix, then*

$$\frac{d}{dx}(e^{\mathbf{A}x}) = \mathbf{A}e^{\mathbf{A}x} = e^{\mathbf{A}x}\mathbf{A},$$

and $\mathbf{A}$ *commutes with* $e^{\mathbf{A}x}$.

It is left as an exercise for the reader to prove the following theorem.

Theorem 7.6.3. *If* **A** *is a square matrix function of x, then a necessary and sufficient condition that*

$$\frac{d}{dx}(e^{\mathbf{A}(x)}) = \frac{d}{dx}(\mathbf{A}(x))e^{\mathbf{A}(x)} = e^{\mathbf{A}(x)}\frac{d}{dx}(\mathbf{A}(x)) \tag{7.6.6}$$

is that

$$\frac{d}{dx}(\mathbf{A}(x))\,\mathbf{A}(x) = \mathbf{A}(x)\frac{d}{dx}(\mathbf{A}(x)).$$

An immediate consequence of Theorem 7.6.3 is the following corollary.

Corollary 7.6.3. *If* A(x) *is a diagonal matrix, then* Eq. (7.6.6) *holds.*

Exercises 7.6

1. If $\mathbf{AB} = \mathbf{BA}$, prove that $\mathbf{A}^2\mathbf{B}^2 = \mathbf{B}^2\mathbf{A}^2$, and in general that $\mathbf{A}^h\mathbf{B}^k = \mathbf{B}^k\mathbf{A}^h$ for h and k positive integers.

2. Determine which (if any) of the following matrices are such that the derivative of exp $\mathbf{A}(x)$ is defined if $\mathbf{A}(x)$ is

(a) $\begin{bmatrix} e^k & 0 \\ 0 & \sin x \end{bmatrix}$, (b) $\begin{bmatrix} e^k & e^{-x} \\ e^{-x} & 1 \end{bmatrix}$, (c) $\begin{bmatrix} 2x & 3x \\ 4x & 2x \end{bmatrix}$, (d) $\begin{bmatrix} e^k & 2 \\ x & e^k \end{bmatrix}$.

3. Upon considering the matrices in exercise 2 by pairs, **A** and **B**, determine which pairs, if any, are such that exp **A** exp **B** = exp(**A** + **B**).

4. Determine in two ways the inverse of exp **A**, if

$$\mathbf{A} = \begin{bmatrix} 0 & 1 & 2 \\ 0 & 0 & 1 \\ 0 & 0 & 0 \end{bmatrix}.$$

5. Either determine a matrix $\mathbf{B}(x)$ such that $\frac{d}{dx}\mathbf{X}(x) = \mathbf{B}(x)\mathbf{X}(x)$, or show that no such matrix exists, if

$$\mathbf{X}(x) = \begin{bmatrix} e^x & -e^{-x} \\ -e^{-x} & x+3 \end{bmatrix}.$$

6. Work exercise 4 if

$$\mathbf{A}(x) = \begin{bmatrix} 1 & e^x \\ -e^{-x} & 1 \end{bmatrix}.$$

7. For the matrix $\mathbf{A}(x)$ in exercise 6, either determine $\frac{d}{dx} \exp \mathbf{A}(x)$, or explain why it cannot be determined.

8. Prove Theorem 7.6.3.

7.7. *Matrix Differential Equations and Systems of Differential Equations*

This section provides a brief introduction to an application of some of the preceding material to the topic of different al equations.

Let the variables $y_1, y_2, \cdots, y_n$ be functions of the variable x such that

$$
\begin{aligned}
y_1' &= a_{11}y_1 + a_{12}y_2 + \cdots + a_{1n}y_n + b_1(x) \\
y_2' &= a_{21}y_1 + a_{22}y_2 + \cdots + a_{2n}y_n + b_2(x) \\
&\cdots \\
y_n' &= a_{n1}y_1 + a_{n2}y_2 + \cdots + a_{nn}y_n + b_n(x),
\end{aligned} \tag{7.7.1}
$$

where the primes indicate differentiation with respect to x, the $b_i(x)$ are integrable functions of x, and the a_{ij} are constants. In matrix form, Eq. (7.7.1) is

$$\frac{d}{dx}\mathbf{y} = \mathbf{Ay} + \mathbf{b}. \tag{7.7.2}$$

If $\mathbf{b} \equiv \mathbf{0}$ in Eq. (7.7.2), the equation is a *homogeneous matrix differential equation*; otherwise, it is a *nonhomogeneous matrix differential equation.*

An "obvious" solution to the *homogeneous* equation Eq. (7.7.2) apparently would be $\mathbf{y} = e^{\mathbf{A}x}$. However, this is not correct, since the left side is a vector and the right side is a square matrix. If the solution of the homogeneous problem Eq. (7.7.2) is required to satisfy an initial condition, i.e.,

$$\frac{d}{dx}\mathbf{y} = \mathbf{Ay}, \qquad \mathbf{y}(0) = \mathbf{y}_0,$$

then a "formal" solution is

$$\mathbf{y} = e^{\mathbf{A}x}\mathbf{y}_0.$$

Although this formal solution satisfies the system, we have seen in the preceding sections some of the difficulties associated in dealing with the infinite series involved.

The general problems associated with the solution of Eq. (7.7.2), and of more complicated matrix equations, are beyond the scope of this book. (See references 2, 3, 4, and 9 at the end of this chapter.)

If we consider the change of dependent variables in Eq. (7.7.2) by

$$\mathbf{v} = \mathbf{Pz}. \tag{7.7.3}$$

where $\mathbf{P}$ is an $n \times n$ nonsingular constant matrix, then

$$\frac{d}{dx}\mathbf{y} = \mathbf{P}\frac{d}{dx}\mathbf{z} \quad \text{and} \quad \mathbf{P}\frac{d}{dx}\mathbf{z} = \mathbf{APz} + \mathbf{b}, \quad \text{or}$$

(7.7.4)
$$\frac{d}{dx}\mathbf{z} = \mathbf{P}^{-1}\mathbf{APz} + \mathbf{P}^{-1}\mathbf{b}.$$

If $\mathbf{A}$ is similar to a diagonal matrix, then, by a proper choice of the matrix $\mathbf{P}$,

(7.7.5)
$$\mathbf{P}^{-1}\mathbf{AP} = \begin{bmatrix} \lambda_1 & 0 & \cdots & 0 \\ 0 & \lambda_2 & \cdots & 0 \\ \cdot & \cdot & \cdots & \cdot \\ 0 & 0 & \cdots & \lambda_n \end{bmatrix},$$

where the λ_i are the characteristic roots of $\mathbf{A}$. The system of equations associated with Eq. (7.7.4) is then

(7.7.6)
$$\frac{d}{dx} z_i = \lambda_i z_i + h_i(x), \qquad i = 1, 2, \cdots, n,$$

where $h_i(x)$ is the element in the ith row of $\mathbf{P}^{-1}\mathbf{b}$.

From elementary differential equations, the solutions of Eq. (7.7.6) are

(7.7.7)
$$z_i = c_i e^{\lambda_i x} + e^{\lambda_i x} \int e^{-\lambda_i x} h_i(x)\, dx, \qquad i = 1, 2, \cdots, n,$$

where the c_i are arbitrary constants of integration. These results can be substituted back into Eq. (7.7.3) to give the solution to the original set of equations, Eq. (7.7.1).

If $\mathbf{A}$ is not similar to a diagonal matrix, then (as is shown in more advanced works) $\mathbf{A}$ is similar to a triangular matrix. (See Section 7.8.) Then there exists a matrix $\mathbf{P}$ such that $\mathbf{P}^{-1}\mathbf{AP} = \mathbf{T}$, where $\mathbf{T}$ is a triangular matrix with the characteristic values of $\mathbf{A}$ on the principal diagonal. That is, from $\mathbf{y}' = \mathbf{Ay} + \mathbf{b}$, the substitution

(7.7.8)
$$\mathbf{y} = \mathbf{Pz}$$

yields

(7.7.9)
$$\mathbf{z}' = \mathbf{P}^{-1}\mathbf{APz} + \mathbf{P}^{-1}\mathbf{b} = \mathbf{Tz} + \mathbf{h},$$

where $\mathbf{h} = \mathbf{P}^{-1}\mathbf{b}$. This matrix equation may be written as the system of differential equations

(7.7.10)
$$\begin{aligned} \frac{dz_1}{dx} &= \lambda_1 z_1 + t_{12} z_2 + \cdots + t_{1n} z_n + h_1 \\ \frac{dz_2}{dx} &= \lambda_2 z_2 + \cdots + t_{2n} z_n + h_2 \\ &\cdots \\ \frac{dz_n}{dx} &= \lambda_n z_n + h_n, \end{aligned}$$

in which some of the λ_i may be equal. The t_{ij} in Eq. (7.7.10) are the non-zero off-diagonal elements of **T** and hence are constants. (Some or all of the t_{ij} may be zero.)

The last equation in Eq. (7.7.10) may be solved as Eq. (7.7.7). This result can then be substituted into the preceding equation to give another first order linear equation which can be solved the same way. Proceeding in this manner, all of the other equations can be solved to give the vector **z** which, when substituted into Eq. (7.7.8), gives the required solution to Eq. (7.7.1).

Example 7.7.1. Solve the system of equations

$$y_1' = y_1 + 2y_2$$
$$y_2' = 2y_2 + y_1$$

by the methods of this section.

The vector differential equation is

$$\begin{bmatrix} y_1 \\ y_2 \end{bmatrix}' = \begin{bmatrix} 1 & 2 \\ 2 & 1 \end{bmatrix} \begin{bmatrix} y_1 \\ y_2 \end{bmatrix}; \quad \text{if}$$

$$\mathbf{P} = \begin{bmatrix} 1/\sqrt{2} & 1/\sqrt{2} \\ 1/\sqrt{2} & -1/\sqrt{2} \end{bmatrix},$$

then $\mathbf{y} = \mathbf{Pz}$ yields

$$\frac{d}{dx}\mathbf{z} = \mathbf{P}^{-1}\mathbf{APz} = \mathbf{Dz},$$

where **D** is a diagonal matrix with $\lambda_1 = 3$, $\lambda_2 = -1$, the characteristic values of **A**, on the diagonal. The matrix **P** is found by the methods of Section 6.7. The solution of

$$\frac{d}{dx}\mathbf{z} = \begin{bmatrix} 3 & 0 \\ 0 & -1 \end{bmatrix}\mathbf{z} \quad \text{is} \quad \mathbf{z} = \begin{bmatrix} c_1 & e^{3x} \\ c_2 & e^{-x} \end{bmatrix}, \quad \text{and hence}$$

$$\mathbf{y} = \begin{bmatrix} 1/\sqrt{2} & 1/\sqrt{2} \\ 1/\sqrt{2} & -1/\sqrt{2} \end{bmatrix} \begin{bmatrix} c_1 & e^{3x} \\ c_2 & e^{-x} \end{bmatrix} \quad \text{or} \quad \begin{aligned} y_1 &= (c_1 e^{3x} + c_2 e^{-x})/\sqrt{2} \\ y_2 &= (c_1 e^{3x} - c_2 e^{-x})/\sqrt{2} \end{aligned}$$

are the solutions to the given equations.

Instead of the system of equations given in Eq. (7.7.1), the system is often given as

$$\begin{aligned} f_{11}(D)y_1 + f_{12}(D)y_2 + \cdots + f_{1n}(D)y_n &= g_1(x) \\ f_{21}(D)y_1 + f_{22}(D)y_2 + \cdots + f_{2n}(D)y_n &= g_2(x) \\ \cdots \\ f_{n1}(D)y_1 + f_{n2}(D)y_2 + \cdots + f_{nn}(D)y_n &= g_n(x) \end{aligned} \tag{7.7.11}$$

in which $D = d/dx$, $f_{ij}(D)$ is a polynomial in D with constant coefficients, and the $g_i(x)$ are integrable functions of x. For example,

$$(D^2 + D + 1)y_1 + (D - 1)y^2 = 4e^x - x,$$
$$(D + 1)y_1 + (D^2 + 2D)y_2 = 2, \tag{7.7.12}$$

is a special case of Eq. (7.7.11).

Equation (7.7.11) can be written as

$$\mathbf{Fy} = \mathbf{g} \tag{7.7.13}$$

in which

(7.7.14)

$$\mathbf{F}(D) = \begin{bmatrix} f_{11}(D) & \cdots & f_{1n}(D) \\ \cdots & & \\ f_{n1}(D) & \cdots & f_{nn}(D) \end{bmatrix}, \quad \mathbf{y} = \begin{bmatrix} y_1 \\ \vdots \\ y_n \end{bmatrix}, \quad \text{and} \quad \mathbf{g}(x) = \begin{bmatrix} g_1(x) \\ \vdots \\ g_n(x) \end{bmatrix}.$$

If the highest ordered differential operation in $f_{11}(D)$ is D^k, then we define $y_1 = x_1$, $y_1' = x_1' = x_2, \cdots, y_1^{(k-1)} = x_{k-1}' = x_k$ and substitute these in the first term of the first equation in Eq. (7.7.11). For the second term we let $y_2 = x_{k+1}$, $y_2' = x_{k+1}' = x_{k+2}$, etc. Proceeding in this manner, the system in Eq. (7.7.11) can eventually be written as

$$\frac{d}{dx}\mathbf{x} = \mathbf{Ax} + \mathbf{g},$$

the same type of equation as Eq. (7.7.2). Although this method may be used, it is often simpler to proceed directly from Eq. (7.7.13).*

If the highest derivative occurring in Eq. (7.7.11) is k, the system of equations can also be written as

$$(\mathbf{D}^k\mathbf{A}_k + \mathbf{D}^{k-1}\mathbf{A}_{k-1} + \cdots + \mathbf{DA}_1 + \mathbf{A}_0)\mathbf{y} = \mathbf{g}, \tag{7.7.15}$$

where
$$\mathbf{D}^j = \begin{bmatrix} \frac{d^j}{dx^j} & 0 & & 0 \\ 0 & \frac{d^j}{dx^j} & \cdots & 0 \\ \cdots & & & \\ 0 & 0 & \cdots & \frac{d^j}{dx^j} \end{bmatrix}, \quad j = 1, 2, \cdots, k,$$

the $\mathbf{A}_j$, $j = 1, 2, \cdots, k$, are constant coefficients matrices, $\mathbf{y}$ is the vector

*The details of this procedure can be found in the very readable paper "A Simple Matrix Approach to Linear Differential Equations" by L. C. Barret and C. R. Wylie, Jr., *American Mathematical Monthly*, V.63 (1956), pp. 472–478.

$[y_1 \ \cdots \ y_n]'$, and $\mathbf{g}$ is the vector $[g_1 \ \cdots \ g_n]'$. (Note that the letter D is used for several different purposes in this section: $\mathbf{D}$ as a diagonal matrix, D as a differential operator, and finally $\mathbf{D}$ as the matrix differential operator as used in Eq. (7.7.15).)

As a final example, the system of equations,

$$\begin{aligned}(2D^2 + 1)y_1 + (D^2 + 4)y_2 &= x^2 + 4x + 2 \\ (D^2 + D + 2)y_1 + (D^2 + D)y_2 &= 2x^2 + 2x + 7,\end{aligned} \tag{7.7.16}$$

can be written as

$$(\mathbf{D}^2\mathbf{A}_2 + \mathbf{D}\mathbf{A}_1 + \mathbf{A}_0)\mathbf{y} = \mathbf{g}(x), \tag{7.7.17}$$

where
$$\mathbf{D}^2 = \begin{bmatrix} \dfrac{d^2}{dx^2} & 0 \\ 0 & \dfrac{d^2}{dx^2} \end{bmatrix}, \qquad \mathbf{D} = \begin{bmatrix} \dfrac{d}{dx} & 0 \\ 0 & \dfrac{d}{dx} \end{bmatrix},$$

$$\mathbf{A}_2 = \begin{bmatrix} 2 & 1 \\ 1 & 1 \end{bmatrix}, \qquad \mathbf{A}_1 = \begin{bmatrix} 0 & 0 \\ 1 & 1 \end{bmatrix}, \qquad \mathbf{A}_0 = \begin{bmatrix} 1 & 4 \\ 2 & 0 \end{bmatrix},$$

$$\mathbf{y} = \begin{bmatrix} y_1 \\ y_2 \end{bmatrix}, \quad \text{and} \quad \mathbf{g}(x) = \begin{bmatrix} x^2 + 4x + 2 \\ 2x^2 + 2x + 7 \end{bmatrix}.$$

Exercises 7.7

1. Verify that the following are solutions to the corresponding equations.
   (a) For Eq. (7.7.12), $y_1 = e^x$, $y_2 = x + 1$.
   (b) For Eq. (7.7.16), $y_1 = x^2 + 2$, $y_2 = x - 1$.

2. For the case $n = 2$, write the solutions found in Eq. (7.7.7) in vector form and substitute the result in Eq. (7.7.3) to obtain the required solution.

3. Solve the system of equations

   (a) $y_1' = 2y_1 + 2y_2$, $y_2' = 2y_1 - y_2$ (b) $y_1' = 4y_1 + 2y_2$, $y_2' = 2y_1$

   by methods of this section.

4. In $y^{(n)} + a_1 y^{(n-1)} + \cdots + a_n y = 0$, let $y = y_1$, $y' = y_1' = y_2$, $y'' = y_2' = y_3$, $\cdots$, $y^{(n-1)} = y_{n-1}' = y_n$, and write the result as a vector differential equation. Determine the characteristic equation for the system.

5. By defining $y_1 = x_1$, $y_1' = x_1' = x_2$, $y_2 = x_3$, and $y_2' = x_4$, rewrite Eq. (7.7.12) as the equation $\dfrac{d}{dx}\mathbf{x} = \mathbf{A}\mathbf{x} + \mathbf{g}$, in the same form as Eq. (7.7.2).

6. Write the system of equations in Eq. (7.7.12) in the form of Eq. (7.7.15).

7. Verify that Eq. (7.7.17) is the same as Eq. (7.7.16).

8. If $\mathbf{Y}(x)$ and $\mathbf{A}(x)$ are $n \times n$ matrices, show that the problem of solving

$$\mathbf{Y}'(x) = \mathbf{A}(x)\mathbf{Y}(x)$$

is equivalent to the problem of finding n solutions to the vector equation

$$\mathbf{y}'(x) = \mathbf{A}(x)\mathbf{y}(x).$$

7.8.† Additional Results for Matrices and Determinants

Several special matrices and determinants, which are often encountered in the literature, are of great importance in mathematics. Some of these are mentioned in this section, along with a theorem that is used in the study of differential equations. These results are merely stated; no attempt is made to prove or verify that the statements given are correct. Further discussion of these topics may be found in the references listed at the end of this chapter.

I. The square matrix $\mathbf{A}_i$ is

$$\mathbf{A}_i = \begin{bmatrix} \lambda_i & 1 & 0 & \cdots & 0 \\ 0 & \lambda_i & 1 & \cdots & 0 \\ 0 & 0 & \lambda_i & \cdots & 0 \\ \cdots & & & & \\ 0 & 0 & 0 & \cdots & \lambda_i \end{bmatrix}; \tag{7.8.1}$$

that is, $\mathbf{A}_i$ is a matrix with the elements $\lambda_i \neq 0$ on the main diagonal, the elements 1 in each position on the *superdiagonal*, and zero elements otherwise. Note that i does *not* refer to the order of the matrix.

It can be shown that every nonsingular matrix $\mathbf{A}$ with elements from $\mathscr{F}_c$ is similar to a matrix $\mathbf{J}$ where

$$\mathbf{J} = \begin{bmatrix} \mathbf{A}_1 & \mathbf{0} & \cdots & \mathbf{0} \\ \mathbf{0} & \mathbf{A}_2 & \cdots & \mathbf{0} \\ \cdots & & & \\ \mathbf{0} & \mathbf{0} & \cdots & \mathbf{A}_s \end{bmatrix}, \tag{7.8.2}$$

the $\mathbf{A}_i$ being defined by Eq. (7.8.1). The λ_i, $i = 1, 2, \cdots, m$, with $s \leqq m$, are the characteristic values of $\mathbf{A}$ but are not necessarily distinct. Such a matrix $\mathbf{J}$ is said to be in *Jordan* canonical form*. Thus there exist matrices $\mathbf{C}$, not unique, such that

$$\mathbf{C}^{-1}\mathbf{A}\mathbf{C} = \mathbf{J}. \tag{7.8.3}$$

Furthermore it can be shown that two matrices are similar if and only if they have the same Jordan form, except possibly the order in which the submatrices $\mathbf{A}_i$ occur in $\mathbf{J}$. The matrix $\mathbf{J}$ is a diagonal matrix if and only if each of the $\mathbf{A}_i$ is a matrix of order 1.

II. The following is a very useful result in the study of differential equations.

*Named after the French mathematician Camille Jordan (1838–1922).

Theorem 7.8.1. *If* $\mathbf{A}$ *is a square matrix, then*

$$\det e^{\mathbf{A}} = e^{\operatorname{tr}\mathbf{A}}. \tag{7.8.4}$$

Since $e^{\operatorname{tr}\mathbf{A}}$ is a scalar that is never zero, $e^{\mathbf{A}}$ is nonsingular and possesses an inverse. By Theorem 7.6.1, $e^{\mathbf{X}}e^{\mathbf{Y}} = e^{\mathbf{X}+\mathbf{Y}}$ if $\mathbf{XY} = \mathbf{YX}$; thus $e^{-\mathbf{A}}$ is the inverse of $e^{\mathbf{A}}$, since $e^{\mathbf{A}}e^{-\mathbf{A}} = e^{\mathbf{0}} = \mathbf{I}$. (See Corollary 7.6.2.)

III. The determinant

$$W(y_1, y_2, \cdots, y_n) = \begin{vmatrix} y_1 & y_2 & \cdots & y_n \\ y_1' & y_2' & \cdots & y_n' \\ \cdot & \cdot & \cdots & \cdot \\ y_1^{(n-1)} & y_2^{(n-1)} & \cdots & y_n^{(n-1)} \end{vmatrix} \tag{7.8.5}$$

is called the *Wronskian** of the functions $y_1, \cdots, y_n$. If $y_1, \cdots, y_n$ are solutions of a linear homogeneous ordinary differential equation of order n, then $W \neq 0$ is a necessary and sufficient condition that these functions be *linearly independent* over some interval (a, b). If the functions are *linearly dependent*, then $W \equiv 0$. However, for functions in general, $W \neq 0$ is not a necessary condition for linear independence.

IV. If we have n differentiable functions of n independent variables, $f_i(x_1, x_2, \cdots, x_n)$, $i = 1, 2, \cdots, n$, then the *Jacobian*† of these functions is the determinant

$$\frac{\partial(f_1, \cdots, f_n)}{\partial(x_1, \cdots, x_n)} = \begin{vmatrix} \dfrac{\partial f_1}{\partial x_1} & \dfrac{\partial f_1}{\partial x_2} & \cdots & \dfrac{\partial f_1}{\partial x_n} \\ \dfrac{\partial f_2}{\partial x_1} & \dfrac{\partial f_2}{\partial x_2} & \cdots & \dfrac{\partial f_2}{\partial x_n} \\ \cdot & \cdot & \cdots & \cdot \\ \dfrac{\partial f_n}{\partial x_1} & \dfrac{\partial f_n}{\partial x_2} & \cdots & \dfrac{\partial f_n}{\partial x_n} \end{vmatrix}. \tag{7.8.6}$$

This determinant is used in the transformation of variables from one system to another, and in establishing whether or not the given functions are *functionally dependent*. In particular, it is both necessary and sufficient that the Jacobian vanish identically for the given n functions to be such that a relation $\Phi(f_1, f_2, \cdots, f_n) = 0$ exists in which none of the x_i's appear explicitly.

V. The *Gramian*, or *Gram determinant*, of the real column vectors $\mathbf{x}_j$ is

$$G = \begin{vmatrix} \mathbf{x}_1'\mathbf{x}_1 & \mathbf{x}_1'\mathbf{x}_2 & \cdots & \mathbf{x}_1'\mathbf{x}_n \\ \mathbf{x}_2'\mathbf{x}_1 & \mathbf{x}_2'\mathbf{x}_2 & \cdots & \mathbf{x}_2'\mathbf{x}_n \\ \cdot & \cdot & \cdots & \cdot \\ \mathbf{x}_n'\mathbf{x}_1 & \mathbf{x}_n'\mathbf{x}_2 & \cdots & \mathbf{x}_n'\mathbf{x}_n \end{vmatrix}; \tag{7.8.7}$$

*Named after the Polish mathematician Höené Wronski (1778–1853).
†Named after the German mathematician C. G. J. Jacobi (1804–1851).

the element in the ij-position is $\bar{\mathbf{x}}_i' \mathbf{x}_j$ if the vectors are complex. (There is a corresponding definition of a Gramian involving the inner products of the elements of a set of functions.)

The vectors in G in Eq. (7.8.7) are *linearly dependent* if and only if $G = 0$; otherwise $G > 0$ and the vectors are *linearly independent*. Also G has nonzero elements only on the main diagonal if the vectors are mutually orthogonal; these nonzero elements are all ones if the vectors form an orthonormal set of vectors.

References

Ayers, F., Jr., *Theory and Problems of Matrices*. Schaum, 1962.

Bellman, R., *Introduction to Matrix Analysis*. McGraw-Hill, 1960.

Birkhoff, G., and C. G. Rota, *Ordinary Differential Equations*. Ginn, 1962.

Coddington, E. A., and N. Levinson. *Theory of Ordinary Differential Equations*. McGraw-Hill, 1962.

Courant, R., and D. Hilbert. *Methods of Mathematical Physics, Vol. I.* Interscience, 1953.

Curtis, C. W., *Linear Algebra*. Allyn and Bacon, 1963.

Davis, H. F., *Fourier Series and Orthogonal Functions*. Allyn and Bacon, 1963.

Finkbeiner, D. T., II, *Introduction to Matrices and Linear Transformations*. Freeman, 1960.

Hochstadt, H., *Differential Equations*. Holt, Rinehart and Winston, 1964.

Macduffee, C. C., "Vectors and Matrices," *The Carus Mathematical Monographs No. 7*. The Mathematical Association of America, 1943.

Miller, F. H., *Partial Differential Equations*. Wiley & Sons, 1941.

Parker, W. V., and J. C. Eaves. *Matrices*. Ronald Press, 1960.

Perlis, S., *Theory of Matrices*. Addison-Wesley, 1952.

Wylie, C. R., Jr., *Advanced Engineering Mathematics*. McGraw-Hill, 1960.

Appendix[†]

Topics from Abstract Algebra

This appendix defines certain terms from modern algebra which are used in this book. It is intended as a review for the reader who is already familiar with basic set and field theory. It can also serve as an introduction for the reader who is unfamiliar with the terminology.

A.1. Groups

After defining an abstract mathematical *group*, we shall examine some mathematical systems to determine whether they meet the requirements for a group.

First, we require a *set of elements* denoted by $S = \{A, B, C, \cdots\}$ (which may be finite or infinite), a knowledge of the meaning of the *equality* of elements (denoted by $=$), and a *binary operation* that combines elements of S (denoted by $\oplus$). Among the possible examples of the binary operation $\oplus$ are addition $(+)$, multiplication $(\cdot)$, rotations, permutations, and division $(\div)$.

Then, the set forms a *group* under the given binary operation provided that the first four of the following five conditions are met:

(1) The *closure property* holds:

(A.1.1) $$A \oplus B = C.$$

That is, for any two elements A and B of the set, a unique element C is obtained, under the given binary operation, that is also an element of the set. Two or all three of the elements of Eq. (A.1.1) may be the same, or they may all be distinct.

(2) The *associative property* holds:

$$A \oplus (B \oplus C) = (A \oplus B) \oplus C. \tag{A.1.2}$$

This merely means that either the first or second operation can be performed first to give the same result. Since checking this property is often tedious, we shall not be too concerned with it in the examples and exercises given in this Appendix.

(3) In the set there is a unique *identity* element, designated by E, such that

$$A \oplus E = E \oplus A = A \tag{A.1.3}$$

for an arbitrary element A of the set S.

(4) For each element A of the set there is a unique element A^{-1}, called the *inverse* of A, such that

$$A \oplus A^{-1} = A^{-1} \oplus A = E. \tag{A.1.4}$$

In some instances an element may be its own inverse, so that $A = A^{-1}$. (Note that A^{-1} does not necessarily mean $1/A$.)

(5) The *commutative property* is

$$A \oplus B = B \oplus A, \tag{A.1.5}$$

for arbitrary elements A and B of S. Although not all groups possess this property, some very important groups do. A group possessing the commutative property is said to be a commutative group or an *Abelian** group.

Example A.1.1. Consider the counterclockwise rotations of 0°, 120°, or 240° of an equilateral triangle about its center; designate these rotations by A, B, and C respectively. Show that the set of rotations form a group under the operation $\oplus$, where $\oplus$ stands for "followed by."

Here $B \oplus C$ means a counterclockwise rotation of the triangle of 120° followed by a counterclockwise rotation of 240°. We see that this has the same result as a rotation of 0°; that is, $B \oplus C = A$. It readily follows that:

(1) The closure property holds, since one counterclockwise rotation followed by another (or by itself) is equivalent to one of the three rotations.
(2) The associative property holds.
(3) The identity element is A, the rotation of 0°.
(4) Each element possesses an inverse; the inverse of A is A, the inverse of B is C, and the inverse of C is B.

Thus these rotations form a group. Is the group Abelian?

*Named after the Norwegian mathematician Niels Henrik Abel (1802–1829).

Example A.1.2. Do the even integers form a group under ordinary addition?

It is readily determined that (1) the sum of even integers is an even integer, (2) even integers may be added in any order, (3) the identity element is zero, an even integer, and (4) the inverse of any even integer is its negative, still an even integer. Hence, the set of even integers forms a mathematical group under ordinary addition. It may also be shown that the group is a commutative group.

Example A.1.3. Given the set of elements $\{a, b, c\}$ and the operation $\oplus$ defined by

$\oplus$	a	b	c
a	a	c	b
b	b	a	c
c	c	b	a

(*i.e.*, $b \oplus c = c$, etc.). Do the elements of the set form an abstract group under this operation?

(1) The elements in the square are either a, b, or c, so the closure property is satisfied.

(2) The element a is a *right identity* element, since $a \oplus a = a$, $b \oplus a = b$, and $c \oplus a = c$; *i.e.*, an element of the set operating on a yields the original element. However, since $a \oplus b = c$, the element a is not a *left identity*; in fact there is no left identity element. Thus we do not have a group.

It is of interest to observe that, since a is the right identity element, then each element is its own inverse, since $a \oplus a = a$, $b \oplus b = a$, and $c \oplus c = a$. Note also that the associative property does not hold in every case; *e.g.*, $b \oplus (a \oplus b) \neq (b \oplus a) \oplus b$.

Exercises A.1

1. Is the group in Example A.1.1 Abelian? Why?
2. Does the set of elements $\{0, 1\}$ form a group under ordinary multiplication?
3. For the set of elements $\{0, 1\}$ with the operation, $+$, defined by $0 + 1 = 1$, $1 + 0 = 1$, $0 + 0 = 0$, and $1 + 1 = 0$, is a group formed?
4. Do the elements $1, -1, i, -i$, where $i = \sqrt{-1}$, form a group with respect to ordinary multiplication?
5. Does the set of all integers form a group under ordinary addition?
6. Do the positive integers form a group under ordinary multiplication?

7. Do the rational numbers form a group under ordinary multiplication? If the additive identity is excluded, does the set form a group?

8. Does the set of real numbers form a group under ordinary addition? If the additive identity is excluded, do they form a group under ordinary multiplication?

9. Excluding zero, do the complex numbers form a group under ordinary multiplication? Do they form a group under ordinary addition?

10. Show that the set of integral multiples of 5 forms a group with respect to addition. Does the set form a group with respect to multiplication?

11. Do the sixth roots of 1 form a group under multiplication? Do the fifth roots of 32 form a group under multiplication?

12. If the multiplication table for the elements $\{a, b, c\}$ is

(a)

$\oplus$	a	b	c
a	b	c	a
b	c	a	b
c	a	b	c

,

(b)

$\oplus$	a	b	c
a	c	b	a
b	a	c	b
c	b	a	c

,

assume the associative property, then
(1) Find the identity element, if any.
(2) State the inverse of each element, if any.
(3) Prove or disprove that the elements form a group under this multiplication.

13.* Given Eq. (A.1.1), Eq. (A.1.2), and $A \oplus E = A$ from Eq. (A.1.3) and $A \oplus A^{-1} = E$ from Eq. (A.1.4), prove that $A^{-1} \oplus A = E$. That is, prove that one part of Eq. (A.1.4) is a consequence of the other.

14.* Given Eq. (A.1.1), Eq. (A.1.2), and $A \oplus E = A$ from Eq. (A.1.3) and $A \oplus A^{-1} = E$ from Eq. (A.1.4), prove that $E \oplus A = A$. That is, prove that one part of Eq. (A.1.3) is a consequence of the other. (Hint: The results of exercise 13 may be used if desired.)

15.* Show that the set of elements

$$\left\{r, \frac{1}{r}, 1 - r, \frac{1}{1 - r}, \frac{r - 1}{r}, \frac{1}{r - 1}\right\}$$

forms a group under the operation $\oplus$, where $\oplus$ is the operation of replacing r in the second element by the first element. Is the group Abelian?†

A.2. *Fields*

A set of objects S forms a *field* under *two* binary operations, say ($\oplus$) and ($\oplus$), provided that:
(1) The set forms an Abelian group under ($\oplus$).

†This group is known as the cross-ratio group; for an application of it, see Earl D. Rainville, *Intermediate Differential Equations*, 2nd ed. (New York: Macmillan, 1964), p. 271.

(2) The set of all elements except the identity under ($\oplus$) forms an Abelian group under ($\oplus\!\!\!|$).
(3) The *distributive law*,

(A.2.1) $$A \,\text{⦶}\, (B \oplus C) = A \,\text{⦶}\, B \oplus A \,\text{⦶}\, C,$$

is satisfied for arbitrary elements of S.

Example A.2.1. If a and b are rational numbers, show that elements of the form $a + b\sqrt{2}$ form a field under the operations of ordinary addition ($+$) and multiplication ($\cdot$).

Under addition the closure, associative, and commutative properties hold, since these properties hold for all rational numbers. The identity element under addition is $0 + 0\sqrt{2} = 0$, and the inverse of $a + b\sqrt{2}$ is $-a - b\sqrt{2}$.

Under multiplication it is not difficult to show that the closure, associative, and commutative properties hold. The multiplicative identity is $1 + 0\sqrt{2} = 1$, and the inverse of $u + v\sqrt{2}$, if $u^2 - v^2 \neq 0$, is

$$\frac{1}{u + v\sqrt{2}} = \frac{u}{u^2 - 2v^2} - \frac{v\sqrt{2}}{u^2 - 2v^2},$$

an element of the type $a + b\sqrt{2}$, a and b rational.

Since division by zero is undefined, we must be sure that $u^2 - 2v^2 \neq 0$. Since u and v are defined as rational, $u^2 - 2v^2 = 0$ requires that $u = v = 0$. Then $u + v\sqrt{2}$ would be the additive identity, $0 + 0\sqrt{2}$, which need not (and does not) have a multiplicative inverse. Therefore $u^2 - 2v^2 \neq 0$, and the division is defined.

Finally, since the distributive property of Eq. (A.2.1) can be shown quite readily to hold, the set of elements of the form $a + b\sqrt{2}$, a and b rational, forms a field under the operations of ($+$) and ($\cdot$).

One of the primary reasons for considering the concept of a field is to introduce the *number fields* $\mathscr{F}_r$ and $\mathscr{F}_c$. The binary operations in these fields are ordinary addition ($+$) and multiplication ($\cdot$). The number field $\mathscr{F}_r$ is defined to be

(A.2.2) $$\mathscr{F}_r = \{x;\ +,\ \cdot \mid x \text{ a real number}\}.$$

The number field $\mathscr{F}_c$ is defined to be

(A.2.3) $$\mathscr{F}_c = \{z;\ +,\ \cdot \mid z \text{ a complex number}\};$$

that is, z is a number of the form $x + iy$ where x and y are real and $i = \sqrt{-1}$. Other number fields are important as well (such as in number 4 of Exercises A.2), but our chief concern shall be with these two. In case we do not wish to specify a particular number field, we shall use the symbol $\mathscr{F}$ without a subscript. Note that any number field is a subfield of the complex number field $\mathscr{F}_c$.

The elements of a number field, or functions that assume values from a number field, are called *scalars*. These elements and functions are simply the quantities the student has been dealing with almost entirely in his previous mathematics training. They include all numbers (rational and irrational, real and imaginary), and all functions of numbers (such as sin, cos, log, or ln).

In determining whether a set of elements forms a field, we have eleven properties to check. Five properties must be satisfied under the first binary operations ($\oplus$); five under the second ($\oplus\!\!\!|$); and one for the combination, the distributive law of Eq. (A.2.1). If any one of these eleven properties is not satisfied, the set does not form a field under these operations.

Exercises A.2

1. Prove that $\mathscr{F}_r$ forms a field under ordinary addition and multiplication.

2. Prove that $\mathscr{F}_c$ forms a field under ordinary addition and multiplication.

3. Does the set of numbers $\{a + ib\}$, a and b rational, form a field under the operations of addition and multiplication of complex numbers?

4. If a number field $\mathscr{F}$ (under ordinary addition and multiplication) must contain $\sqrt{3}$,
   (a) Must it contain 3, 1, 0, $5\sqrt{3}$? Why?
   (b) Must it contain numbers of the form $a + b\sqrt{3}$? If so, describe a and b.
   (c) Describe the smallest number field that contains $\sqrt{3}$.

5. May Eq. (A.2.1) also be written as

$$A \oplus\!\!\!| (B \oplus C) = (B \oplus C) \oplus\!\!\!| A = B \oplus\!\!\!| A \oplus C \oplus\!\!\!| A$$

   for elements that form a field?

6. If the operations of $\oplus$ and $\oplus\!\!\!|$ are defined by the following tables for the set of elements $\{a, b, c\}$,

$\oplus$	a	b	c
a	a	b	c
b	b	c	a
c	c	a	b

and

$\oplus\!\!\!|$	a	b	c
a	a	a	a
b	a	b	c
c	a	c	b

,

   verify that the set forms a field.

A.3. Linear Spaces

In this section we define a *linear space** over a scalar field $\mathscr{F}$ for a set of objects S. We first present the definition formally and then discuss it informally. After this we consider some examples of linear spaces to give the definition more meaning.

Let S be a set $\{a, b, \cdots\}$ which forms an Abelian group under the operation $(+)$, and let $\mathscr{F}$ be a scalar field, $\{\alpha, \beta, \cdots\}$ under operations $(+)$ and $(\cdot)$. We define an operation called *scalar multiplication*, denoted by $(\cdot)$ or simply by the juxtaposition of the symbols, between elements of S and elements of $\mathscr{F}$. Then S forms a *linear space* over $\mathscr{F}$ provided that:

(A.3.1)
(1) $\alpha a = a\alpha$ is an element of S, a closure property.
(2) $(\alpha + \beta)a = (\alpha a) + (\beta a)$, a distributive property.
(3) $\alpha(a + b) = (\alpha a) + (\alpha b)$, another distributive property.
(4) $(\alpha\beta)a = \alpha(\beta a)$, an associative property.
(5) $1a = a$, an identity for each element of S.

Two sets are involved: the set S of undefined objects, and the set of objects forming the scalar field $\mathscr{F}$. (See Section A.2.) Notice that S forms a group under $(+)$ and $\mathscr{F}$ forms a field under operations $(+)$ and $(\cdot)$ (or merely the juxtaposition of the symbols). Thus the symbol $(+)$ is used in two senses: as the group operation between elements of S (as in (3) of Eq. (A.3.1)), and as one of the binary operations in the scalar field $\mathscr{F}$ (as in (2) of Eq. (A.3.1)). No confusion should arise from the two uses of the same symbol.

This definition tells us how we can combine the elements of the two sets by the kinds of commutative and associative operations given in Eq. (A.3.1). The apparently obvious condition given in (5) is not as trivial as it might seem. One instance in which (1), (2), (3), and (4) of Eq. (A.3.1) are satisfied, but (5) is not, is given in the following example.

Example A.3.1. Let the set S consist of all directed line segments (vectors) in the xy-plane, with addition in S defined in an obvious manner (the parallelogram law of vector addition). Let the operation ⦶ between a scalar from $\mathscr{F}_r$ and an element of S consist of taking the projection on the x-axis of the element of S after multiplying the length of the element of S by the scalar. Thus 2 ⦶ a is the projection of $a + a$ on the x-axis. Then in Eq. (A.3.1) the first four properties hold, but (5) does not (unless a lies along the x-axis), since 1 ⦶ a must lie along the x-axis while a need not. What is the length of 1 ⦶ a? Further examination of this example is left as an exercise.

*Other texts may refer to a *linear space* as a *vector space* or as a *linear vector space*. In this book (Chapter 5), a *linear vector space* is defined as a special type of linear space. The term *space* is used in general if some type of algebraic or geometric structure is imposed on a set of elements (often called *points*).

Example A.3.2. Let S consist of all polynomials of the form $\alpha a + \beta y$ where α and β are real numbers and x and y are merely symbols. That is, $\mathscr{F}$ is the $\mathscr{F}_r$ of Eq. (A.2.2) and x and y are symbols that combine as follows. Addition in S is defined by

$$(\alpha_1 x + \beta_1 y) + (\alpha_2 x + \beta_2 y) = (\alpha_1 + \alpha_2)x + (\beta_1 + \beta_2)y.$$

Scalar multiplication is defined by

$$\gamma(\alpha x + \beta y) = (\gamma\alpha)x + (\gamma\beta)y.$$

Does S form a linear space?

It follows directly from the definition of addition given above that S forms an Abelian group under this operation. Also it is readily verified that the properties of Eq. (A.3.1) are satisfied by the given scalar multiplication. Hence, S forms a linear space; the additive identity is $0x + 0y$, and the inverse of $\alpha x + \beta y$ is $(-\alpha)x + (-\beta)y$.

Example A.3.3. Let S consist of all polynomials in the variable x with rational coefficients. The operation of addition is the ordinary addition of polynomials, and scalar multiplication is the ordinary multiplication by a rational number. Show that S forms a linear space over the rationals.

The sum of two polynomials is a polynomial, so S is closed under addition, which is also associative and commutative. The polynomial 0 is the additive identity, and the inverse of the polynomial

$$\sum_{i=0}^{n} \alpha_i x^i \quad \text{is} \quad \sum_{i=0}^{n} (-\alpha_i) x^i.$$

Thus, S forms an Abelian group under addition.

By definition, properties (1) and (5) of Eq. (A.3.1) are satisfied; the other properties follow immediately from the definitions of addition and scalar multiplication. Therefore S forms a linear space over the rational numbers.

Exercises A.3

1. Show that $\mathscr{F}_r$ forms a linear space over the rationals.
2. Show that $\mathscr{F}_c$ forms a linear space over $\mathscr{F}_r$.
3. Show that the set of all real-valued continuous functions on the interval [0, 1] forms a linear space over $\mathscr{F}_r$.
4. Show that the set of ordered triples of real numbers (a_1, a_2, a_3) with addition defined by

$$(a_1, a_2, a_3) + (b_1, b_2, b_3) = (a_1 + b_1, a_2 + b_2, a_3 + b_3)$$

and scalar multiplication defined by

$$\alpha(a_1, a_2, a_3) = (\alpha a_1, \alpha a_2, \alpha a_3)$$

is a linear space over $\mathcal{F}_r$.

5. Draw figures illustrating Example A.3.1 and show that (1) through (4) of Eq. (A.3.1) are satisfied but (5) is not.

6.* Prove that $(0)a = 0$. (Hint: Start with $1a = a$.) Here the first zero is the zero of the scalar field; the second zero is the zero of the additive group of the linear space.

7.* Prove that the inverse of a is $(-1)a$.

A.4. Linear Algebras

Now that we have the idea of a linear space at our disposal, we go one step further and define a *linear algebra*. Again we use the two sets of objects of Section A.3: the set of objects $S = \{a, b, \cdots\}$ that forms a group under the operation $(+)$, and the set of objects $\mathcal{F} = \{\alpha, \beta, \cdots\}$ that forms a field under the operations $(+)$ and $(\cdot)$.

We now assume that the set S forms a linear space over $\mathcal{F}$ (in accordance with Section A.3), and in addition has a multiplication defined. Then S forms a *linear algebra* over $\mathcal{F}$ provided that:

(A.4.1)
(1) ab is an element of S, the closure property.
(2) $(ab)c = a(bc)$, the associative property.
(3) $a(\alpha b + \beta c) = \alpha(ab) + \beta(ac)$, a distributive property.
(4) $(\alpha b + \beta c)a = \alpha(ba) + \beta(ca)$, another distributive property.

For a field (in Section A.2), the set of objects S is required to form an Abelian group under two operations, as well as to satisfy the distributive property of Eq. (A.2.1). For a linear algebra, the set S meets most of the eleven field requirements, but not all of them. First S must form an Abelian group under one operation, called addition, (part of the requirement for a linear space). Then under a second operation called multiplication, in Eq. (A.4.1), (1) is the closure property, (2) is the associative property, and (3) and (4) give the left and right distributive property. However, for a linear algebra (unlike a field) a multiplicative identity is not required, and neither is an inverse for each element under multiplication. Keep in mind that we are here referring only to the elements of S; a linear algebra requires the scalars of $\mathcal{F}$ as well.

Example A.4.1. Let S consist of all polynomials in x which have rational coefficients, with ordinary polynomial addition and multiplication and scalar multiplication holding. Does S form a linear algebra over the rationals?

We saw in Example A.3.3 that S is a linear space. Therefore all that is needed is to check the properties of Eq. (A.4.1). These properties can be verified; the details are left as an exercise for the reader.

Example A.4.2. If a and b are rational numbers, show that numbers of the form $a + b\sqrt{2}$ form a linear algebra over the rationals under the operations of ordinary addition and multiplication. (Note that this is both a stronger and a weaker statement than the statement of Example A.2.1. Here we have said less about the multiplication, but we have added the idea of a scalar multiplication.)

Under addition, the closure, associative, and commutative properties hold because these properties hold for all rational numbers. The identity element is $0 + 0\sqrt{2}$, and the inverse of $a + b\sqrt{2}$ is $(-a) + (-b)\sqrt{2}$. The properties of Eq. (A.3.1) hold, since the α and β are rational numbers and the a and b (of Eq. (A.3.1)) are of the form $a + b\sqrt{2}$; thus, the equations reduce to the associative and distributive laws for multiplication. The properties of Eq. (A.4.1) hold for the same reasons. Therefore, numbers of the form $a + b\sqrt{2}$ form a linear algebra.

Exercises A.4

1. Show that $\mathscr{F}_c$ forms a linear algebra over $\mathscr{F}_r$.
2. Show that $a(\alpha b) = \alpha(ab) = (\alpha a)b$.
3. Verify the details of Example A.4.1.
4. Verify the details of Example A.4.2.
5. Given a linear algebra, what other mathematical systems are involved? That is, is a linear algebra also a group? A field? A linear space?
6. Show that the set of all polynomials in x with coefficients from the field of real numbers forms a linear algebra over $\mathscr{F}_r$. (Addition and multiplication are to be taken in the usual sense.)

Index